Foundations
of
Analysis

PRENTICE-HALL MATHEMATICS SERIES

Albert A. Bennett, Editor

EDWARD J. COGAN

Faculty of Science and Mathematics
Sarah Lawrence College

Foundations

of

Analysis

PRENTICE-HALL, INC.

Englewood Cliffs, N. J.
1962

© 1962 by **PRENTICE-HALL, INC.**
Englewood Cliffs, N. J.

To my wife

FRANCES

Preface

It appears that in the attempt to achieve a thorough understanding of the nature of mathematical analysis, even the most diligent student encounters obstacles of considerable proportions. One of these is that it is difficult to ascertain on what basic mathematical objects and on what relations among these the useful techniques of analysis rest. Another is that it is often unclear by what logical means the relationships and techniques developed in analysis may be derived from basic elements. One approach to a resolution of these difficulties is to acquaint the student with situations in which the techniques of analysis are applied, and with concrete interpretations of the abstract relations studied. Certainly no one can hope to understand the subject without these. Of course, the student who has studied elementary calculus successfully has met many applications of analysis. Such a student is prepared to raise questions of a more fundamental and abstract nature. The intimate connections between the study of calculus and precollege studies in mathematics, for example, cannot be appreciated fully without confronting some of these questions squarely. This is especially true in our day when efforts are being made at the secondary school level to convey the content of mathematics with more emphasis on understanding abstract mathematical conceptions than in earlier programs.

The book is divided into three chapters, the first of which introduces the notions of set, function, predicate, and proof. Some important logical laws are presented as well as traditional ways of abbreviating rigorous proofs. The chapter closes with a discussion of cardinal numbers intended to motivate the choice of Peano's axioms for natural numbers. Chapter 2 develops the system of real numbers, beginning with natural numbers, and uses Cauchy sequences of rational numbers in the final extension.

The third chapter concerns real functions of one argument, and discusses ordinary and uniform continuity, limits, derivatives, and definite and indefinite integrals. Chapter 2 is somewhat more formal than the other two chapters, since the material in Chapter 1 is meant to be a discussion of underlying notions that, for later purposes, are considered as undefined, and it is assumed that by the end of Chapter 2 the reader has developed enough maturity to realize the strictly logical principles that justify steps omitted from abbreviated proofs. Exercises at the end of each section are intended (1) to fix the ideas developed in that section, (2) to complete proofs abbreviated or omitted in that section, (3) to introduce notions allied to the material in that section, but not essential for the development of the analysis that follows it.

The author is indebted to many for assistance and encouragement: to his students, who suffered through very rough early drafts, and made valuable suggestions for their revision; to colleagues, who made important suggestions concerning the correctness of proofs and expository style; and to those at Prentice-Hall, Inc., who did an effective job in converting the manuscript to print. Special gratitude is due to Mrs. Edith Spoley, who prepared a number of editions of the manuscript. These share in the book's merits; the author alone is responsible for its defects.

EDWARD J. COGAN

Sarah Lawrence College

Contents

Foundations
of
Analysis

CHAPTER 1

Language and Logic

1 · BASIC NOTIONS

Mathematics is a language which shares some of the purposes and uses of other languages used by human beings. Its fundamental use is as a medium of communication, and as such, it is a device by which ideas of a certain kind may be passed from one individual to another or preserved to be used at a later time. Mathematics also has as its basic units of communication, *sentences* or *statements;* and contains criteria which enable us to decide which of its sentences are true and which are false. As with other languages, the sentences of mathematics are combinations of symbols which are agreed upon by those who use the language. The criteria that determine which combinations of symbols are to be called sentences form the *syntax* of mathematics, and those that determine which sentences are true form its *logic*. The purpose of this chapter is to acquaint the reader with some of the properties of both the syntax and logic of mathematical languages in general.

Naturally, we describe these properties in English, and before proceeding it is useful to agree on the way certain words, used repeatedly, are to be understood. Once it is agreed that these words are understood in the same way by all who participate in the discussion to follow, then other

1

words can be defined in terms of these. To insist on defining these initial words would mean that others would be used in the definitions, and defining these would require still other words. The result of an insistence that every word be defined is either that an infinite number of words is introduced with no hope of definitions for all of them, or that some of our definitions are *circular* so that each word of a certain pair is defined in terms of the other. Since neither alternative is satisfactory for mathematical languages, we are compelled to agree to use some words without defining them. This does not mean that a description in terms of familiar ideas cannot be provided for these words, which name some of the basic ideas in the ensuing discussion. Such a description is provided in this section.

An attribute of mathematical languages that is not shared by natural languages like English is its precision. This precision, if fully achieved, assures us that no ambiguity can arise in the use of a word that is defined, nor in the application of a criterion for deciding what combinations of symbols are sentences, or which sentences are true. The definitions that introduce new words and the criteria for making syntactical and logical judgments must possess a property referred to as *definiteness*, if the required precision is to be obtained. Suppose, for example, that a group of students is to be divided into three groups: bright, average, and stupid. The task of agreeing on the group to which a student is assigned might be a difficult one indeed unless the criteria for the division were definite and agreed to initially by all who participate in making the decision. One way to introduce definiteness in this case is to divide the range of their IQs or of their scores on some examination into three intervals that exhaust the range and do not overlap.

We may say that a criterion is definite if, once there is agreement on it, no quarrel can arise in using it to make decisions, regardless of who makes the decision or when it is being made. This is certainly the case whenever a mechanical device can be designed that can apply the criterion. For if a criterion is introduced by a sequence of rules for making decisions, and if a machine of some kind can apply the rules, then agreement on the acceptability of the criterion provides assurance that no quarrel can arise in its application. A criterion is said to be *definite* in what follows, if a mechanical device can be designed to apply it.

As an example of a definite criterion that is part of a definition, consider the following:

> "An integer is *even* if the quotient obtained in dividing it by 2 is an integer."

Surely the criterion for evenness as defined here can be applied mechanically, for there are machines that both divide and identify a number as an integer.

It is often desirable in mathematical discussions to consider aggregates or collections of objects that have some property in common. Thus we may consider the collection of all integers that are perfect squares, or the collection of all the points in a given triangle. For our purposes, if the criteria for deciding whether or not a given object belongs to the collection are definite (in the sense just explained) we call the collection a *set*. The notion of set pervades the study of mathematics at all levels and along all branches, and it is useful to introduce the usual notation relating to sets here.

Roughly speaking, a set is specified when a property is given that is shared by the objects in it but not by other objects. Once this is done, we use a capital script letter to name the set. If it is possible to list the names of the objects belonging to the set, this list, enclosed in braces ({ }), serves also to name the set. Thus we may agree on "$\mathcal{A}$" as a name of the set consisting of the integers 1, 2, and 3, or we may use $\{1, 2, 3\}$ as its name.

The objects in a given set are called its *elements*, and if sets $\mathcal{A}$ and $\mathcal{B}$ contain exactly the same elements, we say that $\mathcal{A}$ *equals* $\mathcal{B}$, and write $\mathcal{A} = \mathcal{B}$. Thus, in the example above, we have $\mathcal{A} = \{1, 2, 3\}$. If an object a is an element of a set $\mathcal{A}$ we write $a \in \mathcal{A}$. If a is not an element of $\mathcal{A}$, we write $a \notin \mathcal{A}$. In the above example, the following statements are true:

$$1 \in \mathcal{A}$$
$$2 \in \mathcal{A}$$
$$5 \notin \mathcal{A},$$

while the statements

$$3 \notin \mathcal{A}$$
$$4 \in \mathcal{A}$$

are false. If, of two sets $\mathcal{A}$ and $\mathcal{B}$ every element of $\mathcal{A}$ is also an element of $\mathcal{B}$, we say that $\mathcal{A}$ is a *subset* of $\mathcal{B}$ and write $\mathcal{A} \subset \mathcal{B}$. Thus, if $\mathcal{A} = \{1, 2, 3\}$ as above, then $\{1, 3\} \subset \mathcal{A}$ and $\mathcal{A} \subset \{1, 2, 3, 4, 5\}$ are true statements. Obviously if $\mathcal{A} \subset \mathcal{B}$ and $\mathcal{B} \subset \mathcal{A}$ are both true, then $\mathcal{A} = \mathcal{B}$ is true as well.

Note that the words represented by "$\in$", "$=$", and "$\subset$" are verbs each of which requires a pair of nouns to yield a sentence. For the first of these, the second noun is the name of a set, and for the other two, both nouns must name sets.

Occasions arise in mathematical contexts in which we wish to discuss certain members of a given set without specifying them precisely. One example occurs when we wish to assert simply that there is an element of a given set that possesses some property, and another occurs when we wish to assert that every element of a given set has a property. Thus, we might wish to say that there is no greatest integer using the following form:

For any integer, there is a larger integer.

In this example, we must not be specific about the first integer mentioned, since the assertion is a general one, for it gives a property of "any integer." Similarly, we *cannot* name a specific second integer, for its choice depends on how the first integer is chosen. To make statements such as these in mathematics, we use lower case italic letters as names of elements specified only to the extent that they name elements of a given set. A letter used in this way is called a *variable*, and the specified set is called its *domain*. If the set of all integers is the domain of variables used, then the sentence above may be written:

For any x there is a y, such that $x < y$.

These matters are explained more fully in Sec. 2.

Given two sets α and $\mathcal{B}$ we often consider assignments that associate one or more elements of $\mathcal{B}$ with each element of α. Such an assignment is called a *function* if to each element of α exactly one element of $\mathcal{B}$ is assigned. α is called the *domain* of the function, and $\mathcal{B}$ its *image space*. For example, let α and $\mathcal{B}$ both coincide with the set of all human beings living or deceased, then the natural law that assigns a father to each human being is a function with domain α and image space $\mathcal{B}$. Note that every human in the domain is assigned a father, but not every human in $\mathcal{B}$ is assigned to someone in α, for not every member of $\mathcal{B}$ is a father.

We shall denote functions by single letters, with or without subscripts, and occasionally by combinations of letters. Each element in the domain of a function is called an *argument*, and if f is a function and x an argument of f, then the element of the image space assigned to x by f is called its *value* and is denoted by $f(x)$. Thus, if α and $\mathcal{B}$ both coincide with the set of integers, then the assignment of $2x - 1$ to each element x of α is a function with domain α and image space $\mathcal{B}$, since for every integer x, $2x - 1$ is a unique integer. Note that not every element of $\mathcal{B}$ is assigned by this function as a value, for $2x - 1$ is an odd integer for each integer x. However, all odd integers are values of this function. The subset of the image space consisting of all the values of a function f is called the *range* of f.

Let $\alpha = \{1, 2, 3\}$ and $\mathcal{B} = \{4, 5, 6\}$. Then each of the following tables defines a function with domain α and image space $\mathcal{B}$:

1.

x	1	2	3
$f(x)$	4	4	6

2.

x	1	2	3
$g(x)$	5	5	5

3.

x	1	2	3
$h(x)$	6	4	5

4.

x	1	2	3
$j(x)$	4	6	5

The range of f is $\{4, 6\}$, that of g is $\{5\}$, while $\mathcal{B}$ is the range of h and j. Note that the table

x	1	1	2	2	2	3	3
y	4	5	6	5	4	4	5

defines an assignment from $\mathcal{B}$ to α that is not a function, since more than one element of $\mathcal{B}$ is assigned to elements of α. In order that an assignment f be a function we must have:

> If x and y are elements of the domain of f and $x = y$, then $f(x) = f(y)$.

For some fun tions, like h and j above, not only is a unique value assigned to each argument, but for each value there is exactly one argument to which it is assigned. Such a function is called a *one-one correspondence* and has the additional property:

> If x and y are elements in the domain of f and $f(x) = f(y)$, then $x = y$.

A one-one correspondence pairs off the elements in its domain and range so that exactly one element of each is in each pair.

Let $\alpha = \{1, 2, 3\}$ and $\mathcal{B} = \{1, 4, 9\}$, and for each x in α let $g(x) = x^2$. Then g is a one-one correspondence with domain α and range $\mathcal{B}$. On the other hand, if $\alpha = \{-1, 0, 1\}$ and $\mathcal{B} = \{0, 1\}$, then g is a function with domain α and range $\mathcal{B}$ but not a one-one correspondence.

Throughout this book we shall be concerned with certain sets of numbers and here we assign names that we use consistently for these sets. In Sec. 4 of Chap. 2, the properties of the *natural numbers* are developed. Conventional names for these numbers are 0, 1, 2, and so on, and the name of the set of all natural numbers is $\mathfrak{N}$. The *integers* are investigated in Secs. 8 and 9 of that chapter. They are denoted by $0, 1, -1, 2, -2$, and so on, and the name of the set of all integers is $\mathscr{I}$. The remainder of Chap. 2 is devoted to rational numbers which are denoted by fractions p/q of integers with $q \neq 0$. The set of all rational numbers is denoted by $\mathcal{Q}$. The real numbers are treated in the beginning of Chap. 3 and $\mathcal{R}$ denotes the set of all real numbers.

Let n be any natural number other than 0, and let $\mathcal{Q}$ be any nonempty set with at most n elements. If a is a function whose domain is the set $\{1, 2, \ldots, n-1, n\}$ and whose range is $\mathcal{Q}$, we call the set $\{\mathcal{Q}, a\}$ an *ordered n-tuple* with elements in $\mathcal{Q}$. The elements of $\mathcal{Q}$ are considered to be arranged by a in an order that corresponds to the natural order of its domain. If, for an integer i, we denote the value of a by a_i rather than $a(i)$, the ordered n-tuple is denoted by $(a_1, a_2, \ldots, a_n)$, using parentheses to avoid confusion with the simpler notion of (unordered) sets. In case $n = 2$, (a_1, a_2) is called an *ordered pair*.

Consider $\mathcal{Q} = \{1\}$. The only ordered triple (3-tuple) with elements in $\mathcal{Q}$ is $(1, 1, 1)$. If $\mathcal{B} = \{1, 2\}$, there are eight ordered triples with elements in $\mathcal{B}$. They are $(1, 1, 1)$, $(1, 1, 2)$, $(1, 2, 2)$, $(2, 2, 2)$, $(1, 2, 1)$, $(2, 2, 1)$, $(2, 1, 2)$, $(2, 1, 1)$.

The domain of a function f may consist entirely of ordered n-tuples, as would be the case if a number of distinct elements must be determined before a value can be assigned. Thus before the postage on a parcel can be determined, one must know its weight, the zone of its destination, and the class in which it is to be handled. Clearly the order in which these three numbers are made known is significant in determining the postage to be charged. If, for some positive integer n, the domain of a function f is made up of ordered n-tuples, then f is said to be a *function of n arguments* and its value for the n-tuple $(a_1, a_2, \ldots, a_n)$ is denoted by $f(a_1, a_2, \ldots, a_n)$.

Suppose that f is a function of n arguments such that all its first arguments are elements of a set $\mathcal{Q}_1$, all its second arguments are elements of a set $\mathcal{Q}_2$, and so on. If we are to distinguish the sets from which distinct elements of an n-tuple are assigned, it is useful to introduce the notion of cartesian product.

Let $\mathcal{Q}_1, \mathcal{Q}_2, \ldots, \mathcal{Q}_n$ be n sets where n is a natural number greater than 1. The set of all n-tuples $(a_1, a_2, \ldots, a_n)$ for which $a_1 \in \mathcal{Q}_1$, $a_2 \in \mathcal{Q}_2, \ldots, a_n \in \mathcal{Q}_n$ is called the *cartesian product* of the given sets and denoted by $\mathcal{Q}_1 \times \mathcal{Q}_2 \times \cdots \times \mathcal{Q}_n$. If all the sets are equal to some set $\mathcal{Q}$, their cartesian product is denoted by $\mathcal{Q}^n$.

For example, let $\alpha_1 = \{0, 1, 2\}$ and $\alpha_2 = \{1, 2\}$. Then

$$\alpha_1 \times \alpha_2 = \{(0, 1), (0, 2), (1, 1), (1, 2), (2, 1), (2, 2)\}.$$

Note also that $\alpha_2^2 = \{(1, 1), (1, 2), (2, 1), (2, 2)\}$.

The terminology used throughout the book is defined in terms of the notions introduced here. There is some interest in defining some of these notions formally in terms of the others, thus reducing the number of undefined ideas. It is known that this can be done if the notion of "set" alone is left undefined. The notions of function, one to one correspondence, and ordered n-tuple can be defined as sets of certain kinds. The same is true if the notion of "function" is taken as the only primitive idea. However, while such an exercise has important logical implications, using this procedure would tend to obscure rather than clarify the elementary ideas of mathematics that we seek to expose in what follows.

EXERCISES

1. Explain why the definitions of words listed in a given dictionary are circular. Discuss the difficulties that would be encountered in any attempt to eliminate these circularities from a dictionary of a natural language. Must a dictionary that translates French words into English contain circular definitions? Explain.

2. Mention rules other than those of the text which provide definite criteria for dividing a group of students into the categories: bright, average, stupid.

3. In each case below, give rules if possible that provide definite criteria for dividing the given set of objects into the subsets listed:
   (a) Students at Columbia University
       Subsets: freshmen, sophomores, juniors, seniors, graduate students, unclassified students.
   (b) Real numbers
       Subsets: rational numbers, irrational numbers.
   (c) Working men
       Subsets: laborers, white collar workers, professional workers.
   (d) Girls
       Subsets: blondes, brunettes, redheads.

   If rules cannot be found, explain why they cannot.

4. The following statements are definitions of the word in italics. Which of them provide definite criteria for applying the name defined to an object? If possible, alter the definition so that such criteria are provided in case they are not already.

(a) The lead in a pencil is called *hard* if it does not smudge the paper on which one writes with it.

(b) An integer is said to be *odd* if it is not even.

(c) Of two numbers a and b, a *is greater than* b, if their difference $a - b$ is positive. (Assume that definitions of "difference" and "positive" do provide definite criteria.)

(d) A subject at college is *difficult* if no one can get an A in it.

(e) A woman is *beautiful* if more than three men admire her during every week of March, 1962.

5. Given the following sets:

$\alpha = \{1, 3, 5, 7, 9\}$
$\mathcal{B} = \{1, 2, 3, 4, 5, 6, 7, 8, 9\}$
$\mathcal{C} = \{3, 5, 7\},$

which of the following are true statements?

(a) $\alpha \subset \mathcal{C}$

(b) $\mathcal{C} \subset \mathcal{B}$

(c) $\alpha \in \mathcal{B}$

(d) $5 \in \mathcal{C}$

(e) $5 \not\subset \mathcal{B}$

(f) $4 \not\subset \alpha$

(g) $4 \in \mathcal{B}$

(h) $2 \subset \mathcal{C}$

6. In each of the following, b is assigned to a by the relation expressed. Is the assignment a function? If so, name a reasonable domain and range. If not, explain why not.

(a) b is the mother of a.

(b) b is the brother of a.

(c) b is the husband or the father of a.

(d) b is 7 more than twice a.

(e) b is the square root of a.

(f) a and b are twins.

(g) a and b are partners in a bridge tournament.

(h) b is the oldest sister of a.

(i) b is the number of elements in the set a.

(j) b is the subset of a having one fewer element than a.

(k) b is less than a.

(l) b is the negative of a.

(m) b is the reciprocal of a.

7. Which of the relations of Exercise 6 are one-one correspondences? Of those that are functions, but not one-one correspondences, limit the range in some way, if possible, so that they become one to one.

8. Let n be a function such that for any finite set α, $n(\alpha)$ is the number of elements contained in α. Show that

(a) If $n(\alpha) = n(\mathfrak{B})$, then there is a one-one correspondence with domain α and counterdomain $\mathfrak{B}$.

(b) If there is a one-one correspondence with domain α and counterdomain $\mathfrak{B}$, then $n(\alpha) = n(\mathfrak{B})$.

9. List the elements of $\alpha \times \mathfrak{B}$, $\mathfrak{B} \times \alpha$, and α^2 if $\alpha = \{1, 2, 3\}$ and $\mathfrak{B} = \{0, 2\}$.

10. Let n be the function defined in Exercise 8, k be a positive integer, and α be a finite set. Show that the number of k-tuples whose elements are members of α is $[n(\alpha)]^k$.

11. Let n be the function defined in Exercise 8 and α and $\mathfrak{B}$ be finite sets. Show that $n(\alpha \times \mathfrak{B}) = n(\alpha) \cdot n(\mathfrak{B})$.

2 · PREDICATES

In this section we begin a discussion of the syntax of mathematical languages, which is continued into the two sections that follow. The syntax of a language provides rules that permit us to decide what strings of symbols are sentences. If we are presented with a list of nouns in a natural language, such as English, then the simplest device for producing sentences from nouns of this list is to introduce a verb, or predicate. In the sentence "Socrates is a philosopher" for example, we can consider the verb "is" as a device that converts the pair of nouns "Socrates" and "philosopher" into a sentence. The word "is", to this extent, is called a predicate. On the other hand, we could consider the phrase "is a philosopher" to be a predicate, since it is a device that converts the single noun "Socrates" into the given sentence. Thus the part of a sentence to be called its predicate often depends on what we consider the sentence to be asserting. In the first case the sentence is considered to state a relation between two things; in the second it is considered to state a property of one thing.

In the development of a mathematical system, an important concern is whether its sentences are true or false. To be sure, it is also important to know what a sentence asserts, but this is a matter of what objects the nouns denote, and what properties and relations are asserted by the predicates. In studying mathematics we momentarily set aside our concern for the meaning or interpretation of a sentence, concentrating only on whether the sentence is true or false. It is the logic of a mathematical language that provides rules for making this decision. The rules of logic are formulated in such a way that they may be applied independently of the meaning assigned to a sentence being proved. To this extent mathematics is *abstract*.

To give an example, we consider the following rule, used often in elementary algebra:

$$\text{If } x = y \text{ is true, then } x + a = y + a \text{ is true.} \qquad (1)$$

We may interpret x, y, and a as numerals, "$=$" as the relation of equality, and "$+$" as the operation of addition. Then the rule asserts something about sentences of arithmetic. Or we may interpret x and y as names of rectangles, "$=$" as the relation of congruence, and "$+ a$" as the operation of magnifying the dimensions of a rectangle by a factor of a, so that (1) is a rule of geometry. However we interpret (1), we apply it always in the same definite way to decide whether a sentence is true.

We take the abstractness of mathematical procedure into account by distinguishing sentences only as to their truth and falsity. Thus we ask of a predicate not what it asserts of the nouns in its sentence, but only whether the sentence it assigns to these nouns is true or false.

We can consider a mathematical *predicate* to be a function of one or more arguments whose arguments are nouns, and which assigns to each argument (or to each n-tuple of arguments) one of the values T (for "true") or F (for "false"). Just which of these values a predicate assigns for a choice of argument (or arguments) is determined by the logic of the language. A predicate that takes a single noun as an argument is called a *property* or *unary* predicate. If the elements of the domain of a predicate are ordered pairs of nouns, it is called a *relation* or a *binary* predicate. If the elements of the domain of a predicate are ordered n-tuples then the predicate is said to be *n-ary*. The range of any predicate is the set $\{T, F\}$. The domain of a predicate is often called its *universe*. It consists of all nouns of the language to which the predicate makes an assignment.

Consider the unary predicate e having the set $\mathcal{I}$ of all integers as its universe. In order to define this predicate we must specify in some way, usually by listing axioms for e, for what elements x of $\mathcal{I}$ its value $e(x)$ is T and for what arguments its value is F. Let us adopt the following axioms for e:

e1. $e(0) = T$

e2. $e(1) = F$

e3. If $e(x) = T$, then $e(x + 2) = e(x - 2) = T$

e4. If $e(x) = F$, then $e(x + 2) = e(x - 2) = F$.

Note that a combination of $e1$ and $e3$ allows us to establish $e(2) = e(-2) = T$, and combining this again with $e3$, we obtain $e(4) = e(-4) = T$. In fact, no matter what *even* integer x is, the axioms allow us to prove that $e(x) = T$. In the same way we can use $e2$ and $e4$ to prove that for any *odd* integer x, $e(x) = F$. The decision as to whether e assigns T or F to a given integer x is based only on the axioms $e1$–$e4$ and logical rules for combining them. The interpretation given e plays no role in the proofs of the results.

In fact, a result of the consequences of the axioms is that we may interpret the predicate e in a very natural way. Since $e(x)$ is true if and only if x is an even integer we may assign to the sentence $e(6)$, for example, the meaning "6 is an even integer." Further $e(3)$ means "3 is an even integer" and the fact that this is false is reflected in the axioms for e by the provability of $e(3) = F$.

A binary predicate that occurs in most mathematical languages is the predicate q satisfying the following axioms:

$q1$. For each x, $q(x, x) = T$

$q2$. For each x and each y, if $q(x, y) = T$, then $q(y, x) = T$

$q3$. For each x, each y, and each z, if $q(x, y) = T$ and $q(y, z) = T$, then $q(x, z) = T$.

Of course the arguments of q occur in ordered pairs, since q is binary. Often the universe of a binary predicate is the set $\mathcal{Q}^2$ of all ordered pairs of elements of a given set $\mathcal{Q}$. If this is true for the predicate q satisfying the axioms $q1$–$q3$, we call q an *equivalence relation* over $\mathcal{Q}$. Note that $q(x, y)$ can be interpreted as "x and y are identical." If $\mathcal{Q}$ is a set of numerals, we may interpret $q(x, y)$ as "x and y stand for the same number." Equivalence relations are discussed further in Section 7.

One difference between the studies of arithmetic and algebra is that our interest in the first is directed toward the study and proofs of statements about specific numbers, while in the second we deal with number properties and relations expressed in general. For example, we establish in the study of arithmetic the statement

$$4(2 + 3) = 4 \cdot 2 + 4 \cdot 3$$

while in the study of algebra we are more likely to investigate the more general property that for each number x, y, and z in the set of numbers under study, the relation

$$x(y + z) = xy + xz$$

is true. The goal of the former is to establish (in this case) the effect of combining the operations of addition and multiplication and applying the combination to the particular numbers 4, 2, and 3. The latter establishes a relation among these operations and the equality predicate which holds for all members of some universe of numbers.

In order to state properties of predicates and operations in the most general way without limiting ourselves merely to particular statements that can be written in terms of them, we must introduce into the language some device for naming them. Of course, we do so when we introduce letters as names of functions, for both operations and predicates are particular kinds of functions. We might let "p" stand for the operation of addition, "m" stand for the operation of multiplication, and "q" for the predicate of equality, as before. Then $p(2, 4)$ is another name for the sum of 2 and 4, usually denoted by $2 + 4$, and $m(1, 3)$ is another name for the product $1 \cdot 3$. Then the statement $4(2 + 3) = 4 \cdot 2 + 4 \cdot 3$ can be written in the form

$$q(m(4, p(2, 3)), p(m(4, 2), m(4, 3))).$$

Though this provides a consistent device for naming functions and predicates which has important theoretical advantages when dealing with their abstract properties, such a form for the statement is completely unacceptable for use here because it is unfamiliar and cumbersome, and because there are more familiar devices for making such a statement. We are not in the habit of denoting operations and predicates by letters. Instead we use conventional signs like "$+$," "$\cdot$," and "$=$" to write the sentences of arithmetic, and we use variables in place of numerals to express the operations and predicates themselves.

In referring to the predicate of equality we often use the form $x = y$, agreeing that x and y are variables that name unspecified elements of a given set. Note that "$x = y$" is not a sentence because, for one thing, the variables do not name specific numbers, and, for another, there is no way to decide whether it is true or false. Neither is "$x = y$" the name of the predicate of equality. But it does represent this predicate q of equality in that the value assigned to an ordered pair (a, b) in the universe of q can be obtained by substituting a for x and b for y in "$x = y$." Thus "$x = y$" is the name of the value that predicate q assigns to an unspecified ordered pair (x, y) in its universe. We call this form an *open statement* since we think of the variables as blanks to be filled by nouns. It becomes a (closed) statement when appropriately chosen nouns are substituted for the variables.

In general, then, an open statement is a statement-like expression used to represent a predicate and composed of conventional symbols of the language together with occurrences of variables in positions conventionally assigned to nouns. In the same way, we may represent operations by forms similar to those that represent the results of the operations. Thus we often represent the addition operation by the form $x + y$, because the plus sign is used conventionally in statements in which addition plays a part. The form "$x + y$" is called an *expression* and represents the sum of an unspecified ordered pair (x, y) of elements of the domain of its definition. A specific sum can be obtained by the substitution of specific numerals for x and y.

Similar considerations apply in general. If an n-ary predicate is assigned a name, say p, we represent the associated open statement by $p(x_1, x_2, \ldots, x_n)$, and if f is an n-ary operation, then the associated expression is represented by $f(x_1, x_2, \ldots, x_n)$.

The process of substitution of numerals for variables proceeds according to the following rule: If a numeral a is substituted for an occurrence of a variable x, then a must simultaneously be substituted for every occurrence of x in the open statement or expression. To understand the result of failing to follow this rule consider the expressions

$$x^2 + 8x \quad \text{and} \quad x^2 + 16.$$

Note that even though the second expression can be obtained by substituting 2 for the second occurrence of x in the first, the two expressions do not represent the same operation. Note that the first of these assigns to 3, for example, the number $3^2 + 8 \cdot 3$ or 33, while the second assigns $3^2 + 16$ or 25 to 3. Similarly the predicates represented by

$$x^2 + x = x(x + 1) \quad \text{and} \quad x^2 + 1 = x(x + 1)$$

are not the same even though the second can be obtained by substituting 1 for the second occurrence of x in the first. Note that the first is true for all real numbers x, while the second is true only for the number 1.

If an open statement or expression with two or more variables is changed by the substitution of a noun for every occurrence of one of its variables, the open statement or expression obtained represents a different predicate or operation. Thus, the open statement

$$x^2 + xy^2 - 3xyz = yz^2$$

represents a ternary predicate which expresses a relation among three numbers. If 3 is substituted for x we obtain

$$9 + 3y^2 - 9yz = yz^2$$

which represents a binary predicate expressing a relation between two numbers. Now if 1 is substituted throughout for z, we have

$$9 + 3y^2 - 9y = y$$

which represents a unary predicate or property. Similarly $x - 2y + z$ represents an operation on three numbers, $3 - 2y + z$ a binary operation, and $3 - 2 + z$ (or $1 + z$) a unary operation.

Our interest in open statements lies beyond the fact that we can convert them into sentences by substitutions. In considering a particular predicate two questions arise that can often be answered without reference to particular nouns to which this predicate applies. Our concern may not be to find out to what nouns the predicate assigns the value T, but rather solely the fact that there are such nouns in its universe. Thus, if a lady on a shopping trip finds some article that she "simply must have," the price of which is $45, her concern is to determine if she has available some number, x, of dollars that is greater than or equal to 45. She has no need to know what that number x is—merely that it exists. A number of common situations in mathematics are similar, and to describe such a situation we use a device called the existential quantifier. If a unary predicate p is represented by an open statement in the single variable x, then the fact that p assigns T to some element of its universe is expressed by writing $(E\ x)p(x)$, and "$(E\ x)$" is called an *existential quantifier*. The statement $(E\ x)p(x)$ may be read "For some x, $p(x)$ is true," "There exists an x such that $p(x)$ is true," or simply "For some x, $p(x)$." This statement is true if p assigns T to at least one of its arguments, and false if p assigns F to all of its arguments. In the universe of integers,

$$(E\ x)[x^2 = 1]$$

is true since there are two integers x for which $x^2 = 1$, while the statement

$$(E\ x)[x^2 = 3]$$

is false. Note that the decision of whether an existential statement is true or false depends on the universe considered. Both of the statements are true in the universe of real numbers, while neither of them is true in the universe of even integers.

It is convenient to be able to express also the fact that a predicate p assigns T to each element in its universe. If it does, we write $(x)p(x)$ and read this statement as "For all x, $p(x)$ is true," "For each x, $p(x)$ is true," or simply "For each x, $p(x)$." In this statement, "(x)" is called a *universal quantifier*. If for a given predicate p the statement $(x)p(x)$ is true, we say that p is *universally true*. For example, a property of the number 1 is that its product with any number is that number. This is expressed by the statement $(x)[x \cdot 1 = x]$.

If an open statement with two or more variables is preceded by a quantifier in one of the variables, a predicate is represented that has one fewer argument than the predicate represented originally. Thus,

$$(y)[x + y = y + x]$$

represents a unary predicate which assigns T to each real number x. Thus if the real numbers form the universe then

$$(x)(y)[x + y = y + x]$$

is a true statement.

If a predicate is defined by preceding an open statement by a number of quantifiers in variables that occur in it, it is important to distinguish between the variables of the open statement that are in the quantifiers and those that are not. To denote this distinction, we say that the variables that occur in the quantifiers are *bound* variables, while the others are *free*. The substitutions of constants for bound variables cannot be interpreted in a useful way and are not allowed. Thus the substitution of 3 for x in $(x)[x \cdot 1 = x]$ yields $(3)[3 \cdot 1 = 3]$ to which no reasonable meaning can be assigned, though we may (sometimes profitably) substitute y for x throughout. On the other hand the same substitution in the open statement

$$(y)[x + y = y + x]$$

yields the statement

$$(y)[3 + y = y + 3]$$

which is true in some universes.

EXERCISES

1. Each of the open statements below represents a predicate with arguments in the given universe $\mathfrak{U}$. Name the set of all elements of $\mathfrak{U}$ to which the predicate assigns the value T, using your own interpretation of the predicate and universe given.

   (a) $x + y < 5$; $\mathfrak{U}$: ordered pairs of positive integers.
   (b) x is a state whose name begins with the letter "A"; $\mathfrak{U}$: all states of the United States.
   (c) $x^2 - 5x - 6 = 0$; $\mathfrak{U}$: all positive integers.
   (d) $x^2 - 5x - 6 = 0$; $\mathfrak{U}$: all rational numbers.
   (e) $x^2 > x$; $\mathfrak{U}$: all rational numbers.

    (f) x lies west of y; $\mathfrak{U}$: ordered pairs of states of the United States that border Mexico.

    (g) x is a subset of y; $\mathfrak{U}$: all ordered pairs of subsets of $\{1, 2, 3, 4\}$.

2. Show that $e(6) = \mathrm{T}$ and that $e(-5) = \mathrm{F}$, using the axioms $e1$–$e4$.

3. Use the conventional properties of arithmetic to show that if $e(x) = \mathrm{T}$ for an integer x then $(\mathrm{E}\ y)[x = 2y]$ is true in the universe $\mathscr{I}$ of integers.

4. Show that if x is an integer for which $(y)[x = 2y + 1]$ is true, then $e(x) = \mathrm{F}$.

5. Tell whether each of the following statements is true or false in the universe $\mathscr{I}$ of integers.

    (a) $(x)e(x)$
    (b) $(\mathrm{E}\ x)e(x)$
    (c) $(x)q(x, x)$
    (d) $(\mathrm{E}\ x)q(x, x)$
    (e) $(x)(y)q(x, y)$
    (f) $(x)(\mathrm{E}\ y)q(x, y)$
    (g) $(\mathrm{E}\ x)(y)q(x, y)$

6. Show that if $q(x, y) = \mathrm{T}$ and $q(z, y) = \mathrm{T}$, then $q(x, z) = \mathrm{T}$, using the axioms $q1$–$q3$ for equivalence relations.

7. Consider the following axioms for a *strict order relation* m:

    $m1$. For each x, $m(x, x) = \mathrm{F}$.
    $m2$. For each x and each y, if $m(x, y) = \mathrm{T}$, then $m(y, x) = \mathrm{F}$.
    $m3$. For each x, each y, and each z, if $m(x, y) = \mathrm{T}$ and $m(y, z) = \mathrm{T}$, then $m(x, z) = \mathrm{T}$.
    $m4$. For each x and each y, if x and y are distinct, then either $m(x, y) = \mathrm{T}$ or $m(y, x) = \mathrm{T}$.

Verify that the predicates represented in conventional notation by the open statements below are strict order relations:

    (a) $x < y$; $\mathfrak{U}$: all integers.
    (b) $x > y$; $\mathfrak{U}$: all integers.
    (c) x is a factor of y; $\mathfrak{U}$: all positive integer powers of 3.

8. Show that no equivalence relation is a strict order relation.

9. Verify that the predicates represented in conventional notation below are not strict order relations:

    (a) $x \le y$; $\mathfrak{U}$: all integers.
    (b) $x \ge y$; $\mathfrak{U}$: all integers.
    (c) x is a factor of y; $\mathfrak{U}$: all integers.
    (d) $x \subset y$; $\mathfrak{U}$: all subsets of any set.

10. The *converse* of a binary relation r is a relation s defined so that $s(x, y) = r(y, x)$ for each x and each y. In the universe $\mathcal{I}^2$ of ordered pairs of integers write an open statement that represents the converse of the relation represented by:

   (a) $x < y$
   (b) $x > y$
   (c) $x = y$
   (d) x is a factor of y
   (e) $x + y = y^2$

11. For predicates q and e and operations p and m as in the text, write the following open statements in conventional notation:

   (a) $q(p(x, p(y, z)), p((x, y), z))$
   (b) $e(m(2, x), p(x, 3))$
   (c) $q(m(x, y), m(y, x))$
   (d) $e(p(m(1, x), 1), 3)$.

12. If "x is a factor of y" is the predicate defined by the open statement $(E z)[y = zx]$, discuss whether this predicate is definite in the sense of Section 1. Show that this predicate satisfies properties $q1$ and $q3$, but not $q2$.

13. Show that the converse of an equivalence relation is an equivalence relation and that the converse of a strict order relation is a strict order relation.

3 · PREDICATE CONNECTIVES

When an English sentence is a simple one it is usually so because we can analyze it into a single predicate and some nouns about which the predicate says something. By using conjunctions to join simple sentences together (according to fixed rules) sentences may be obtained that have quite complicated structures. These conjunctions are words like "and," "or," "although," and so on. We need to express some of these more complicated ideas in mathematical languages as well. In mathematics, however, we can continue to think of all sentences as simple ones if we make some minor changes from English syntax. To do this we consider the "compounding" operation to be performed on predicates rather than sentences and then a compound sentence is the value assigned by a compound predicate to a given n-tuple of arguments. For example, we may think of the compound sentence $2 \leq 3$ either as a compound formed by joining the two sentences $2 < 3$ and $2 = 3$ by "or," or as the value for the argument pair $(2, 3)$ of the compound predicate $x \leq y$.

If we are to take the latter course, then we must adjust our syntax to include two situations that may arise. First, in order that our rules apply in cases in which the predicates have arguments from distinct universes, we introduce vacuous or useless variables so that they can be redefined with a common universe. No difficulty arises when we combine predicates represented by $x < y$ and $x = y$ to obtain the predicate represented by $x \leq y$, for the three predicates share the same set of ordered pairs as universe in most meaningful discussions. Suppose we wish to combine the predicates represented by $x < y$ and $y < z$ to yield a predicate represented by $x < y < z$. The first two of these have sets of ordered pairs as universes, while the universe of the third is a set of ordered triples. To simplify our work, we consider the universe of each of the first two predicates to coincide with the universe of the predicate to be defined. Then the third element of an ordered triple is vacuous for the first predicate, and the first element is vacuous for the second. In each case the truth value assigned to an ordered triple does not depend on what is substituted for the vacuous variable.

The second consideration is that we would like to include the conjunctions of sentences as special cases of the devices we are about to define for predicates. To do this we consider any true sentence to be a predicate that assigns T to each argument in any universe, and a false sentence to be one that assigns F to each argument in any universe. Thus, the predicate which takes ordered triples as arguments and is represented by

$$\text{if } 1 + 1 = 2 \text{ and } x = y, \text{ then } xz + (1 + 1) = yz + 2$$

is made up of the sentence $1 + 1 = 2$, and the predicates represented by

$$x = y \quad \text{and} \quad xz + (1 + 1) = yz + 2.$$

These three are all considered to be ternary predicates with a universe that coincides with that of their compound.

The devices that combine predicates into compounds are called connectives. Thus a *connective* is a function that takes predicates as arguments and assigns a predicate as a value. We consider only unary and binary connectives here, since those that are more complicated may be defined by combining these. Since our fundamental concern with a predicate is whether it assigns T or F to an argument, a compound predicate is defined whenever it is specified how the assignment made by the compound depends on the assignments made by its parts. In order to define a connective, then, we must specify for every combination of truth values of the connected predicates what truth value the compound predicate assigns.

We define the *negation* $\sim p$ of a predicate p as a predicate which assigns F to those arguments to which p assigns T and vice versa. We can specify this definition by a *truth table* which gives the assignment of the compound for all possible assignments of its parts as follows:

p	$\sim p$
T	F
F	T

so that the decision as to the assignment $\sim p$ makes is automatic as soon as the value assigned by p is known. Some predicates that are negations are represented by open statements in a conventional way. Thus if p is represented by $x = y$ then $\sim p$ is represented by $x \neq y$. Similarly for $x < y$, $x > y$, and so on. The negation $\sim p$ can always be represented by placing the negation sign "$\sim$" before the open statement that represents p.

Given two predicates p and q with the same universe, their *disjunction* $p \vee q$ is a predicate with the same universe and is defined by the table

p	q	$p \vee q$
T	T	T
T	F	T
F	T	T
F	F	F

If either of two predicates or both assign T to an argument, then their disjunction does also. In the remaining case that both predicates assign F, their disjunction also assigns F. In algebra and arithmetic the conventional abbreviation for the disjunctions $(x = y) \vee (x < y)$ and $(x = y) \vee (x > y)$ are $x \leq y$ and $x \geq y$ respectively. Thus, for example, $2 \leq 5$ is true, since it is an abbreviation of $(2 = 5) \vee (2 < 5)$, and $2 < 5$ is true. On the other hand $7 \leq 3$ is false since $7 < 3$ and $7 = 3$ are both false.

Connectives may be compounded to form other connectives. Thus if p and q are predicates we may combine the connectives $\sim$ and $\vee$ with them to define the predicate $\sim(p \vee q)$ whose truth table can be deduced from the truth tables of $\sim$ and $\vee$. To do this, p and q are combined first to yield $p \vee q$, and negation is applied to the result:

p	q	$p \vee q$	$\sim(p \vee q)$
T	T	T	F
T	F	T	F
F	T	T	F
F	F	F	T

The last column characterizes the new connective defined. Since the new predicate assigns T only when both p and q assign F, the connective is interpreted in English as "neither . . . nor . . . ." We use the single symbol "|" to denote this binary connective and define $p|q$ so that its truth table coincides with that of $\sim(p \lor q)$.

Another important connective that can be defined from $\sim$ and $\lor$ is the one whose value for predicates p and q is $\sim[(\sim p) \lor (\sim q)]$. Its truth table is

p	q	$\sim p$	$\sim q$	$(\sim p) \lor (\sim q)$	$\sim[(\sim p) \lor (\sim q)]$
T	T	F	F	F	T
T	F	F	T	T	F
F	T	T	F	T	F
F	F	T	T	T	F

so that the new predicate assigns T only if p and q both assign T. Thus the new predicate is rendered in English as "p and q." We abbreviate this predicate by "$p \land q$." Conventional usage in algebra and arithmetic introduces $x < y < z$ as an abbreviation for $(x < y) \land (y < z)$. Similarly for $x > y > z$. The predicate $p \land q$ is said to be the *conjunction* of the predicates p and q.

We wish to define a connective which reflects in mathematical language the logical properties of the conjunction "if . . . then . . ." of English. To do this, note that if p and q are predicates, we want the predicate "if p then q" to assign T in case p and q both assign T, and F in case p assigns T and q assigns F. This is because the usual meaning of "if p then q" is that q is true whenever p is true. This requires part of the truth table for this connective to be

p	q	
T	T	T
T	F	F
F	T	
F	F	

and the sense in which the new connective is used provides no criteria for determining what assignment is made in the last two cases. Now q itself and the connective $p \land q$ have truth tables that satisfy these requirements, but to have the new connective coincide with either of these would be contrary to the interpretation in mind. Another connective that agrees with these in the first two cases, but only in those, is $(\sim p) \vee q$. Its truth table is

p	q	$(\sim p) \vee q$
T	T	T
T	F	F
F	T	T
F	F	T

which assigns T whenever p assigns F. The predicate $(\sim p) \vee q$ agrees with the intended interpretation since it makes the appropriate assignment in the first two cases, and yet it coincides with neither q nor $p \wedge q$. The proposed predicate satisfies the requirements of the interpretation and in doing so assigns F in as few cases as possible. This becomes a decided advantage in using $(\sim p) \vee q$ to render "if p then q" in mathematical discourse. We abbreviate this compound predicate by $p \rightarrow q$ and call it the *conditional* of p and q. If it assigns T, then q assigns T in all cases that p assigns T. Hence we may render it in English also as "p is a sufficient condition for q." Since this means that p cannot assign T unless q assigns T, we obtain the renditions "p only if q" and "q is a necessary condition for p."

Examples of conditionals investigated in algebra are

$$x < y \rightarrow x + z < y + z$$

$$x = y \rightarrow zx = zy.$$

To demonstrate that these are true for all choices of x, y, and z, it must be shown that whenever x and y are chosen so that the part before the arrow (called the *antecedent*) is true, the other part (called the *consequent*) is also true for these choices and any z.

For predicates p and q the conditionals $p \rightarrow q$ and $q \rightarrow p$ are called *converses* of each other. In comparing the truth tables of a pair of converses

p	q	$p \rightarrow q$	$q \rightarrow p$
T	T	T	T
T	F	F	T
F	T	T	F
F	F	T	T

note that they both assign T in exactly those cases that p and q assign the same value. This is described by saying that "p is a necessary and sufficient condition for q" or "p if and only if q." A connective called the *biconditional* is defined to reflect this usage as the conjunction $(p \rightarrow q) \wedge (q \rightarrow p)$ of the pair of converses and is abbreviated by $p \leftrightarrow q$. Its truth table is

p	q	$p \leftrightarrow q$
T	T	T
T	F	F
F	T	F
F	F	T

Note that this truth table also agrees with the truth table for the conditional in the first two cases. We now have interpretations of all four connectives that assign T in the first case and F in the second case of their truth tables.

Predicate connectives can be used to define some of the predicates of a language in terms of others in the way illustrated above by the definition above of "unequal to," "less than or equal to," and so on. One can show that there are four unary connectives, sixteen binary connectives, sixty-four ternary connectives, and in general 2^{2n} n-ary connectives for any positive integer n. It is not surprising that pairs of connectives can be defined that have identical truth tables. The definition of $p \rightarrow q$ insists that its truth table be the same as that of $(\sim p) \vee q$. The reader may check that $\sim[p \wedge (\sim q)]$ has the same truth table as well. Predicates having the same truth table assign the same truth value to each n-tuple of arguments regardless of the universe in which they are defined. Such predicates can be used interchangeably as parts of statements in the language being used and are said to be *logically equivalent*. Thus two predicates are logically equivalent if they are defined using connectives that have the same truth table. Consider the truth table for $\sim[(\sim p) \wedge (\sim q)]$ for example:

p	q	$\sim p$	$\sim q$	$(\sim p) \wedge (\sim q)$	$\sim[(\sim p) \wedge (\sim q)]$
T	T	F	F	F	T
T	F	F	T	F	T
F	T	T	F	F	T
F	F	T	T	T	F

which is the same as that of $p \vee q$. The fact that the truth tables of these two predicates coincide is proof that they are equivalent. Logical equivalence is a relation among predicates that implies that the predicates related assign the same truth value to every argument in *every* universe they have in common.

Another relation between predicates p and q of importance here occurs in case q assigns T to every argument to which p assigns T in any universe that p and q have in common. In this case we say that p *logically implies* q. This means that the knowledge that $p(a) = $ T for a given argument a is sufficient to assert that $q(a) = $ T as well.

These relations may be defined relative to a given universe $\mathfrak{U}$. We say that p is equivalent to q (p implies q) in the universe $\mathfrak{U}$ if $p(a) = q(a)$ $[q(a) = $ T whenever $p(a) = $ T$]$ for every element a of $\mathfrak{U}$. Obviously, if p is logically equivalent to q, then p is equivalent to q in every universe, and similarly for implication. Note, however, that $x > 0$ is equivalent to $[(y \neq 0) \wedge (x = y^2)]$ in the universe of real numbers, since every positive real number is the square of a nonzero number and the square of every nonzero real number is positive. In the universe of integers, however, the predicates are not equivalent since there are positive integers that are not squares of integers. Thus, the predicates are not logically equivalent.

On the other hand the predicate $x < y < z$ logically implies the predicate $y < z$, for the former is an abbreviation for $(x < y) \wedge (y < z)$ and for any predicates p and q, $p \wedge q$ logically implies q. To see this consult the truth tables for $p \wedge q$ and q and note that $p \wedge q$ assigns T only if q assigns T.

Using connectives one can define predicates that assign T to each of their arguments in any universe whatsoever. Such predicates are said to be *logically true*. An example of a logically true predicate is $p \vee (\sim p)$, where p is any predicate, for its truth table is

p	$\sim p$	$p \vee (\sim p)$
T	F	T
F	T	T

every entry of which is T. A predicate like $p \wedge (\sim p)$ that assigns F to every argument of any universe is said to be *logically false*.

EXERCISES

1. Using connectives and open statements of the form $x = y$, $x < y$, and $x > y$, write predicates of which the following are abbreviations.

(a) $2 \not< x$

(b) $x < y \leq z$

(c) $x < y \not< 6$

(d) $3 \leq x \leq 7$

(e) $3 > x > z > 1$

(f) $x \not\leq 4$

(g) $x = y < z$

(h) $x \neq z \not> 2$

2. Explain why $x < y > z$ cannot be considered as an abbreviation of a compound predicate in the same sense that $x < y < z$ can. Attempt to define the sentence obtained from $x < y > z$ by considering special choices of substitutions of integers for x, y, and z. Why does the attempt fail?

3. Let $\mathfrak{U}$ be the set of all ordered triples (x, y, z) of integers. For each of the following binary predicates defined in the universe $\mathfrak{U}$ which element of the ordered triples is vacuous? Tell whether the predicate assigns T or F to the triple given.

   (a) $x < y$: $(1, 5, 1)$
   (b) $x = y$: $(3, 2, 1)$
   (c) $z \leq x$: $(1, 1, 1)$
   (d) $(E\ x)[z = xy]$: $(1, 4, 8)$
   (e) $(E\ y)[x^2 + y^2 = z^2]$: $(3, 9, 5)$
   (f) $(E\ x)[x^2 + y^2 < z^2]$: $(2, 1, 1)$

4. Give the truth table for each of the following compound predicates.

   (a) $[\sim(\sim p) \vee q] \wedge (\sim q)$ (f) $p \leftrightarrow \sim q$
   (b) $(\sim p) \to q$ (g) $\sim[p \wedge (\sim q)]$
   (c) $(\sim p) \to (\sim q)$ (h) $p \to (q \to p)$
   (d) $(p \wedge q) \to p$ (i) $p \to (p \wedge q)$
   (e) $(p \vee q) \to q$ (j) $p \to (p \vee q)$

5. Inspecting the truth tables obtained in Exercise 4 as well as the truth tables for p and for q, list those predicates from Exercise 4 that are

   (a) logically true
   (b) logically false
   (c) pairs of logically equivalent predicates
   (d) pairs of predicates in which the first implies the second.

6. Prove that p and q are logically equivalent if and only if $p \leftrightarrow q$ is logically true.

7. Prove that p logically implies q if and only if $p \to q$ is logically true.

8. Prove that any predicate logically implies a logically true predicate, and that a logically false predicate logically implies any predicate.

9. Prove that all logically true predicates are logically equivalent, and that all logically false predicates are logically equivalent.

10. Give an example other than the one in the text of a pair of predicates that are equivalent in some universe but not logically equivalent. Give an example of a pair of predicates in which the first implies the second in some universe but does not logically imply it.

11. Show that the number of entries in the truth table of an n-ary connective is 2^n, and devise a system for listing them similar to that given in the text for listing the entries for unary and binary connectives.

12. Show that there are 16 distinct binary connectives. For any positive integer n show that there are 2^{2n} distinct n-ary connectives.

13. Show that all sixteen binary connectives are compounds of

   (a) $\sim$ and $\vee$
   (b) $\sim$ and $\wedge$
   (c) $\sim$ and $\rightarrow$
   (d) The single connective $|$.

14. Show that some binary connectives cannot be defined as compounds of $\vee$, $\wedge$, $\rightarrow$, and $\leftrightarrow$.

15. Show that some binary connectives cannot be defined as compounds of $\sim$ and $\leftrightarrow$.

4 · SOLUTION SETS AND THEIR DIAGRAMS

If p is a predicate with universe $\mathfrak{U}$, it is often important to consider the subset of $\mathfrak{U}$ consisting of all elements a for which $p(a) = \mathrm{T}$. This subset of $\mathfrak{U}$ is called the *solution set* of p and of any open statement that represents p. If a predicate and its universe are both well-defined, then the solution set of the predicate is also well-defined in that universe. Both predicate and universe must be specified before the solution set can be determined. In this section we consider solution sets of open statements, relations among them, and operations on them. The discussion assumes that here each open statement contains the single variable x so that all predicates are unary. Analogous considerations may be discussed for n-ary predicates for any positive integer n. In this case what is represented here as a single argument is to be interpreted as an ordered n-tuple.

If a predicate is denoted by a lower case letter (say p), we shall denote its solution set in a specified universe $\mathfrak{U}$ by the corresponding script capital letter ($\mathscr{P}$, in this case). Otherwise any script capital can be assigned to denote a solution set, or the set may be named by listing its elements within braces. If an open statement is given in a specified universe $\mathfrak{U}$, then "$\{x| \ldots\}$" acts as a name for its solution set, where the three dots are replaced by the open statement. This device is known as the *set builder* and all occurrences of x in it are bound.

For example, let $\mathfrak{U}$ be the set of all integers and p be the predicate such that $p(x)$ means that x is an even integer. An open statement that represents p in terms of arithmetic notions is $(\mathrm{E}\ y)[x = 2y]$ in the single free variable x. The solution set of p in $\mathfrak{U}$ is named by any one of the following:

$$\mathscr{P}; \quad \{\ldots, -4, -2, 0, 2, 4, \ldots\}; \quad \text{or} \quad \{x|(\mathrm{E}\ y)[x = 2y]\}.$$

The last two names permit one to check easily the truth of a statement that a given integer is even. The first name is used in theoretical work in which only the association between predicate and solution set need be made explicit.

Note that the solution set depends on the choice of universe, for if the example is changed so that the universe contains only the positive integers, then the solution set named by $\{x|(E\ y)[x = 2y]\}$ is no longer listed as above, but as $\{2, 4, 6, \ldots\}$.

Recall that two predicates p and q with a common universe $\mathfrak{U}$ are equivalent in $\mathfrak{U}$ if $p(a) = q(a)$ for every a in $\mathfrak{U}$. This means that the solution sets $\mathcal{P}$ and $\mathcal{Q}$ contain the same elements of $\mathfrak{U}$. In this case we say that $\mathcal{P}$ and $\mathcal{Q}$ are *equal* and write $\mathcal{P} = \mathcal{Q}$. Since $p(a) \leftrightarrow q(a)$ is true if and only if $p(a) = q(a)$, we define $\mathcal{P} = \mathcal{Q}$ to mean $(x)[p(x) \leftrightarrow q(x)]$.

It can be shown in the universe of integers, for example, that

$$2x + 1 = 3 \quad \text{and} \quad x = 1$$

are equivalent, that is, that the statement

$$(x)[(2x + 1 = 3) \leftrightarrow (x = 1)]$$

is true. Thus the solution sets of these open statements are equal by definition. The solution set is, of course, $\{1\}$.

Recall that p implies q in $\mathfrak{U}$ if $q(a) = T$ for every a in $\mathfrak{U}$ for which $p(a) = T$. Using connectives, this statement is equivalent to saying that $(x)[p(x) \rightarrow q(x)]$ is true in $\mathfrak{U}$. In this case every element of $\mathcal{P}$ is also an element of $\mathcal{Q}$, so we say that $\mathcal{P}$ *is a subset* of $\mathcal{Q}$ and write $\mathcal{P} \subset \mathcal{Q}$. Note, for example, that in the universe of integers

$$\{x\,|\,x = 1\} \subset \{x\,|\,x^2 = x\}$$

for $(x)[x = 1 \rightarrow x^2 = x]$ is true in that universe. However, the converse inclusion

$$\{x\,|\,x^2 = x\} \subset \{x\,|\,x = 1\}$$

is false, for the example $x = 0$ shows that the converse implication

$$(x)[x^2 = x \rightarrow x = 1]$$

is false.

The reader is asked to show in the exercises that $\mathcal{P} = \mathcal{Q}$ if and only if $\mathcal{P} \subset \mathcal{Q}$ and $\mathcal{Q} \subset \mathcal{P}$, where $\mathcal{P}$ and $\mathcal{Q}$ are any solution sets. If $\mathcal{P}$ is not empty, $\mathcal{P} \subset \mathcal{Q}$, and $\mathcal{P} \neq \mathcal{Q}$ we say that $\mathcal{P}$ is a *proper* subset of $\mathcal{Q}$.

Certain predicates p in a universe $\mathfrak{U}$ have the property that $p(a) = T$ for every a in $\mathfrak{U}$. Such predicates have the entire universe $\mathfrak{U}$ as a solution set and are said to be *universally true*. If q is any predicate and p is universally true, then $(x)[q(x) \rightarrow p(x)]$ is true. Thus $Q \subset U$ for every solution set Q. An example of a universally true predicate in the universe of integers is represented by

$$x^2 + x = x(x + 1)$$

since it is true when any integer is substituted for x. On the other hand, some predicates are universally false in a given universe, like the predicate $3x = 5$ in the universe of integers. No element of the universe is in the solution set of such a predicate and we say that its solution set is *empty*. We denote the empty set (we need only one) by ε. If p is universally false in a universe U, then $(x)[p(x) \rightarrow q(x)]$ for any predicate q. Thus $\varepsilon \subset Q$ for any solution set Q. We have, for example,

$$\{x|\, 3x = 5\} = \{x|\, x^2 = 2\} = \{x|\, 1 < x < 2\} = \varepsilon$$

in the universe of integers.

A *set operation* is a function that takes sets as arguments and assigns a set as a value. We define here a unary and several binary set operations whose values are used to denote sets related in a particular way to the arguments of the operations.

If p is a predicate in the universe U and $\mathcal{P}$ its solution set, then the *complement of* $\mathcal{P}$ is the set of all elements of U that are not elements of $\mathcal{P}$. The complement of $\mathcal{P}$ is denoted by $\mathcal{P}'$ and is the solution set of the predicate $\sim p$. If $U = \{1, 2, 3, 4, 5\}$ and $\mathcal{P} = \{1, 3, 5\}$, then $\mathcal{P}' = \{2, 4\}$. If U is the set of all integers and $\mathcal{P} = \{x|\, x < 2\}$, then

$$\mathcal{P}' = \{x|\, x \geq 2\} = \{x|\, x > 1\}.$$

Note that $U' = \varepsilon$ and $\varepsilon' = U$, and if $\mathcal{P} \subset Q$, then $Q' \subset \mathcal{P}'$. To prove the last relation, note that $p(x) \rightarrow q(x)$ is logically equivalent to $\sim q(x) \rightarrow \sim p(x)$, so that $(x)[p(x) \rightarrow q(x)]$ is true in any universe if and only if $(x)[\sim q(x) \rightarrow \sim p(x)]$ is true. Proofs of the first two relations are left as exercises.

Let p and q be predicates in a universe U and

$$\mathcal{P} = \{x|p(x)\} \quad \text{and} \quad Q = \{x|q(x)\}.$$

The set of all elements of U for which p and q both assign the value T is called the *intersection* of $\mathcal{P}$ and Q. This set is denoted by $\mathcal{P} \cap Q$ and is the solution set of $p(x) \wedge q(x)$. The set of all elements of U for which either p or q both assign the value T is called the *union* of $\mathcal{P}$ and Q. This set is denoted by $\mathcal{P} \cup Q$ and is the solution set of $p(x) \vee q(x)$.

Let $U = \{1, 2, 3, 4, 5, 6, 7, 8\}$, $\mathcal{P} = \{1, 2, 3, 4\}$ and $Q = \{2, 4, 6, 8\}$. Then $\mathcal{P} \cap Q = \{2, 4\}$ and $\mathcal{P} \cup Q = \{1, 2, 3, 4, 6, 8\}$. Note that for any set $\mathcal{P}$, $\mathcal{P} \cap \varepsilon = \varepsilon$ and $\mathcal{P} \cup U = U$. To prove the first of these relations, note that if q is universally false, then $p \wedge q$ is equivalent to q in the universe $\mathfrak{u}$ and $\mathcal{E} = \{x|q(x)\}$. The proof of the second relation is left as an exercise.

Since it can be shown that $p \wedge q$ logically implies p, we have $\mathcal{P} \cap \mathcal{Q} \subset \mathcal{P}$. Similarly $\mathcal{P} \cap \mathcal{Q} \subset \mathcal{Q}$. Since it can be shown that p logically implies $p \vee q$, we have $\mathcal{P} \subset \mathcal{P} \cup \mathcal{Q}$. Similarly $\mathcal{Q} \subset \mathcal{P} \cup \mathcal{Q}$.

Given two solution sets $\mathcal{P}$ and $\mathcal{Q}$ in a universe $\mathfrak{u}$, the set $\mathcal{P} \cap \mathcal{Q}'$ consisting of all elements of $\mathfrak{u}$ that are elements of $\mathcal{P}$ but not elements of $\mathcal{Q}$ is called the *difference* of $\mathcal{P}$ and $\mathcal{Q}$ and denoted by $\mathcal{P} - \mathcal{Q}$. It is the solution set of $p(x) \wedge \sim q(x)$. Since this open statement is equivalent to the negation of $p(x) \rightarrow q(x)$, the solution set of this open statement is $(\mathcal{P} - \mathcal{Q})'$.

Let $\mathfrak{u} = \{100, 101, 102, 103, 104, 105\}$ and define predicates p, q, r, as follows:

$$p(x): x \text{ is even}$$

$$q(x): x \text{ is divisible by 5}$$

$$r(x): x \text{ has two identical digits.}$$

Then,

$$\mathcal{P} = \{x|p(x)\} = \{100, 102, 104\}$$

$$\mathcal{Q} = \{x|q(x)\} = \{100, 105\}$$

$$\mathcal{R} = \{x|r(x)\} = \{100, 101\}.$$

Then the solution set of "x has two identical digits or is even" is

$$\mathcal{R} \cup \mathcal{Q} = \{100, 101, 102, 104\}.$$

Note that the complement of this set is $\{103, 105\}$. The solution set of "x is divisible by both 2 and 5" is $\mathcal{P} \cap \mathcal{Q} = \{100\}$. The solution set of "if x is divisible by 5, then it has two identical digits" is $\{100, 101, 102, 103, 104\}$ since both antecedent and consequent are true when $x = 100$, and the antecedent is false (so the conditional is true) in the other four cases. Note that $\mathcal{Q} - \mathcal{R} = \{105\}$, so that the solution set is $(\mathcal{Q} - \mathcal{R})'$. This was to be expected since the given open statement is $q(x) \rightarrow r(x)$.

Consider now an example dealing with solution sets of binary predicates. Let $\mathcal{S} = \{1, 2, 3, 4\}$ and $\mathfrak{u} = \mathcal{S}^2$ so that $\mathfrak{u}$ is the set of all ordered pairs of elements in $\mathcal{S}$. We define binary predicates p, q, and r as follows:

$$p(x, y): x + y = 4$$

$$q(x, y): x + 2y = 7$$

$$r(x, y): 3x > y + 1.$$

Then,

$$\mathcal{P} = \{(x, y)|p(x, y)\} = \{(1, 3), (2, 2), (3, 1)\},$$

$$\mathcal{Q} = \{(x, y)|q(x, y)\} = \{(1, 3), (3, 2)\},$$

$$\mathcal{R} = \{(x, y)|r(x, y)\} = \{(1, 1), (2, 1), (2, 2), (2, 3), (2, 4), (3, 1),$$
$$(3, 2), (3, 3), (3, 4), (4, 1), (4, 2), (4, 3), (4, 4)\}.$$

Thus,

$$\mathcal{P} \cup \mathcal{Q} = \{(1, 3), (2, 2), (3, 1) \ (3, 2)\}$$

is the solution set of $[x + y = 4] \vee [x + 2y = 7]$,

$$\mathcal{P} \cap \mathcal{Q} = \{(1, 3)\}$$

is the solution set of $[x + y = 4] \wedge [x + 2y = 7]$,

and

$$\mathcal{R}' = \{(1, 2), (1, 3), (1, 4)\}$$

is the solution set of

$$\sim[3x > y + 1] \quad \text{or} \quad 3x \leq y + 1.$$

The set

$$\mathcal{P} - \mathcal{Q} = \{(2, 2), (3, 1)\}$$

is the solution set of

$$[x + y = 4] \wedge \sim[x + 2y = 7] \quad \text{or} \quad \sim[(x + y = 4) \to (x + 2y = 7)].$$

In dealing with solution sets, it is convenient to devise graphical techniques for exhibiting relations among the sets in a given discussion. One such graphical device is called a *Venn diagram* and can be used with two or three subsets of any universe whatever. If the universe of open statements considered is a set of numbers or of n-tuples of numbers, then a *coordinate system* can be used to good advantage to display the relations among solution sets. We close this section with a discussion of these two graphical techniques.

In using Venn diagrams, the universe under discussion is represented by a rectangular region in a plane and every solution set by a circular region interior to it. The basic diagrams for discussion about one, two, and three solution sets of the universe are drawn in Figure 1(a)–(c). Note that a single set $\mathcal{C}$ makes it possible for us to consider the universe as the union of at most two disjoint sets $\mathcal{C}$ and $\mathcal{C}'$. Given any two sets $\mathcal{C}$ and $\mathcal{B}$, the union may be considered as the union of at most four disjoint sets: $\mathcal{C} \cap \mathcal{B}'$, $\mathcal{C} \cap \mathcal{B}$, $\mathcal{C}' \cap \mathcal{B}$, and $\mathcal{C}' \cap \mathcal{B}'$. Three subsets divide the universe into at most 8 mutually disjoint sets in a similar way. Note that the maximum number of disjoint sets is provided for in each diagram of Figure 1, and numbers are assigned to the regions. Note that the numbers are assigned in the same order that cases are listed in truth tables for the

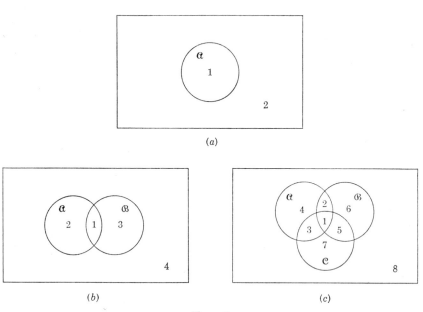

(a)

(b)   (c)

Figure 1

predicates that define the solution sets. Thus if α is the solution set of a predicate p, we characteristically list the cases for any unary connective defined on p as

$$p$$

	p
1.	T
2.	F

and region 1 represents the set of all a in $\mathfrak{u}$ such that $p(a) = T$ and region 2 the set of all a in $\mathfrak{u}$ for which $p(a) = F$. Similarly, if the predicates p and q have solution sets α and $\mathfrak{B}$ respectively, a truth table lists the cases for a binary connective involving them as follows:

	p	q
1.	T	T
2.	T	F
3.	F	T
4.	F	F

and the number assigned to a region in Figure 1(b) is the number of the only truth table case in which a complex predicate involving p and q assigns T. Region 3, for example, represents $\mathcal{P}' \cap \mathcal{Q}$ which is the truth set of $(\sim p) \wedge q$. This predicate is true only in case $p(a) = F$ and $q(a) = T$, which is the third case in the table. We follow this procedure for three predicates listing the cases as

	p	q	r
1.	T	T	T
2.	T	T	F
3.	T	F	T
4.	T	F	F
5.	F	T	T
6.	F	T	F
7.	F	F	T
8.	F	F	F

A Venn diagram is used to exhibit a set defined from others by means of the operations defined in this section. This may be done by agreeing to write in the number of a region only if that region is part of the set to be displayed. Consider the set $(\mathcal{P} \cup \mathcal{Q})'$. In a Venn diagram with two sets $\mathcal{P}$ includes regions 1 and 2, $\mathcal{Q}$ includes regions 2 and 3, so that their union includes regions 1, 2, and 3. Thus, the only region included in $(\mathcal{P} \cup \mathcal{Q})'$ is region 4 and its Venn diagram is Figure 2. By observing relationships

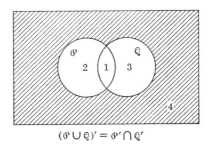

$$(\mathcal{P} \cup \mathcal{Q})' = \mathcal{P}' \cap \mathcal{Q}'$$

Figure 2

among the Venn diagrams of sets one can conclude that analogous relations hold between the sets themselves. Thus if two sets have identical diagrams, they must be equal, and if the diagram of a set $\mathcal{P}$ is included in the diagram of $\mathcal{Q}$, then we must have $\mathcal{P} \subset \mathcal{Q}$. Note that Figure 2 is also the diagram of $\mathcal{P}' \cap \mathcal{Q}'$. Since $\mathcal{P}$ includes regions 1 and 2, $\mathcal{P}'$ includes regions 3 and 4 and since Q includes regions 2 and 3, Q′ includes regions 1 and 4. Thus ℘′ ∩ Q′ includes region 4 alone.

If the universe consists of single numbers, it is usually represented by a collection of points on a straight line. Thus, for example, the universe {1, 2, 3, 4, 5, 6, 7, 8} may be represented as in Figure 3. Then the ele-

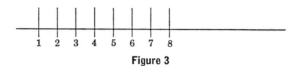

Figure 3

ments of a solution set are indicated by distinguishing the corresponding points in some way—enclosing them in circles, squares, or triangles—if several sets are to be included in the same diagram. In Figure 4 the ele-

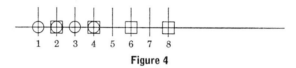

Figure 4

ments of the set ℘ = {1, 2, 3, 4} are indicated with circles and the elements of Q = {2, 4, 6, 8} are indicated with squares. Note that the elements of ℘ ∩ Q are those that are in both a circle and a square, and the elements of ℘ ∪ Q are those that are in either a circle or a square or both.

If the universe consists of ordered pairs of numbers, then all first elements are plotted on one of two intersecting lines and all second elements on the other. Conventionally the line on which first elements are plotted is horizontal, and the other line is vertical. A point of the plane determined by these lines corresponding to an element (a, b) of the universe

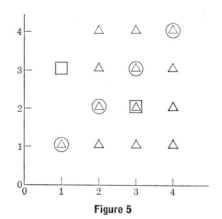

Figure 5

is located as the intersection of a vertical line through the point a on the horizontal and a horizontal line through b on the vertical. Then elements of solution sets may be distinguished by circles, triangles, and squares as before. Figure 5 represents the universe S^2 where $S = \{1, 2, 3, 4\}$ and the solution sets of the open statements

$$x = y, \quad x + 2y = 7, \quad \text{and} \quad 3x > y + 1$$

represented by circles, squares, and triangles respectively.

EXERCISES

1. Let $\mathcal{U} = \{1, 2, 3, 4, 5, 6, 7, 8, 9\}$, $\mathcal{P} = \{1, 4, 5, 6, 8\}$, $\mathcal{Q} = \{1, 4, 9\}$, and $\mathcal{R} = \{5, 6, 7\}$. List the elements in each of the following sets.

(a) $\mathcal{P} \cap \mathcal{Q}'$
(b) $(\mathcal{P} - \mathcal{R}) \cup (\mathcal{P} - \mathcal{Q})$
(c) $\mathcal{P}' \cup \mathcal{R}$
(d) $\mathcal{P} \cap \mathcal{R}'$
(e) $(\mathcal{Q} - \mathcal{P})' \cap \mathcal{R}$

(f) $\mathcal{P}' - \mathcal{R}$
(g) $\mathcal{Q} \cap (\mathcal{P} \cup \mathcal{R})$
(h) $(\mathcal{Q} \cap \mathcal{P}) \cup (\mathcal{Q} \cap \mathcal{R})$
(i) $[(\mathcal{P} - \mathcal{Q}) \cup (\mathcal{P} - \mathcal{R})] - \mathcal{P}$
(j) $\mathcal{P} \cup \mathcal{Q} \cup \mathcal{R} \cup \mathcal{P}'$

2. For the universe $\mathcal{U}$ of Exercise 1, define predicates p, q, and r as follows:

$p(x) = x$ is an even number
$q(x) = x$ is a prime number
$r(x) = x$ is a divisor of 70.

List the solution sets of the following statements.

(a) $\sim[p \wedge (\sim q)]$
(b) $r \wedge \sim(p \vee q)$
(c) $p \rightarrow (\sim r)$
(d) $p \rightarrow (q \rightarrow r)$

(e) $p \rightarrow (q \rightarrow p)$
(f) $p \wedge (\sim p)$
(g) $r \vee [q \wedge (\sim q)]$
(h) $(r \rightarrow p) \wedge (q \leftrightarrow p)$

3. Let $\mathcal{U}$ be any set and p and q be any predicates with universe $\mathcal{U}$. Let u be a predicate that assigns T to every element of $\mathcal{U}$ and e be a predicate that assigns F to every element of $\mathcal{U}$. Use truth tables to show that each of the following predicates is *universally true* (assigns T to every element of $\mathcal{U}$).

(a) $\sim e \leftrightarrow u$
(b) $\sim u \leftrightarrow e$
(c) $p \vee q \leftrightarrow q \vee p$
(d) $p \wedge q \leftrightarrow q \wedge p$
(e) $p \wedge q \leftrightarrow p$
(f) $p \wedge q \rightarrow q$
(g) $p \rightarrow p \vee q$
(h) $q \rightarrow p \vee q$
(i) $(p \rightarrow q) \leftrightarrow [(\sim q) \rightarrow (\sim p)]$

(j) $\sim(p \wedge q) \leftrightarrow (\sim p) \vee (\sim q)$
(k) $\sim(p \vee q) \leftrightarrow (\sim p) \wedge (\sim q)$
(l) $p \vee u \leftrightarrow u$
(m) $p \wedge u \leftrightarrow p$
(n) $p \wedge e \leftrightarrow e$
(o) $p \vee e \leftrightarrow p$
(p) $p \rightarrow u$
(q) $e \rightarrow p$

4. Let $\mathcal{U}$ be any set and $\mathcal{P}$ and $\mathcal{Q}$ be solution sets with universe $\mathcal{U}$. Use the results of Exercise 3, interpreting $\mathcal{P}$ as the solution set of p and $\mathcal{Q}$ as the solution set of q, to prove each of the following laws.

(a) $\mathcal{E}' = \mathcal{U}$

(b) $\mathcal{U}' = \mathcal{E}$

(c) $\mathcal{P} \cup \mathcal{Q} = \mathcal{Q} \cup \mathcal{P}$

(d) $\mathcal{P} \cap \mathcal{Q} = \mathcal{Q} \cap \mathcal{P}$

(e) $\mathcal{P} \cap \mathcal{Q} \subset \mathcal{P}$

(f) $\mathcal{P} \cap \mathcal{Q} \subset \mathcal{Q}$

(g) $\mathcal{P} \subset \mathcal{P} \cup \mathcal{Q}$

(h) $\mathcal{Q} \subset \mathcal{P} \cup \mathcal{Q}$

(i) If $\mathcal{P} \subset \mathcal{Q}$ then $\mathcal{Q}' \subset \mathcal{P}'$

(j) $(\mathcal{P} \cap \mathcal{Q})' = \mathcal{P}' \cup \mathcal{Q}'$

(k) $(\mathcal{P} \cup \mathcal{Q})' = \mathcal{P}' \cap \mathcal{Q}'$

(l) $\mathcal{P} \cup \mathcal{U} = \mathcal{U}$

(m) $\mathcal{P} \cap \mathcal{U} = \mathcal{P}$

(n) $\mathcal{P} \cap \mathcal{E} = \mathcal{E}$

(o) $\mathcal{P} \cup \mathcal{E} = \mathcal{P}$

(p) $\mathcal{P} \subset \mathcal{U}$

(q) $\mathcal{E} \subset \mathcal{P}$

5. Use Venn diagrams to verify the relations in Exercise 4.

6. Use Venn diagrams to verify that

$$\mathcal{P} \cap (\mathcal{Q} \cup \mathcal{R}) = (\mathcal{P} \cap \mathcal{Q}) \cup (\mathcal{P} \cap \mathcal{R})$$

and that

$$\mathcal{P} \cup (\mathcal{Q} \cap \mathcal{R}) = (\mathcal{P} \cup \mathcal{Q}) \cap (\mathcal{P} \cup \mathcal{R})$$

for all solution sets $\mathcal{P}$, $\mathcal{Q}$, and $\mathcal{R}$ in a universe $\mathcal{U}$.

7. Use Venn diagrams to verify that

$$\mathcal{P} \cup (\mathcal{Q} \cap \mathcal{P}) = \mathcal{P} \cap (\mathcal{Q} \cup \mathcal{P}) = \mathcal{P}$$

for any solution sets $\mathcal{P}$ and $\mathcal{Q}$ in a universe $\mathcal{U}$.

8. Describe a technique using Venn diagrams for determining the truth value assigned by a complex predicate in case the assignments made by its parts are known.

9. Let $\mathcal{S} = \{1, 2, 3, 4, 5, 6\}$ and $\mathcal{U} = \mathcal{S}^2$. Sketch a graph in a coordinate system of the solution set in $\mathcal{U}$ of each of the following open statements.

(a) $x = 4$

(b) $x + 2y = 8$

(c) $2x - y < 5$

(d) $x^2 - 5x - 6 = 0$

(e) $x^2 - 5x - 6 < 0$

(f) $x^3 - 4x^2 = 0$

(g) $x^3 - 4x > 0$

10. If $\mathcal{P}$ and $\mathcal{Q}$ are sets and $\mathcal{P} \subset \mathcal{Q}$, we say that $\mathcal{P}$ *is smaller than* $\mathcal{Q}$ and $\mathcal{Q}$ *is larger than* $\mathcal{P}$. Show that $\mathcal{P} \cap \mathcal{Q}$ is the largest set that is a subset of both $\mathcal{P}$ and $\mathcal{Q}$ and that $\mathcal{P} \cup \mathcal{Q}$ is the smallest set of which $\mathcal{P}$ and $\mathcal{Q}$ are subsets.

5 · THE NOTION OF PROOF

In this section and the next we consider the notion of mathematical proof and provide explicitly a number of rules according to which it may be concluded that a given statement is true, provided that the truth of other statements is already established. A feature of the rules discussed here is that they are justified on logical grounds alone, and so provide patterns of proof for many branches of mathematics as well as for many nonmathematical areas. Because of this, we call these rules *logical rules*. Those logical rules justified by the way connectives are defined and discussed in the present section, while those justified by the interpretation we place on quantifiers are discussed in Section 6.

What is called a proof in most mathematics textbooks is seldom completely rigorous, even though the statements established are often true. The reason for this is that we have learned to apply certain rules of proof tacitly, so that the author of a textbook may feel confident that gaps in his argument can be filled by most of his readers. Here we shall consider complete proofs of mathematical statements and make explicit the rules applied tacitly in most textbooks. The purpose of this is not to insist on undue fussiness as much as it is to give the reader an awareness of the logical equipment he is expected to bring with him to any mathematical context. In addition to logical rules, properties of equality and properties of sets often serve to fill the gaps in textbook proofs. The procedure of abbreviating complete proofs is illustrated at the end of Section 6. We call an abbreviated proof correct if it can be expanded into a proof, as defined here, by providing justifications for the steps omitted.

We turn next to two questions. First, what is a logical rule? Second, what is a valid proof?

A *logical rule* is a convention that identifies a statement s as true once it is known that a certain finite number n of statements $p_1, p_2, \ldots, p_n$ are true, and one that is justified solely on grounds of the formal relationships among the statements involved. This means that we shall seek to justify the rules provided here by the interpretations we have already given to logical connectives and quantifiers. For the case of rules justified by logical connectives, we show that a logical rule is correct by demonstrating that every row in which the truth tables of the *premises* $p_1, p_2, \ldots, p_n$ of the rules are assigned T is also a row in which the *conclusion* s of the rule is also assigned T. Here we write logical rules in the form

$$p_1, p_2, \ldots, p_n \vdash s, \tag{2}$$

where $p_1, p_2, \ldots, p_n$ are the premises and s is the conclusion. It is easy to show that (2) is correct if and only if $p_1 \wedge p_2 \wedge \cdots \wedge p_n$ logically implies s in the sense of Section 3. Several examples are given below.

Virtually all the proof rules of mathematics, logical or otherwise, have premises, so that to establish the truth of any statement requires us to know that certain other statements are true. It may be that these other statements are conclusions of rules as well, in which case their truth depends on the truth of the premises of the rules. It is evident that if we required proofs for all mathematical statements, we would obtain a situation similar to one that develops when we require that all words of a language be defined. That is, such a requirement leads either to the need for infinitely many proofs to establish a single statement or to *circular arguments* in which a conclusion of a rule serves as premise in a rule applied earlier. Since neither of these situations is desirable, we begin the study of a branch of mathematics by agreeing that certain statements of the language are accepted as true without proof. These statements, called *axioms*, serve two important purposes. On the one hand, they provide true statements for use as premises of rules. On the other hand, they characterize concisely the set of objects and relations to be studied. Thus, the true statements, or *theorems*, of a mathematical language are either axioms or statements implied by the axioms.

Given a set of axioms of a mathematical language, any sequence $r_1, r_2, \ldots, r_m$ of statements of the language is called a *proof* if for every $i = 1, 2, \ldots, m$, either

(1) r_i is an axiom, or
(2) r_i is the conclusion of a rule whose premises are statements r_j with $j < i$.

Note that the premises r_j used in establishing r_i occur before r_i in the proof. Such a proof is usually called a proof of r_m, the last statement of the sequence, although every statement in the sequence is a theorem.

In turning to the development of specific logical rules, we note first the following table:

p	q	$p \rightarrow q$
T	T	T
T	F	F
F	T	T
F	F	T

for the conditional. Since the only row in which p and $p \rightarrow q$ both contain T is the first, and since q contains T there, we have justified the rule

$L1.$ $p, p \rightarrow q \vdash q.$

$L1$ is called the *rule of detachment* and reflects a fundamental property of the conditional: its consequent is true whenever its antecedent is. This rule provides a device for eliminating a conditional statement from an argument. A proof using $L1$ would proceed as follows:

(1) p axiom, or conclusion of an applied rule
(2) $p \rightarrow q$ axiom, or conclusion of an applied rule
(3) q by $L1$, from 1 and 2.

If there is a proof of q on the assumption that p is true, we write $p \gg q$. In this case q is true whenever p is true, so that p implies q. This means that $p \rightarrow q$ is logically true, by Exercise 7 of Section 3, so that the existence of a proof of q from p guarantees that $p \rightarrow q$ is true. Thus we have a rule for introducing a conditional into a proof.

$L2.$ $p \gg q \vdash p \rightarrow q$

A part of a proof applying $L2$ proceeds as follows:

  $i.$ p assumption, or axiom, or conclusion of an applied rule,
  $j.$ q axiom, or conclusion of an applied rule
$j + 1.$ $p \rightarrow q$ by $L2$, from i, and j.

Note that a feature of $L2$ is that if q can be proved on the assumption that p is true, then one can assert that $p \rightarrow q$ is true independently of any assumption about the truth of p. This is because the conditional is true when its antecedent is false. The validity of $L2$ can be considered an important reason for adopting the definition we have of the conditional.

We consider now rules that introduce and eliminate occurrences of other connectives in proofs of statements. Noting the truth table for conjunction:

p	q	$p \wedge q$
T	T	T
T	F	F
F	T	F
F	F	F

we find that to know that p and q are both true is sufficient for the assurance that $p \wedge q$ is true. Thus we have the rule

$L3.$ $p, q \vdash p \wedge q$

for introducing conjunctions. Conversely, if $p \land q$ is true, then both p and q are true. Thus rules for eliminating conjunctions are

   L4. $p \land q \vdash p$

   L5. $p \land q \vdash q$.

By inspecting the truth table for the disjunction, the validity of the following rules can be demonstrated.

   L6. $p \vdash p \lor q$

   L7. $q \vdash p \lor q$

   L8. $p \lor q, \sim q \vdash p$

Rules concerning negation are

   L9. $p \vdash \sim(\sim p)$

   L10. $\sim(\sim p) \vdash p$.

Another important rule dealing with negation is the rule

   L11. $p \gg [q \land (\sim q) \vdash \sim p$

which holds because according to the last row of the table for the conditional a logically false statement can be proved only from a false assumption. Thus p is false if $q \land (\sim q)$ follows from it, and $\sim p$ is true.

Both *L2* and *L11* permit the conclusion that a statement is true on the basis of the existence of a proof on the assumption p. Thus their character differs from that of the other rules somewhat. Once either rule has been applied, and its conclusion asserted, the assumption p no longer plays the role of premise in the main proof of which this application is a part. We say that such an assumption p is *discharged* when either *L2* or *L11* is applied. The only assumptions in the main proof are those that are not discharged in this way. The proof given in the paragraph below illustrates these points.

The validity of rules may be established with the aid of rules already known to be valid by carrying out proofs using the latter rules with statements specified only in the way they are built up from others by using connectives. Such procedures, called *proof schemes*, assure us that the indicated inference can be drawn regardless of what these other statements are. Thus, the validity of

   L12. $p \to q \vdash (\sim q) \to (\sim p)$

is assured since the premise and conclusion are logically equivalent. However, its validity may be also established using other rules as follows:

(1) p assumption
(2) $p \to q$ assumption
(3) q by $L1$ from 1 and 2
(4) $\sim q$ assumption
(5) $q \wedge (\sim q)$ by $L3$ from 4 and 5
(6) $\sim p$ by $L11$ from 1 and 5, discharging 1
(7) $(\sim q) \to (\sim p)$ by $L2$, from 4 and 7, discharging 7.

Since the only undischarged premise is 2, these seven steps constitute a proof of $L12$.

In $L11$, the negation of a statement can be shown to be true if a contradiction can be proved when the truth of the statement itself is assumed, hence a proof using this rule is said to be a *proof by contradiction*. A proof using $L12$ is called a *proof by contraposition* because its premise and conclusion are contrapositives of each other. The rule

$L13.$ $(\sim p) \to (\sim q) \vdash q \to p$

is another rule of contraposition. Its proof is left to the reader.

It is convenient to note another rule concerning conditionals:

$L14.$ $p \to q, q \to r \vdash p \to r$

which we shall refer to as the *rule of transitivity*. Its validity may be established, as with other rules, by truth tables, or by the following proof:

(1) p assumption
(2) $p \to q$ assumption
(3) q by $L1$, from 1 and 2
(4) $q \to r$ assumption
(5) r by $L1$, from 3 and 4
(6) $p \to r$ by $L2$, from 1 and 5, discharging 1.

The rules introduced here can be used to establish the fact that a predicate built up of connectives is logically true. A proof demonstrating this is distinguished from other proofs given here by the fact that *all* assumptions used are discharged by applications of $L2$ or $L11$ before the completion of the proof.

The predicate $p \to (q \to p)$ is logically true, as can be shown by inspection of its truth table. A proof that this is so using the rules of this section is the following:

(1) q assumption
(2) p assumption
(3) $q \to p$ by $L2$, from 1 and 2, discharging 1
(4) $p \to (q \to p)$ by $L2$, from 2 and 3, discharging 2.

It should now be apparent to the reader that the rules described here are not used explicitly in mathematical proofs even by the most meticulously rigorous mathematician. Indeed most proofs encountered in mathematics books are highly intuitive, sometimes to the point that the logical rules applied in a derivation are difficult to discern. To insist that every logical rule used in a proof be cited would force mathematical procedure to be unnecessarily long and tedious. The purpose for listing the rules above, and those of quantifiers in the next section, is to acquaint the reader with the notion of a valid logical principle and the role it plays in the structure of a mathematical theory. It is hoped that the reader recognizes in these rules patterns of inference he has encountered repeatedly, and that, in addition, he acquires some awareness of their justification.

The reader will note that conventional procedure is adopted in Chapters 2 and 3, where parts of proofs are condensed into steps justified by the simultaneous application of several logical rules. This is done in the interest of saving time and space, and because our fundamental concern in those chapters is with numbers and functions, rather than with mathematical languages in general. Such a condensed proof can be called rigorous if it can be expanded into a complete proof using a single valid rule at each step.

EXERCISES

1. Use the truth table for disjunction to justify $L6$–8.

2. Use the truth table for negation to justify $L9$–10.

3. Prove $L13$, using rules $L1$–12 to justify the steps of the proof.

4. Show that $a \leq b$ follows from the assumption that $a < b$.

5. Show that $a \leq b$ follows from the assumption that $a = b$.

6. Show that $a > b$ follows from the assumption that $a > b > c$.

7. Show that $b > c$ follows from the assumption that $a > b > c$.

8. Does $a > c$ follow from the assumption $a > b > c$ using the rules of this section? Explain.

9. Using the rules of this section, prove each of the following rules of procedure:

   (a) $p \rightarrow (q \rightarrow r) \vdash (p \wedge q) \rightarrow r$
   (b) $p \vdash p$
   (c) $p, q \rightarrow (\sim p) \vdash \sim q$

(d) $p \rightarrow (q \rightarrow r) \vdash q \rightarrow (p \rightarrow r)$
(e) $p \rightarrow (q \wedge r) \vdash (p \rightarrow q) \wedge (p \rightarrow r)$
(f) $(p \vee q) \rightarrow r \vdash (p \rightarrow r) \vee (q \rightarrow r)$.

10. Using the rules of this section prove that each of the following is logically true:

(a) $p \vee (\sim p)$
(b) $(p \rightarrow q) \rightarrow [p \rightarrow (p \rightarrow q)]$
(c) $[p \rightarrow (q \rightarrow r)] \rightarrow [(p \rightarrow q) \rightarrow (p \rightarrow r)]$
(d) $(\sim p) \vee (\sim q) \rightarrow \sim (p \wedge q)$.

11. State rules for introducing and eliminating the biconditional in a proof. Use truth tables to justify the rules chosen.

6 · RULES FOR QUANTIFIERS

Consider the sentence

$$(E\,x)\{(y)(y + x = x + y = y) \wedge (z)[(y)(y + z = y) \rightarrow z = x]\} \qquad (3)$$

which asserts a familiar property of algebra. The sentence asserts that there is an element of the universe having two properties: (1) its sum with any number is that number itself, and (2) any other element of the universe having property (1) is equal to it. The first property is fundamental to the number 0 and to its role in addition, and the second property asserts that there is only one number that plays this role. We say that it asserts the *uniqueness* of the element whose existence is assured by the statements.

We note that the rules of procedure of the preceding section cannot be used to prove this sentence from any set of axioms that are not themselves conjunctions, conditionals, and the like. Since the axioms we use are mostly simple, rather than compound, sentences, the procedure indicated in proving (3) is to break it up into two parts, thus:

$$(y)(y + x = x + y = y), \quad (z)[(y)(y + z = y) \rightarrow z = x].$$

If each part is proved, then their conjunction follows by $L3$. To prove (3) from this conjunction it would be necessary to have some sort of rule for introducing an existential quantifier. Note too that this procedure would require that rules of procedure be applied to open statements as well as sentences. This is to be expected since in much of mathematical work, open statements are used more frequently than are the sentences obtained from them by using quantifiers. Thus in stating a law of factoring in algebra, we would write

$$x^2 - y^2 = (x + y)(x - y)$$

rather than
$$(x)(y)[x^2 - y^2 = (x + y)(x - y)].$$

The difficulty involved in using open statements in this way lies in the fact that it is not clear which of the variables can be replaced by the name of any element of the universe, and for which of the variables substitution is allowed from a limited subset of the universe. This distinction is erased as soon as quantifiers are eliminated. Thus, in the class of integers, every pair of integers has a difference. This can be expressed using quantifiers as
$$(x)(y)(E\,z)[x + z = y]$$
but the open statement $x + z = y$ itself communicates nothing about existence.

No difficulty occurs in reasoning only with open statements, when an open statement is treated as being equivalent to the universal statement obtained from it by preceding it with a string of universal quantifiers. To reflect this we have the following rules for the introduction and elimination of the universal quantifier in a proof:

$L15.$ $p(x) \vdash (x)p(x)$

$L16.$ $(x)p(x) \vdash p(x).$

Adopting these rules permits the proofs of other rules in which only universal quantifiers are involved. For example, an interchange of universal quantifiers before a binary predicate does not affect the truth of the resulting statement:

$L17.$ $(x)(y)p(x, y) \vdash (y)(x)p(x, y).$

Proof:

(1) $(x)(y)p(x, y)$ assumption
(2) $(y)p(x, y)$ by $L16$, from 1
(3) $p(x, y)$ by $L16$, from 2
(4) $(x)p(x, y)$ by $L15$, from 3
(5) $(y)(x)p(x, y)$ by $L15$, from 4

Other rules relate universal quantifiers with connectives.

$L18.$ $(x)[p(x) \rightarrow q(x)] \vdash (x)p(x) \rightarrow (x)q(x)$

$L19.$ $(x)[p(x) \wedge q(x)] \vdash (x)p(x) \wedge (x)q(x)$

We give a proof of $L18$, leaving a proof of $L19$ for the reader.

(1) $(x)[p(x) \rightarrow q(x)]$ assumption
(2) $p(x) \rightarrow q(x)$ by $L16$, from 1

(3) $(x)p(x)$ assumption
(4) $p(x)$ by $L16$, from 3
(5) $q(x)$ by $L1$, from 4
(6) $(x)q(x)$ by $L15$, from 5
(7) $(x)p(x) \rightarrow (x)q(x)$ by $L2$, from 3 and 6, discharging 3

In considering the existential quantifier, note that $(E\,x)p(x)$ means that $p(u) = T$ for at least one element u in the universe. In order to eliminate an occurrence of an existential quantifier from a proof, we need some way of representing the element whose existence is asserted. Of course, the name that we use may be ambiguous, for it may not be known what element of the universe has the asserted property. We shall use letters, u, v, and w, with or without subscripts as ambiguous names for elements of the universe whose existence is asserted by an existential statement. Care must be taken to use distinct letters for ambiguous names arising from distinct existential quantifiers. With this proviso, we have the rule:

$L20$. $(E\,x)p(x) \vdash p(u)$,   where u is an ambiguous name.

For the introduction of the existential quantifier into an argument, we note that if $p(a)$, where a is a specific name, or $p(u)$ where u is an ambiguous name, can be proved, then we may assert $(E\,x)p(x)$. Thus we have:

$L21$. $p(a) \vdash (E\,x)p(x)$,   where a is a specific name

$L22$. $p(u) \vdash (E\,x)p(x)$,   where u is an ambiguous name.

Of course, if a universal sentence is true, then any instance of it is true, so that we have the rules:

$L23$. $(x)p(x) \vdash p(a)$,   where a is a specific name

$L24$. $(x)p(x) \vdash p(u)$,   where u is an ambiguous name.

The rule $L24$ is valid only in universes that are not empty. Since none of the universes used in the ensuing exposition are empty, we adopt it as a principle of logic.

Using $L20$–22, it can be proved that existential quantifiers are interchangeable:

$L25$. $(E\,x)(E\,y)p(x, y) \vdash (E\,y)(E\,x)p(x, y)$

Proof:

(1) $(E\,x)(E\,y)p(x, y)$ assumption
(2) $(E\,y)p(u, y)$ by $L20$, from 1

(3) $p(u, v)$ by $L20$, from 2
(4) $(\text{E } x)p(x, v)$ by $L22$, from 3
(5) $(\text{E } y)(\text{E } x)p(x, y)$ by $L22$, from 4.

A number of rules giving important relationships between existential and universal quantifiers are needed.

$L26.\ (x)p(x) \vdash (\text{E } x)p(x)$

$L27.\ \sim(x)p(x) \vdash (\text{E } x)[\sim p(x)]$

$L28.\ \sim(\text{E } x)p(x) \vdash (x)[\sim p(x)]$

$L27$ implies that the falsity of a universal statement gives assurance that an element a of the universe exists such that $p(a) = \text{F}$. This rule is not valid in an empty universe. According to $L28$, the falsity of an existential statement implies that $p(a) = \text{F}$ for each element a of the universe. The converses of these rules are also valid:

$L29.\ (\text{E } x)[\sim p(x)] \vdash \sim(x)p(x)$

$L30.\ (x)[\sim p(x)] \vdash \sim(\text{E } x)p(x).$

According to $L29$, to prove that a universal sentence is false it is sufficient to prove that $p(a) = \text{F}$ for at least one element a of the universe. This element a is called a *counterexample*. Thus, in trigonometry, to show that

$$\sin (x + y) = \sin x + \sin y$$

is not universally true in the universe of real numbers, it is sufficient to show that there are real numbers a and b such that

$$\sin (a + b) \neq \sin a + \sin b.$$

If we let $a = \pi/3$ and $b = \pi/6$, we note that

$$\sin (a + b) = \sin (\pi/2) = 1$$

while

$$\sin a + \sin b = (\sqrt{3} + 1)/2.$$

We prove $L29$, leaving proof of $L30$ to the reader.

Proof of L29:

(1) $(\text{E } x)[\sim p(x)]$ assumption
(2) $\sim p(u)$ by $L20$, from 1
(3) $(x)p(x)$ assumption
(4) $p(u)$ by $L24$, from 3
(5) $p(u) \wedge (\sim p(u))$ by $L3$, from 2 and 4
(6) $\sim(x)p(x)$ by $L11$, from 3 and 5, discharging 3.

The remainder of this section is devoted to proofs from the theory of groups to illustrate the use of $L1$–30 in a mathematical context as well as ways in which proofs giving all logical details may be abbreviated. A *group* is a set $\mathfrak{U}$ of objects for which a single binary operation is defined. If x and y are elements of $\mathfrak{U}$, then the result of applying the operation is denoted by xy and called a *product*. One binary predicate, called *equality*, and represented by the open statement $x = y$, is adopted and satisfies the axioms $q1$–3 given in Section 2. They are, restated using quantifiers:

$E1$. $(x)[x = x]$

$E2$. $(x)(y)[x = y \rightarrow y = x]$

$E3$. $(x)(y)(z)[x = y \wedge y = z \rightarrow x = z]$.

The axioms adopted for the product operation are:

$G1$. $(x)(y)(E\ z)(z = xy)$

$G2$. $(x)(y)(z)[x(yz) = (xy)z]$

$G3$. $(x)(y)[(E\ z)(xz = y) \wedge (E\ z)(zx = y)]$.

We take the following sentences as axioms that express an important relation between the predicate and the operation. They are called *monotonic laws*.

$E5$. $(x)(y)(z)(x = y \leftrightarrow xz = yz)$

$E6$. $(x)(y)(z)(x = y \leftrightarrow zx = zy)$

The abstract proofs of theorems from these axioms do not depend on how we interpret them, for the rules of procedure are applied in a mechanical way in a proof. To illustrate the importance of the theory, however, it is desirable to exhibit an interpretation in terms of familiar mathematical ideas. To do this we specify the set $\mathfrak{U}$, the operation, and the predicate in such a way that the axioms are true for the specification chosen.

For one interpretation, let $\mathfrak{U}$ be the set $\mathcal{I}$ of integers, the operation be addition, and the relation be equality. Then the axioms $E1$–$E3$ state respectively that equality is reflexive, symmetric, and transitive (see the next section). $G1$ is a closure law stating that the sum of two integers is an integer; $G2$ asserts the associativity of addition; and $G3$ asserts that every equation $a + x = b$ and $x + a = b$ has a solution. This is equivalent to the statement that the difference of every ordered pair of integers is an integer.

Another interpretation consists in letting $\mathfrak{U}$ be the set $\mathcal{Q}$ of all nonzero rational numbers, interpreting the operation as multiplication, and the relation as equality. The exercises develop other interpretations of a group.

We first show that for each x and y, the solution z of $xz = y$ which exists by $G3$ is unique.

Theorem 1. $(x)(y)(z)(w)[xz = y \land xw = y \to z = w]$

Proof:

(1)	$xz = y \land xw = y$	assumption
(2)	$xz = y$	by $L4$, from 1
(3)	$xw = y$	by $L5$, from 1
(4)	$(x)(y)(x = y \to y = x)$	by $E2$
(5)	$xw = y \to y = xw$	by $L23$, from 4
(6)	$y = xw$	by $L1$, from 3 and 5
(7)	$(x)(y)(z)(x = y \land y = z \to x = z)$	by $E3$
(8)	$xz = y \land y = xw \to xz = xw$	by $L23$, from 7
(9)	$xz = y \land y = xw$	by $L3$, from 2 and 6
(10)	$xz = xw$	by $L1$, from 8 and 9
(11)	$(x)(y)(z)(x = y \leftrightarrow zx = zy)$	by $E6$
(12)	$z = w \leftrightarrow xz = xw$	by $L23$, from 11
(13)	$xz = xw \to z = w$	by Ex. 11, Sec. 6
(14)	$z = w$	by $L1$, from 10 and 13
(15)	$xz = y \land xw = y \to z = w$	by $L2$, from 1 and 14, discharging 1
(16)	$(x)(y)(z)(w)[xz = y \land xw = y \to z = w]$	by $L15$, from 15.

Note that some abbreviation has already occurred in the application of $L15$ and $L23$ which permits the introduction or elimination of a single universal quantifier at a time. The number of steps deleted at each point equals the number of quantifiers introduced or eliminated.

In practice other abbreviations are introduced by using the properties $E1-6$ and the logical rules tacitly, justifying a step by noting that properties of logic, or properties of equality are used. In addition, open statements that are universally true are quoted without quantifiers. Thus a modified proof using these abbreviations may be constructed as follows:

(1)	$xz = y \land xw = y$	assumption
(2)	$xz = y$	by $L4$, from 1
(3)	$xw = y$	by $L5$, from 1
(4)	$y = xw$	properties of equality
(5)	$xz = xw$	properties of equality
(6)	$z = w$	properties of equality

and the theorem follows by $L2$ and $L15$.

The proof that the solution z of $zx = y$ is unique and is left to the reader.

It follows from $G3$ that $(E\ y)(x)(xy = x)$, and, by Theorem 1, y is a unique element of the group. This element is often denoted by e and called the *identity element* of the group. Thus we have $(x)(xe = x)$. We next show that $(x)(ex = x)$ is a theorem as well.

Theorem 2. $(x)(ex = x)$

Proof:

(1) $(ex)e = ex$	definition of e
(2) $ee = e$	definition of e
(3) $(ee)x = ex$	properties of equality
(4) $(ex)e = (ee)x$	properties of equality
(5) $e(ex) = (ee)x$	by $G2$
(6) $e(xe) = (ex)e$	by $G2$
(7) $e(ex) = e(xe)$	properties of equality
(8) $ex = xe$	properties of equality
(9) $xe = e$	definition of e
(10) $ex = e$	properties of equality

and the proof follows by $L15$.

Other properties of a group are left as exercises.

EXERCISES

1. Prove $L19$.

2. Show by an example that the converse of $L19$ is not a valid rule.

3. Show by an example that the converse of $L18$ is not a valid rule.

4. Prove the rule $(x)p(x) \lor (x)q(x) \vdash (x)[p(x) \lor q(x)]$.

5. Is the converse of the rule in Exercise 4 valid? Give a reason for your answer.

6. Prove $L30$.

7. Prove that each of the following rules is valid, given $L1$–30.

   (a) $\sim(x)[p(x) \lor q(x)] \vdash (E\ x)\{[\sim p(x)] \land [\sim q(x)]\}$
   (b) $\sim(E\ x)[p(x) \lor q(x)] \vdash (x)\{[\sim p(x)] \land [\sim q(x)]\}$
   (c) $\sim(x)[p(x) \land q(x)] \vdash (E\ x)\{[\sim p(x)] \lor [\sim q(x)]\}$
   (d) $\sim(E\ x)[p(x) \land q(x)] \vdash (x)\{[\sim p(x)] \lor [\sim q(x)]\}$

8. Express verbally the procedures embodied in the four rules of Exercise 7.

9. Give a counterexample from the universe of real numbers to show that each of the following statements is false there.

(a) $(x)(y)(\text{E } z)(xz = y)$
(b) $(x)(x^2 > 0)$
(c) $(x)(y)(z)(x > y \rightarrow xz > yz)$
(d) $(x)(y)(x^2 + y^2 = (x + y)^2)$
(e) $(x)(y)(|x + y| = |x| + |y|)$
(f) $(x)(y)(x^2 = y^2 \rightarrow x = y)$
(g) $(x)(y)(x^2 = y^2 \rightarrow x = |y|)$

10. Show that the set $\{1, i, -1, -i\}$ forms an interpretation of the axioms for a group under ordinary multiplication and equality, provided that $ii = i^2 = -1$.

11. Give a complete proof of the fact that in a group the solution z of every equation $zx = y$ is unique.

12. Give an abridged proof of the theorem in Exercise 11.

13. $G3$ implies that for each x in a group, the solution z of the open statement $xz = e$ exists. Show that for each x it is unique.

14. Repeat Exercise 13 for the solution w of $wx = e$.

15. Show that the elements w and z of Exercises 13 and 14 are equal.

16. What is the identity element of the group of nonzero rational numbers under multiplication? of the group of Exercise 10?

17. For each x the unique common solution of $xz = e$ and $zx = e$ is called the *inverse* of x. What are the inverses of the elements of the group:

   (a) of integers under addition
   (b) of nonzero rational numbers under multiplication
   (c) of the group in Exercise 10.

18. Name other interpretations of the axioms for a group.

7 · RELATIONS

If p is a binary predicate, then, according to common usage, we say that the sentence $p(a, b)$ expresses a *relation* between the elements a and b of the universe of p. Examples of relations commonly investigated in mathematics are represented by open statements (in appropriate universes) as follows: $x = y$, $x < y$, $x > y$, $x \leq y$, $x \geq y$, $x \subset y$, etc. Note that in representing a relation, it is usual to place the predicate symbol between the arguments, rather than before them. We follow common usage here by writing xpy for $p(x, y)$.

The universe $\mathfrak{U}$ of a binary predicate is a set of ordered pairs. If $\mathfrak{U} = \mathcal{S}^2$ for some set $\mathcal{S}$, then we say that the binary predicate is a *relation over* $\mathcal{S}$.

In this section we consider the properties of some important relations over a set S.

An important relation over a set S is the relation of *identity*, represented by $x = y$. The philosopher and mathematician Leibniz defined the relation of identity to hold between two objects if any property of one of them is also a property of the other. Using quantifiers, one may say that a is identical to b if

$$(p)\{p(a) \leftrightarrow p(b)\}.$$

Note that p occurs as a variable in this statement and its universe is the class of all unary predicates. The rules of logic dealing with such universes are in a sense more complicated than those explained in the preceding sections, and there is no need to develop them here. It is useful to point out that the strength of the relation of identity requires logic beyond the scope developed here.

There are a number of relations that express the fact that certain similarities between pairs of objects of a set S can be proved, and these, called *equivalence relations*, can be characterized in languages using the logical rules described earlier. An equivalence relation expresses the fact that certain objects that are, perhaps, not identical have *some* properties in common. The need to establish equivalence relations arises from the desire to be able to interchange the names of certain mathematical objects in a mathematical context.

For example, "1 + 1" is not identical with "2," but they are equivalent in the sense that they are (by convention) names of the same number, so that each may be replaced by the other in an arithmetical context. To cite another example, the set $\{1, 2, 3\}$ is not identical to the set $\{7, 8, 9\}$, yet they are equivalent in the sense that they have the same number of elements. Thus they are interchangeable in any context in which the only property of a set germane to the discussion is the number of elements it contains as members. Two people, similarly, may have the same boxing prowess, and so may be replaced by one another on a fight card or in an ordered rating of boxers.

An important property of an equivalence relation is that it allows us to express the set S over which it is defined as a union of subsets, each of which contains elements of S that are equivalent to each other in pairs. Further, these subsets are pairwise disjoint, reflecting the fact that objects that are not equivalent belong to distinct subsets. Any representation of S as a union of mutually disjoint subsets is called a *partition* of S, and the subsets are called *cells* of the partition. If each cell of a partition of S

contains elements which are equivalent under some equivalence relation p, we say that the partition is *induced* by p.

For example, if S is a set of people, and apb means "a has the same height as b," then the elements of any cell of the partition induced by p are people of the same height. Similarly, if S is a set of finite subsets and apb means that a and b have the same number of elements, then the elements of a cell of the partition induced by p are all sets with the same number of elements.

For another example, let S be the set $\mathcal{I}$ of integers, and let apb mean that $(a - b)/5$ is an integer. Then two integers are in the same cell of the partition induced by p if their difference is divisible by 5. Note that there are exactly five cells in this partition. One cell contains all multiples of 5, another contains all numbers that are 1 more than a multiple of 5, and so on. The elements of a cell are equivalent in the sense that they all leave the same remainder when divided by 5. These cells are called *integers modulo* 5, and are usually denoted by 0, 1, 2, 3, and 4.

We shall show that if p is a relation over S that induces a partition, then it must have the properties:

$R.\ (x)(xpx)$

$S.\ (x)(y)(xpy \rightarrow ypx)$

$T.\ (x)(y)(z)(xpy \land ypz \rightarrow xpz).$

These are called the *reflexive*, *symmetric*, and *transitive* properties respectively, and any relation p satisfying them is called an *equivalence relation*. Note that these are just the properties $E1$–3 of equality assumed as axioms in the preceding section.

If p is to induce a partition in S, then surely each element x of S must be in the same cell with itself, so the reflexive property must hold. If x is in the same cell with y, then y is in the same cell with x, so p must be symmetric. Further, if x is in the same cell with y and y is in the same cell with z, then x is in the same cell with z, so the transitive property holds.

The preceding paragraph shows that R, S, and T are necessary conditions for p to induce a partition in S. To show that they are sufficient, assume that p has all three properties. We choose an element a_1 of S and let it belong to a subset S_1. We place a second element a_2 in S_1 if and only if a_2pa_1 is true. If not, we place a_2 in a second subset S_2. We proceed in this way with every element a_j of S. If there is an element a_k with $k < j$ for which a_jpa_k, we place a_j in the same subset with a_k. If not, we place a_j in a new subset. Every element is eventually placed in some subset of

$\mathcal{S}$. Suppose that some element a is placed in two distinct subsets $\mathcal{S}_m$ and $\mathcal{S}_n$. Let a_i be the first element placed in $\mathcal{S}_m$ and a_j be the first element placed in $\mathcal{S}_n$. Then apa_i and apa_j are both true. But then a_ipa is true by the symmetric property, and a_ipa_j follows from a_ipa and apa_j by the transitive property. This contradicts the fact that $\mathcal{S}_m$ and $\mathcal{S}_n$ are chosen distinct and proves that all subsets constructed are disjoint from one another.

A consequence of the fact that p induces a partition in $\mathcal{S}$ is that if $a \in \mathcal{S}_1$ and $b \in \mathcal{S}_2$, for two cells $\mathcal{S}_1$ and $\mathcal{S}_2$, and if apb, then $\mathcal{S}_1 = \mathcal{S}_2$; that is, $\mathcal{S}_1$ and $\mathcal{S}_2$ have all their elements in common.

Another kind of relation important in mathematics, as well as in other fields, is the *order relation*. We shall distinguish here several different kinds of order relations. The simplest we shall consider is epitomized by the relation represented by "x is at least as desirable as y." Such relations are important in arranging sets of objects in preference lists. Certainly if p is a relation of this kind every element x of $\mathcal{S}$ is at least as high on the preference list as itself, so that p must be reflexive. Also, if x is at least as high as y and y is at least as high as z on a preference list, then x must be at least as high as z, so the transivity property must hold. A relation having these two properties is called a *quasi order* relation. Besides the preference relation, the relation $x \subset y$ among subsets of a given set, and the relation $x \leq y$ among numbers are quasi order relations. Another example is the relation "x implies y" among predicates.

Note that if p is a quasi order relation there may be elements a and b of $\mathcal{S}$ for which apb and bpa are both true. This would be the case if for two objects on a shopping list, a is at least as desirable as b and vice versa. In such a case the ordering does not help in choosing between the alternatives a and b. On the other hand, some quasi orders have the property that apb and bpa are both true only if $a = b$. Examples of such relations, called *partial order relations*, are those represented by $x \leq y$ and $x \subset y$. In addition to satisfying the reflexive and transitive properties, a partial order relation p has the *antisymmetric* property

A. $(x)(y)(xpy \wedge ypx \to x = y)$.

The relation of implication is another example of a partial order.

A feature of partial order relations is that there may be elements a and b of S for which neither apb nor bpa is true. This is so, for example, in the case of the subset relation and the implication relation. For the relation represented by $x \leq y$, however, at least one of the statements $a \leq b$ and $b \leq a$ must hold for every pair of numbers in the universe. A partial order for which this is true is called a *weak total order*, and has the property

B. $(x)(y)(xpy \lor ypx)$.

Contrasted with the order relations discussed above, which are reflexive, is a relation like that represented by $x < y$. Not only does the reflexive law fail to hold but the stronger condition holds that for each x, xpx is false. Such a relation is said to be *irreflexive* and has the property

I. $(x)[\sim(xpx)]$.

Note that the reflexive property and the irreflexive property are not negations of one another, for there are relations that are neither reflexive nor irreflexive. The relation represented by "x loves y" is an example of such a relation.

The relation $x < y$ is not symmetric. With respect to symmetry even a stronger condition holds: if $x < y$, then $y \not< x$. This is known as the property of *asymmetry*, given by

D. $(x)(y)(xpy \rightarrow \sim(ypx))$.

Since the relation $x < y$ relates every distinct pair of numbers, it satisfies the *connectedness* property

C. $(x)(y)(x \neq y \rightarrow (xpy) \lor (ypx))$.

Finally, since $x < y$ represents an order relation, it must be transitive. Any relation p that has the properties I, D, C, and T is called a *strict total order*.

In the material of Chapters 2 and 3 order relations are discussed over various classes of numbers. If an order relation is defined, then part of our task is to show that it satisfies the properties that here characterize it as to type. In the work to follow weak total orders and strict total orders will be of special concern.

EXERCISES

1. Consider each of the following relations over the given set $\mathcal{S}$:
    (a) x is married to y; $\mathcal{S}$ is a set of married people
    (b) x is married to y; $\mathcal{S}$ is a set of people married to members of $\mathcal{S}$
    (c) $x - y = 0$; $\mathcal{S}$ is the set $\mathcal{R}$ of real numbers
    (d) x is logically equivalent to y; $\mathcal{S}$ is a set of predicates
    (e) x logically implies y; $\mathcal{S}$ is a set of predicates
    (f) $x + y = 1$; $\mathcal{S}$ is the set $\mathcal{R}$ of real numbers
    (g) x lives at least as close to New York City as y; $\mathcal{S}$ is a set of people in the suburbs of New York City

(h) x is at least as old and has worked at factory A at least as long as y; $\mathcal{S}$ is a set of workers at factory A.

Answer the following questions for each relation above:

(a) Which of the properties R, S, T, A, B, C, D, I does the relation satisfy?
(b) Which of the following terms describe the relation: equivalence, quasi order, partial order, weak total order, strict total order?
(c) If the relation is an equivalence relation, describe the partition of $\mathcal{S}$ it induces.

2. Show that the conjunction of two equivalence relations is an equivalence relation. Is this true of their disjunction?

3. If p induces a partition $\{\mathcal{P}_1, \mathcal{P}_2, \ldots, \mathcal{P}_m\}$ in $\mathcal{S}$ and q induces a partition $\{\mathcal{Q}_1, \mathcal{Q}_2, \ldots, \mathcal{Q}_n\}$, show that each cell of the partition induced in $\mathcal{S}$ by $p \wedge q$ is the intersection $\mathcal{P}_i \cap \mathcal{Q}_j$ for some $i \leq m$ and $j \leq n$. The partition induced by $p \wedge q$ is called the *cross* of the partitions induced by p and by q.

4. If $\mathcal{S}$ is a class of people and p is represented by "x and y have the same color eyes" and q is represented by "x and y have the same color hair," describe the partitions induced in $\mathcal{S}$ by p, by q, and by $p \wedge q$.

5. One partition is *finer than* another if each cell of the first is a subset of some cell of the second. Show that the cross of two partitions is finer than both of them.

6. Show that the relation represented by "x is finer than y" over partitions of a set $\mathcal{S}$ is a partial order relation. Give an example of two partitions of a set $\mathcal{S}$ neither of which is finer than the other.

7. If p is represented by xpy, the *converse* of p is a relation p' represented by ypx. Thus, by definition,

$$(x)(y)(xp'y \leftrightarrow ypx)$$

is true. For each of the properties R, S, T, A, B, C, D, I considered in turn, determine whether the fact that p has the property implies that p' has the property. If it is so, prove it. If not, give an example to disprove it.

8. If x and y are integers modulo 5, define their *sum* $x + y$ as the integer modulo 5 containing all sums $a + b$ where $a \in x$ and $b \in y$.

(a) Show that the sum of integers modulo 5 is *well defined*. That is, show that if a and a' are members of x and b and b' are members of y, then $a + b$ and $a' + b'$ are members of the same integer modulo 5.
[Hint: This is the same as showing that if $a - a'$ and $b - b'$ are multiples of 5, then $(a + b) - (a' + b')$ is a multiple of 5.]
(b) Construct an addition table for integers modulo 5 and show that they form a group under addition.

(c) What is the identity element of this group? For each integer modulo 5, what is its group inverse?

9. If x and y are integers modulo 5, define their *product* xy as the integer modulo 5 containing all products ab where $a \in x$ and $b \in y$.

   (a) Show that the product of integers modulo 5 is well defined.
   (b) Construct a multiplication table for integers modulo 5 different from 0 and show that they form a group under multiplication.
   (c) What is the identity element of this group? For each integer modulo 5, what is its group inverse?

10. Develop the theory of arithmetic for integers modulo 6 reflecting the development sketched in Exercises 8 and 9. Why does an attempt to show that integers modulo 6 different from 0 form a group under multiplication fail?

8 · FUNCTIONS AND CARDINAL NUMBERS

This section treats relations that can be used to define functions and one-one correspondences, and uses these notions to define the idea of cardinal numbers, which underlies the theory of natural numbers to be developed in later sections. Recall that, given two sets $\mathcal{A}$ and $\mathcal{B}$, a function with domain $\mathcal{A}$ and image set $\mathcal{B}$ is an assignment of a single element of $\mathcal{B}$ to each element of $\mathcal{A}$. If p is a relation whose universe is the cartesian product $\mathcal{A} \times \mathcal{B}$, then we can interpret the truth of the statement apb to mean that b is assigned to a. Thus every relation assigns elements of $\mathcal{B}$ to elements of $\mathcal{A}$. In order to use a relation to define a function, however, we must be sure that to each element of $\mathcal{A}$ *one and only one element* of $\mathcal{B}$ is assigned. Thus, to insure that p assigns an element of $\mathcal{B}$ to each element of $\mathcal{A}$, it must satisfy the condition

F_1. $(x)(E\,y)(xpy)$.

This is actually a condition on the choice of $\mathcal{A}$. In order to insure that p assigns only one element of $\mathcal{B}$ to each element of $\mathcal{A}$ so that $\mathcal{B}$ is the range of the function, the truth of the two statements xpy and xpz must imply that $y = z$ is true. Thus, in order that p be used to define a function, it must satisfy F_1 and the condition

F_2. $(x)(y)(z)(xpy \land xpz \rightarrow y = z)$.

If p satisfies both F_1 and F_2 then it defines a function f and we usually write "$f(x) = y$" for "xpy" in this case. Thus if p is represented by $2x - y = 1$ in the universe $\mathcal{I}^2$ of ordered pairs of integers, then the function f defined assigns to each integer x the integer $2x - 1$, so we write

$$2x - 1 = y \quad \text{or} \quad f(x) = y \quad \text{or} \quad f(x) = 2x - 1.$$

That all three forms are acceptable is due to the fact that the relation expressed by "$=$" is reflexive, symmetric, and transitive.

In terms of solution sets, the conditions F_1 and F_2 imply that for each x there is one and only one y such that (x, y) is in the solution set of p. This means that if (x, y) and (x, z) are both in the solution set of p, we must have $y = z$.

Let f be a function with domain $\mathcal{A}$ and range $\mathcal{B}$ and g be a function with domain $\mathcal{C}$ and range $\mathcal{D}$. Let $\mathcal{A}_1$ be the subset of $\mathcal{A}$ whose elements x have values that belong to $\mathcal{B} \cap \mathcal{C}$. The function g assigns to each element of $\mathcal{B} \cap \mathcal{C}$ some element of $\mathcal{D}$. Thus there is a function h with domain $\mathcal{A}_1$ for which $h(x) = g(f(x))$ for each x in $\mathcal{A}_1$ and its range is a subset of $\mathcal{D}$. This function h is called the composition of g on f and is denoted by $g[f]$. Thus, the statement $h(x) = z$ may be defined as

$$(E\ y)(f(x) = y \wedge g(y) = z)$$

and $\mathcal{A}_1$ may be defined as $\{x | f(x) \in \mathcal{C}\}$. The construction of compositions is illustrated in Figure 6.

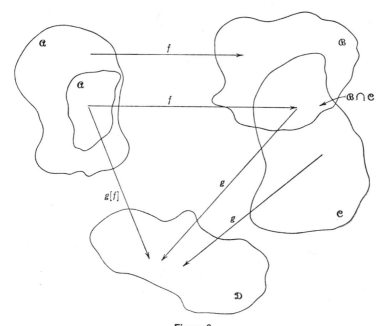

Figure 6

For example, let $\alpha = \mathcal{B} = \mathcal{I}$ and let f be the function defined by $f(x) = 2x - 1$. Let $\mathcal{C}$ be the set of all perfect squares of integers and $\mathcal{D} = \{0, 1, 2, \ldots\}$, and let $g(x) = \sqrt{x}$. Then

$$h(x) = g[f](x) = \sqrt{2x - 1}$$

and the domain α_1 of h is the set of all integers x for which $2x - 1$ is a perfect square. This is illustrated in the graphs of Figure 7.

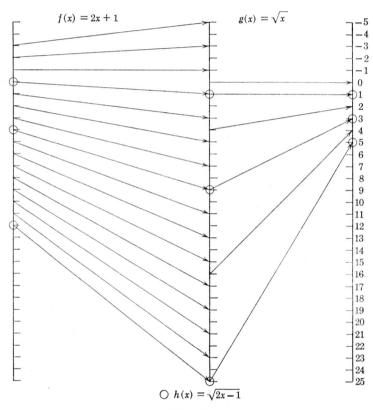

Figure 7

If p and its converse p' both satisfy F_1 and F_2 then not only is one and only one y in $\mathcal{B}$ assigned to each element x of α, but no two elements x are assigned the same element y. Further, every y in $\mathcal{B}$ is assigned. If p defines the function f then p' also defines a function called the *inverse* of f and denoted by $\bar{f}$. The set $\mathcal{B}$ is the range of f since all of its elements are values of f. Similarly, $\mathcal{B}$ is the domain and α the range of $\bar{f}$. If a function f has an inverse function, then it is a one-one correspondence. In order that p define a one-one correspondence it must satisfy F_1, F_2, and the properties

F_3. $(y)(\mathrm{E}\,x)(xpy)$

F_4. $(x)(y)(z)(xpz \wedge ypz \rightarrow x = y)$.

Note that the function f defined by $f(x) = x + 1$ is a one-one correspondence with domain and range g. It assigns to each integer its successor as a value. Its inverse is the function $\bar{f}(x) = x - 1$ assigns to each integer its predecessor. The function defined by $f(x) = 2x - 1$ with g as domain has the set of odd integers as range. Its inverse is the function defined by

$$\bar{f}(x) = \frac{x + 1}{2}.$$

If a function is a one-one correspondence with domain $\mathcal{A}$ and range $\mathcal{B}$, we say that it is a correspondence *from* $\mathcal{A}$ *onto* $\mathcal{B}$.

If f is a correspondence from $\mathcal{A}$ onto $\mathcal{B}$ and g is a correspondence from $\mathcal{B}$ onto $\mathcal{C}$, we leave it to the reader to show that $g[f]$ is a correspondence from $\mathcal{A}$ to $\mathcal{C}$ and that the inverse of $g[f]$ is $\bar{f}[\bar{g}]$.

One-one correspondences are extremely useful in studying the relationship between sets and their cardinal numbers. The notion of cardinal number is defined below and serves to express a property of a set $\mathcal{A}$ usually expressed by "the number of elements in $\mathcal{A}$." In Chapter 2, the natural numbers are introduced axiomatically and the axioms reflect the fact that their structure is concerned primarily with counting procedures. The interpretations of these axioms are usually denoted by $0, 1, 2, \ldots$ and are used to express the number of elements in a set. Here we define cardinal numbers and prepare to show that they form an interpretation of the axioms for natural numbers to be introduced later.

We can use the notion of one-one correspondence to distinguish between two very important types of set: finite and infinite. We note that for finite sets $\mathcal{A}$ and $\mathcal{B}$ a one-one correspondence from $\mathcal{A}$ to $\mathcal{B}$ exists only if they have the same number of elements. This is because the correspondence pairs off the elements of the two sets so that each element of each set is in one and only one pair. Thus, if $\mathcal{A}$ is a finite set and $\mathcal{A}_1$ is a proper subset of $\mathcal{A}$, there can be no one-one correspondence from $\mathcal{A}$ onto $\mathcal{A}_1$, for $\mathcal{A}_1$ has fewer elements than $\mathcal{A}$. On the other hand, if $\mathcal{A}$ is infinite (in intuitive terms) then it is possible to find a proper subset $\mathcal{A}_1$ of $\mathcal{A}$ and a one-one correspondence from $\mathcal{A}$ onto $\mathcal{A}_1$. For example, let $\mathcal{A}$ be the set g of integers, and $\mathcal{A}_1$ be the set of odd integers. Then the function f defined by $f(x) = 2x - 1$ is a one-one correspondence from $\mathcal{A}$ onto $\mathcal{A}_1$

and α_1 is a proper subset of α. It was the mathematician Georg Cantor who first showed in 1877 that this criterion could be used to distinguish between finite and infinite sets. Thus when we say that a set α is *infinite* we mean that there is a proper subset α_1 of α and a one-one correspondence from α onto α_1. If no proper subset exists for which such a one-one correspondence can be found, we say the set is *finite*.

Let α be an infinite set and $\mathfrak{u}$ be the set of all finite subsets of α. We define a relation p over $\mathfrak{u}$ so that xpy means that there is a one-one correspondence from x onto y. Note that x and y are elements of $\mathfrak{u}$ but *finite subsets* of α. We show that p is an equivalence relation.

Note that the identity relation is a one-one correspondence from any set onto itself. Since such a correspondence exists, p must have the reflexive property, thus $(x)(xpx)$ is true. Assume that xpy is true. Then there is a correspondence f from x to y. Since f is one-one, its inverse $\bar{f}$ is a correspondence from y onto x. Thus, p has the symmetric property and

$$(x)(y)(xpy \rightarrow ypx)$$

is true. To prove that p is transitive, assume that xpy and ypz are true. Then there is a one-one correspondence f from x onto y and a one-one correspondence g from y onto z. In this case the composition $g[f]$ is a one-one correspondence from x onto z, so that xpz is true. Thus,

$$(x)(y)(z)(xpy \wedge ypz \rightarrow xpz)$$

is true.

Since p is an equivalence relation, there is a partition induced in $\mathfrak{u}$, each cell of which contains finite subsets of α that are mutually equivalent under the relation p. Each cell of this partition is called a (finite) *cardinal number*. In particular, if x is any finite subset of α, the cell to which it belongs is called the cardinal number of x and denoted by $n(x)$. Note that n is a function whose domain is $\mathfrak{u}$ and whose range is the set $\mathfrak{c}$ of all cardinal numbers.

The relation p expresses the fact that sets have some property in common, since p is an equivalence relation; this is the property of having the same number of elements. The notion of cardinal number is an *abstraction* from the notion of set since it distinguishes sets only as to the cardinal numbers of elements in them and disregards all o her properties. Abstraction in this sense means concentration on some properties of the elements of a universe while neglecting others.

The null set ε is an element of $\mathfrak{u}$, so that $n(\varepsilon)$ exists. We denote it by 0.

For each $a \in \mathcal{C}$, the set $\{a\}$ is an element of $\mathfrak{U}$ and all such unit sets belong to the same cardinal number, which we denote by 1. If x is an element of $\mathfrak{U}$ for which $n(x) = b$, then there is an element $a \in \mathcal{C}$ that is not a member of x. The existence of a is assured since x is a finite subset of the infinite set $\mathcal{C}$. Thus the set $x \cup \{a\}$ has a cardinal number. It can be shown that for any element x of $\mathfrak{U}$ for which $n(x) = b$ and any element a of $\mathcal{C}$ that is not an element of x, $n(x \cup \{a\})$ is the same. We call $n(x \cup \{a\})$ the *successor* of $n(x)$ and denote it by $S(n(x))$. Thus every cardinal number has a unique successor. Define $1 = S(0)$, $2 = S(1)$, $3 = S(2)$, and so on.

It can also be shown that if a and b are cardinal numbers and $S(a) = S(b)$, then $a = b$. To see this, suppose

$$a = n(x) \quad \text{and} \quad b = n(y).$$

If $a \neq b$, then there is no one-one correspondence from x onto y. Let c and d be elements of $\mathcal{C}$ such that c does not belong to x and d does not belong to y. Then there is no one-one correspondence from $x \cup \{c\}$ onto $y \cup \{d\}$. But this contradicts the hypothesis that $S(a) = S(b)$, so that the assumption that $a \neq b$ must be abandoned. Hence $a = b$.

We leave it to the reader to show that 0 is not the successor of any cardinal number.

These properties can be summarized in the following list of sentences in the universe $\mathcal{C}$ of cardinal numbers:

(1) $(E\,x)(x = 0)$
(2) $(x)(E\,y)(y = S(x))$
(3) $(x)(y)(S(x) = S(y) \to x = y)$
(4) $(x)(0 \neq S(x))$.

These statements are interpretations in the domain of cardinals of the first four axioms for natural numbers to be cons dered later.

An interesting point about the structure of the set $\mathcal{C}$ is that every cardinal number other than 0 is the successor of some cardinal number; that is, it has a *predecessor*. It is a consequence of the axioms for natural numbers, as we shall show, that a strict total order relation $x < y$ may be defined that arranges natural numbers in a straight line, or chain, so to speak. Since cardinal numbers can be interpreted in these axioms, the same is true for them. Thus 0 is first in order; its successor 1 is second; $S(1)$, or 2, is third, and so on.

Suppose we wish to define a function f with domain $\mathcal{C}$. If a value is assigned to 0, and if for each x, we are told how the value $f(S(x))$ can be computed from x and the value $f(x)$, then every value of f is determined. We might define f as follows:

$$f(0) = 2$$
$$f(S(x)) = x + f(x),$$

where we assume that addition is defined as usual. To find $f(3)$ for example, we could perform the following computation:

$$
\begin{aligned}
f(3) &= f(S(2)) \\
&= 2 + f(2) \\
&= 2 + f(S(1)) \\
&= 2 + (1 + f(1)) \\
&= 2 + [1 + f(S(0))] \\
&= 2 + \{1 + [0 + f(0)]\} \\
&= 2 + 1 + 0 + 2 \\
&= 5.
\end{aligned}
$$

For any $x \in \mathcal{C}$ we could proceed to find $f(x)$ in this way. Such a definition is said to be *inductive* since an apparently small amount of information can be expanded to provide information about the value assigned to every member of $\mathcal{C}$. To be inductive, the definition must determine the value $f(0)$ and, for each x, it must determine $f(S(x))$ in terms of x and $f(x)$.

We may proceed in the same way to prove inductively for some property p that $(x)p(x)$ is true. Such a proof requires two steps. We demonstrate first that $p(0)$ is true. This is called the *basis* of the proof. Next we show for each x that if $p(x)$ is true, then $p(S(x))$ is also true. This is called the *induction step* of the proof. Since the truth of $p(S(x))$ is implied by the truth of $p(x)$ for each x, it depends, finally, on the truth of $p(0)$. Since, by the basis, $p(0)$ is true, we may assert that $(x)p(x)$ is true. The induction step is a proof of $(x)[p(x) \to p(S(x))]$. To prove it we use the rules $L2$ and $L15$ after demonstrating that the open statement $p(S(x))$ follows from $p(x)$. The use of $L2$ discharges the premise $p(x)$, so that the conclusion is not assumed in the proof, even though it seems to be assumed as the premise $p(x)$.

Let us prove, as an example, that

$$(x)\left(0 + 1 + 2 + \cdots + x = \frac{x(x+1)}{2}\right).$$

Proof: In the basis, we show that

$$0 = \frac{0(0 + 1)}{2}.$$

For the induction step, assume

$$0 + 1 + 2 + \cdots + x = \frac{x(x + 1)}{2}$$

as the *hypothesis of the induction*. On this assumption we must prove that

$$0 + 1 + 2 + \cdots + x + S(x) = \frac{S(x)[S(x) + 1]}{2}.$$

By the hypothesis we have

$$0 + 1 + 2 + \cdots + x + S(x) = \frac{x(x + 1)}{2} + S(x)$$

adding $S(x)$ to both sides of the equation. However,

$$\frac{x(x + 1)}{2} + S(x) = \frac{xS(x)}{2} + S(x)$$

$$= S(x)\left(\frac{x}{2} + 1\right)$$

$$= S(x)\frac{x + 2}{2}$$

$$= S(x)\frac{S(x) + 1}{2}$$

and the result follows by *L*2 and *L*15. Of course, we have used here known properties of addition and multiplication. The proofs that these properties hold will be given in the investigation of natural numbers.

The fact that the cardinal numbers submit to proofs by induction demonstrates that the fifth axiom of natural numbers is satisfied:

(5) $p(0) \wedge (x)[p(x) \rightarrow p(S(x))] \rightarrow (x)p(x).$

EXERCISES

1. The following open statements represent predicates in the universe $\mathcal{I}$ of integers. For each predicate, tell whether it defines a function whose domain is $\mathcal{I}$. If so, is this function a one-one correspondence? If not, attempt to choose a subset of $\mathcal{I}$ so that the predicate has this subset as domain.

    (a) $x + 2y = 9$
    (b) $x^2 + y^2 = 9$

(c) $x + y^2 = 9$
(d) $x^2 + y = 9$
(e) $xy = 9$
(f) $xy = 28$
(g) $y - |x + 2| = 9$

2. Of the predicates of Exercise 1, which have converses that define functions with domain $\mathcal{I}$? with a smaller domain?

3. What are the ranges of the functions defined in Exercises 1 and 2?

4. Prove that if f and g are one-one correspondences, then so are $f[g]$ and $g[f]$.

5. Let f have the domain $\mathcal{I}$ and be defined by $f(x) = 5x + 2$ and let g be defined by $g(x) = x/5$ and have a subset of $\mathcal{I}$ as domain.

   (a) What is the largest subset of $\mathcal{I}$ that is a domain of g?
   (b) Show that $g[f]$ has an empty domain.
   (c) What is the domain of $f[g]$?
   (d) Express $f[g]$ by a single formula.

6. The function defined by the identity relation is called the *identity function* and denoted by x. If f is a one-one correspondence, show that $f[\bar{f}]$ and $\bar{f}[f]$ coincide with the identity function.

7. Show that the inverse of a one-one correspondence is a one-one correspondence.

8. If f and g are one-one correspondences, show that the inverse of $g[f]$ is $\bar{f}[\bar{g}]$.

9. Find a one-one correspondence different from the one given in the text to show that the integers form an infinite class.

10. We define a function f with domain $\mathcal{C}$ inductively as follows:
$$f(0) = 0, f(S(x)) = f(x) + 2x + 1.$$
Prove by induction that $(x)[f(x) = x^2]$ is true.

11. We define g inductively as follows:
$$g(0) = 0, \qquad g(S(x)) = g(x) + x^2.$$
Prove that $(x)[g(x) = x(x + 1)(2x + 1)/6]$ is true.

12. Define h inductively as follows:
$$h(0) = 0, \qquad h(S(x)) = h(x) + x^3.$$
Prove that $(x)[h(x) = x^2(x + 1)^2/4]$ is true.

13. If a and b are cardinal numbers, define their sum $a + b$ as $n(x \cup y)$, where x and y are disjoint and $n(x) = a$ and $n(y) = b$. Show that addition defined thus is well defined by showing that if x' and y' are any other sets satisfying these conditions, then
$$n(x' \cup y') = n(x \cup y).$$

14. We define the sum of two cardinal numbers inductively as follows:
$$a + 0 = a, \qquad a + S(x) = S(a + x).$$
Show that for all cardinal numbers x and y, the sum $x + y$ is the same under either this definition or the one given in Exercise 13.

15. Show that the cardinal number 0 has no predecessor.

BIBLIOGRAPHY

Allendoerfer, Oakley, *Introduction to Mathematics*, McGraw-Hill 1955.

Breuer, Fehr, *The Theory of Sets*, Prentice-Hall 1958.

Hilbert, Ackermann, *Mathematical Logic*, Chelsea 1950.

Kemeny, Snell, Thompson, *Introduction to Finite Mathematics*, Prentice-Hall 1957.

Kerschner, Wilcox, *The Anatomy of Mathematics*, Ronald 1950.

Mathematical Association of America, *Elementary Mathematics of Sets*, University of Buffalo, revised 1958.

Quine, *Methods of Logic*, Holt 1950.

Rosser, *Logic for Mathematicians*, McGraw-Hill 1953.

Russell, *Introduction to Mathematical Philosophy*, Macmillan 1924.

Tarski, *Introduction to Logic*, Oxford 1946.

Stabler, *Introduction to Mathematical Thought*, Addison-Wesley 1953.

Suppes, *Introduction to Logic*, Van Nostrand 1957.

Whitehead, *Introduction to Mathematics*, Oxford 1948.

Wilder, *Foundations of Mathematics*, Wiley 1952.

Numbers and Their Properties

CHAPTER 2

1 · OPERATIONS ON NUMBERS

This chapter treats familiar systems of numbers, operations on them, and relations among them. Beginning with Section 4 the axioms for the set $\mathfrak{N}$ of natural numbers are introduced and operations and predicates are defined. The set $\mathcal{I}$ of integers is defined and its properties examined in Sections 8 and 9. Section 10 is devoted to the definition of the set of rational numbers. Certain limitations in using the elements in each of these sets lead us to define the next set in this sequence. Thus, the fact that subtraction cannot be universally performed among natural numbers leads us to define the integers, and because not all quotients of integers are integers we are led to consider the set $\mathbb{Q}$ of rational numbers. Limitations of a different sort become apparent in operating with rational numbers, and these lead us to define the set $\mathfrak{R}$ of real numbers in Chapter 3. There, functions that have subsets of $\mathfrak{R}$ as domain and range are also investigated.

The procedure of defining a new class of numbers in terms of numbers already defined is called *extension*. The principal reason for using this term is that the new set of numbers is defined so that it contains a subset whose elements reflect the properties of the system being extended. This enables us to construct new systems of numbers embodying properties that former systems lack without losing the stated properties of former systems. Thus, among the integers are the nonnegative integers, which reflect the operational properties of natural numbers; among the rational numbers are fractions of the form $a/1$, where a is an integer, reflecting the properties of the integers.

The first three sections of this chapter deal with arithmetic operations and relations. Here, the goal is to set down and discuss properties of these operations and relations that are commonly known and widely used. Since most of those who work with arithmetic use these properties intuitively and automatically, it is important to point out just how these properties justify the things we always do with numbers. Then, in later sections, the properties themselves are justified.

In the first three sections we assume that our universe is a set $\mathfrak{U}$ of numbers of some kind. We specify $\mathfrak{U}$ in different ways beginning with Section 4. A *binary operation* in $\mathfrak{U}$ is a function with domain $\mathfrak{U}^2$ and range $\mathfrak{U}$. Thus, it assigns a *unique* element of $\mathfrak{U}$ to every ordered pair of elements of $\mathfrak{U}$, and we call this element the *result* of the operation. To begin with, we assume that two operations, addition, and multiplication, are defined in $\mathfrak{U}$, and denote their results for the ordered pair (a, b) by $a + b$ and ab respectively. Since these operations make an assignment to *every* ordered pair in $\mathfrak{U}^2$, we say that $\mathfrak{U}$ is *closed* under the operations. Stated in the language developed in Chapter 1, the properties of closure of addition and multiplication are

O1. $(x)(y)(\mathrm{E}\, z)[x + y = z]$

O2. $(x)(y)(\mathrm{E}\, z)[xy = z]$.

Another property is that the result of an operation is *unique*. For addition and multiplication, the following properties assure uniqueness:

O3. $(x)(y)(z)(w)[x + y = z \wedge x + y = w \rightarrow z = w]$

O4. $(x)(y)(z)(w)(xy = z \wedge xy = w \rightarrow z = w]$.

Closure and uniqueness properties are always present since we have assumed an operation to be a function with domain $\mathfrak{U}^2$. If a relation is defined, however, these properties must be proved before the relation can be entitled an "operation." If the properties O1–4 hold, we think of "$x + y$" and "xy" as names of unique numbers, and in most cases other names for these numbers exist in the language already.

To express the fact that two groups of symbols designate the same number, a predicate of equality is introduced that is reflexive, symmetric, and transitive. Using this predicate all names of numbers are partitioned into equivalence classes such that a member of one of these classes is replaceable in any arithmetical context by another member of this class without affecting the truth of the context. We represent equality by $x = y$.

The fact that equality is reflexive, symmetric, and transitive is expressed by R, S, and T given in Section 7 of Chapter 1. Because of these properties, we can introduce a number of abbreviations into proofs whose statements are equalities. Thus, if a proof of $v = w$ has the steps:

$$x = y \qquad \text{assumption}$$
$$y = x \qquad \text{by } S$$
$$z = y \qquad \text{assumption}$$
$$z = x \qquad \text{by } T$$
$$w = z \qquad \text{assumption}$$
$$w = x \qquad \text{by } T$$
$$v = x \qquad \text{assumption}$$
$$x = v \qquad \text{by } S$$
$$w = v \qquad \text{by } T$$
$$v = w \qquad \text{by } S$$

we may abbreviate it thus:

$$v = x \qquad \text{assumption}$$
$$ = y \qquad \text{assumption, } T$$
$$ = z \qquad \text{assumption, } S, T$$
$$ = w \qquad \text{assumption, } S, T.$$

Note that S is applied to replace an equality by its converse, and T to pass from two equalities to a third. In the abbreviated proof, the premises of a rule are not always expressed.

Because a binary operation acts on an *ordered* pair (a, b) it is convenient to establish a relation between the results of the operation on a pair (a , b) and its *converse* (b, a). If these results are equal for every a and b in $\mathfrak{U}$ we say that the operation is *commutative*. In defining addition and multiplication, we attempt to prove the commutative properties:

O5. $(x)(y)[x + y = y + x]$

O6. $(x)(y)[xy = yx]$.

Since these operations are binary, we must group by pairs any set of elements of $\mathfrak{u}$ to be added or multiplied, and need to state some relationships among the possible groupings. Thus $(a + b) + c$ indicates that c is added to the sum of a and b, while $a + (b + c)$ indicates that the sum of b and c is to be added to a. If both results are equal, we say that the operation is *associative*. Statements of the associative property for addition and multiplication are

O7. $(x)(y)(z)[(x + y) + z = x + (y + z)]$

O8. $(x)(y)(z)[(xy)z = x(yz)]$.

Once the properties O5 and O7 are established, it can be shown that if a finite set of numbers is added, then the result is the same no matter what the order or how they are grouped. Thus, we can show, for example, that

$$(x)(y)(z)(w)\{[x + (y + z)] + w = (x + w) + (y + z)\}.$$

Proof:

$$[x + (y + z)] + w = w + [x + (y + z)] \quad \text{by O5}$$
$$= (w + x) + (y + z) \quad \text{by O7, T}$$
$$w + x = x + w \quad\quad\quad\quad\quad \text{by O5}$$
$$(w + x) + (y + z) = (x + w) + (y + z) \quad *$$
$$[x + (y + z)] + w = (x + w) + (y + z) \quad \text{by T}.$$

Note that we might justify the step marked * by some statement like "when equals are added to equals, the results are equal." This principle is called the *monotonic property* of addition with respect to equality. Statements of this property for addition and multiplication are:

O9. $(x)(y)(z)[x = y \rightarrow x + z = y + z]$

O10. $(x)(y)(z)[x = y \rightarrow xz = yz]$.

The converses of these properties are called *cancellation properties*. They are:

O11. $(x)(y)(z)[x + z = y + z \rightarrow x = y]$

O12. $(x)(y)(z)[xz = yz \rightarrow x = y]$.

In some number systems, O12 does not hold without further restriction as we shall show. Other monotonic and cancellation properties in which z is the first term of the sum, or the first factor in the product, also hold. Their proofs are left for the reader.

Applications of $O9$–12 are especially important in solving linear equations. To solve the equation

$$2x + 1 = 7 + x$$

we might proceed with the following proof:

$$2x + 1 = 7 + x \qquad \text{assumption}$$
$$(x + x) + 1 = (6 + 1) + x \qquad \text{definition}$$
$$(x + 1) + x = (6 + 1) + x \qquad \text{by } O5,\ O7,\ T$$
$$x + 1 = 6 + 1 \qquad \text{by } P11$$
$$x = 6 \qquad \text{by } O11.$$

We have proved $(x)[2x + 1 = 7 + x \to x = 6]$. Of course, this is a proof that the solution of the equation must be unique, that is, that all solutions are equal to 6. To solve the equation, it must also be shown that 6 is a solution. This requires a proof of the converse statement

$$(x)[x = 6 \to 2x + 1 = 7 + x].$$

A short cut to this proof is to note that the converse of every property used in the earlier proof is also a property of arithmetic, so that each step is *reversible*. The steps are listed in reverse order and justified by converses of properties used in the proof above.

If three numbers are combined using addition and multiplication, a relation between the results obtained from distinct sequences of applying the operations plays an important part. This relation between the two operations is called the *distributive* property and is given by

$O13.$ $(x)(y)(z)[x(y + z) = xy + xz]$.

We establish the convention that if no grouping symbols appear, multiplication is performed before addition, so that $xy + xz$ is $(xy) + (xz)$.

Though the properties $O5$–8 and $O13$ are used so naturally when we do arithmetic that it seems somewhat superfluous to list them explicitly, it is important to realize that their validity justifies some very important procedures. An example is found in performing operations on numbers represented in traditional "positional" notation. A numeral in this notation is a sequence of digits taken from the list of numbers from 0 through 9. The number represented by such a numeral is the sum of multiples of powers of 10; for example,

$$374 = 3(10)^2 + 7(10) + 4.$$

It is interesting to investigate the properties used in finding the sum of two numbers represented in this way, say as two digit numerals. We learn from childhood to display the numerals in a column, to carry, and to remember sums of numbers from 0 through 9. Thus, we find that the sum $34 + 58$ is 92. To justify this conclusion, we may reason as follows:

$$\begin{aligned}
34 + 58 &= [3(10) + 4] + [5(10) + 8] && \text{by definition} \\
&= [3(10) + 5(10)] + [4 + 8] && \text{by } O5, 7 \\
&= [3 + 5](10) + 12 && *, \text{ addition table} \\
&= 8(10) + [1(10) + 2] && \text{by addition table, definition} \\
&= [8(10) + 1(10)] + 2 && \text{by } O7 \\
&= [8 + 1](10) + 2 && * \\
&= 9(10) + 2 && \text{by addition table} \\
&= 92 && \text{by definition.}
\end{aligned}$$

Note that "definition" is used as a justification when a numeral in positional notation is replaced by its expanded form, or vice versa, and "addition table" is used when the sum of two numbers is replaced by the conventional numeral that represents it.

As an illustration with multiplication, we justify the equation $12 \cdot 11 = 132$:

$$\begin{aligned}
12 \cdot 11 &= [1(10) + 2][1(10) + 1] && \text{by definition} \\
&= [1(10) + 2]1(10) + [1(10) + 2]1 && \text{by } O13 \\
&= 10[1(10) + 2] + [1(10) + 2] && \text{by } O6, \text{ multiplication table} \\
&= [1(10)^2 + 2(10)] + [1(10) + 2] && \text{by } O13, O6 \\
&= 1(10)^2 + \{[2(10) + 1(10)] + 2\} && \text{by } O7 \\
&= 1(10)^2 + \{(2 + 1)(10) + 2\} && * \\
&= 1(10)^2 + 3(10) + 2 && \text{by addition table, } O7 \\
&= 132 && \text{by definition.}
\end{aligned}$$

The justification of the step marked $*$ is the property

$$(x)(y)(z)[(x + y)z = xz + yz]$$

whose proof is left to the reader.

Having defined addition and multiplication in a system of numbers we may be sure that the sum and product of two numbers exist and are unique as long as the properties $O1$–4 are theorems of the system. Suppose that, given two numbers a and b, we wish to find a number c so that $c + b = a$. In a sense, we wish to find the first element of an ordered pair whose second element and whose sum are known. The operation that assigns such a number c to the ordered pair (a, b) is called *subtraction*. The number c itself is called the *difference* of b from a and denoted by $a - b$. In defining subtraction the properties of existence and uniqueness of differences concern us:

O14. $(x)(y)(\text{E } z)[z + y = x]$

O15. $(x)(y)(z)(w)[z + y = x \wedge w + y = x \rightarrow z = w]$.

If O14–15 are theorems then one and only one number $a - b$ is assigned to every ordered pair (a, b) of elements of $\mathfrak{u}$. From these properties and the definition of difference it follows that

O16. $(x)(y)[(x - y) + y = x]$.

Using O15–16 a number of useful properties of subtraction may be established:

$$(x)(y)(z)[(x - y) - z = x - (y + z)] \tag{4}$$
$$(x)(y)(z)[(x + y) - z = (x - z) + y] \tag{5}$$
$$(x)(y)(z)[x(y - z) = xy - xz]. \tag{6}$$

We prove (4) and (6), leaving the proof of (5) for the reader.

Proof of (4):

$$
\begin{aligned}
[(x - y) - z] + (y + z) &= [(x - y) - z] + (z + y) && \text{by O5} \\
&= \{[(x - y) - z] + z\} + y && \text{by O7} \\
&= (x - y) + y && \text{by O16} \\
&= x && \text{by O16} \\
[x - (y + z)] + (y + z) &= x && \text{by O16} \\
[(x - y) - z] + (y + z) &= [x - (y + z)] + (y + z) && \text{by S, T} \\
(x - y) - z &= x - (y + z) && \text{by O11}
\end{aligned}
$$

Proof of (6):

$$
\begin{aligned}
x(y - z) + xz &= x[(y - z) + z] && \text{by O13} \\
&= xy && \text{by O16} \\
(xy - xz) + xz &= xy && \text{by O16} \\
x(y - z) + xz &= (xy - xz) + xz && \text{by S, T} \\
x(y - z) &= xy - xz && \text{by O11.}
\end{aligned}
$$

If subtraction is defined and has the properties O14–15 then for every element a of $\mathfrak{u}$ there is an element b such that $a + b = a$. Thus,

$b = a - a$. We can show that if $a + b = a$ and $c + d = c$, then $b = d$.
For by monotonic properties

$$(a + b) + c = a + (c + d)$$

follows from the hypotheses. Now using commutative and associative
principles we have

$$b + (a + c) = d + (a + c)$$

and the conclusion follows by O11. Thus we have shown that in a number system with subtraction, there is a number *zero*, denoted by 0 that
has the property:

O17. $(x)[x + 0 = x]$.

Another property of 0 is:

O18. $(x)[0x = 0]$.

Proof:

$$\begin{aligned}
x + 0x &= 1x + 0x && \text{by multiplication table} \\
&= (1 + 0)x && \text{by Exercise 2} \\
&= 1x && \text{by O17, O10} \\
&= x && \text{by multiplication table} \\
0x &= 0 && \text{by O17, O15.}
\end{aligned}$$

The property of the multiplication table used in this proof is $(x)[1x = x]$,
and this is proved below.

To define an inverse for multiplication, we ask if for every a and b
there is a unique c such that $cb = a$. If there is exactly one such c we call
it the *quotient* of a by b and denote it by a/b. The operation that assigns
a/b to (a, b) is called *division*.

Note first that if $b = 0$, and $a \neq 0$, there is no c such that $cb = a$, for
by O18, $c0 = 0c = 0$ for every number c. If $b = 0$ and $a = 0$, then
$cb = a$ is true for every number c, so that c is not unique. Since either
existence or uniqueness fails in these cases, *division by zero is excluded*.
However, in some of the number systems we deal with we shall prove
that division by any number other than 0 gives a unique quotient, so
that the properties

O19. $(x)(y)[y \neq 0 \rightarrow (E\,z)(zy = x)]$

O20. $(x)(y)(z)(w)[y \neq 0 \wedge zy = x \wedge wy = x \rightarrow z = w]$

are theorems.

Note that the impossibility of division by zero limits the validity of
the cancellation law O12, for $x = y$ does not follow from $xz = yz$ if $z = 0$.

To see this note the fact that $0 \cdot 1 = 0 \cdot 2$ is true, but $1 = 2$ is false as a counterexample. The fact that $1 \neq 2$ follows from definitions of number systems to be considered later. Were this not so, our systems of numbers would have the undesirable property that $(x)[x = 0]$. Hence we must replace $O12$ by the restricted property:

O12′. $(x)(y)(z)[z \neq 0 \wedge xz = yz \rightarrow x = y]$.

We leave it to the reader to show that if $ba = a$ and $dc = c$, where a and c are not zero, then $b = d$. This means that there is a number 1 with the property:

O21. $(x)[1x = x]$.

EXERCISES

1. Use $O1$–2 to prove each of the following.
   (a) $(x)(y)(z)(\mathrm{E}\,w)[x(y + z) = w]$
   (b) $(x)(y)(z)(\mathrm{E}\,w)[(x + y)(y + z) = w]$

2. Prove that $(x)(y)(z)[(x + y)z = xz + yx]$ is true.

3. Using $O5$–$12'$, prove each of the following.
   (a) $(x)(y)(z)[x = y \rightarrow z + x = z + y]$
   (b) $(x)(y)(z)[x = y \rightarrow zx = zy]$
   (c) $(x)(y)(z)[z + x = z + y \rightarrow x = y]$
   (d) $(x)(y)(z)[z \neq 0 \wedge zx = zy \rightarrow x = y]$

4. Prove that each of the following is a valid property of arithmetic.
   (a) $(x)(y)(z)(w)[x(y + (z + w)) = xy + (xz + xw)]$
   (b) $(x)(y)(z)[x(y + x) + z(y + z) = y(x + z) + (xx + zz)]$
   (c) $(x)(y)(z)(w)[(x + y)(z + w) = xz + \{yz + (wx + wy)\}]$
   (d) $(x)(y)(z)[(x + y)(x + z) = (xx + (y + z)x) + yz]$

5. Show that 3 is the unique solution of the equation $x + 3 = 2x$, and justify each step of the proof.

6. Use the properties developed in this section to justify the following sums and products.
   (a) $33 + 117 = 150$
   (b) $28 + 75 = 103$
   (c) $25 \cdot 21 = 525$
   (d) $15 \cdot 72 = 1080$

7. Prove (5).

8. Prove that each of the following is a valid property of arithmetic:

   (a) $(x)(y)(z)[x - (y - z) = (x - y) + z]$
   (b) $(x)(y)(z)[(x - y)z = xz - yz]$
   (c) $(x)(y)(z)(w)[(x - y) + (z - w) = (x + z) - (y + w)]$
   (d) $(x)(y)(z)(w)[(x - y) - (z - w) = (x + w) - (y + z)]$

9. Prove that $(x)(y)[xy = 0 \rightarrow x = 0 \lor y = 0]$.

10. Use the result of Exercises 4(d) and 9 to prove that the solution set of

$$x^2 - 5x - 6 = 0 \text{ is } \{2, 3\}.$$

[Note: Prove that 2 and 3 are solutions, and that if x is a solution, then $x = 2$ or $x = 3$.]

11. Prove that each of the following is a valid property of arithmetic:

   (a) $(x)(y)(z)[(x/y)z = (xz)/y]$
   (b) $(x)(y)(z)[(x/y) + z = (x + yz)/y]$
   (c) $(x)(y)(z)(w)[(x/y)(z/w) = (xz)/(yw)]$
   (d) $(x)(y)(z)(w)[(x/y)/(z/w) = (xw)/(yz)]$.

12. We define an assignment n so that for each x in $\mathfrak{U}$, $x + n(x) = 0$.

   (a) Prove that n is a function.
   (b) Prove that n is a one-one correspondence. What is its inverse?
   (c) Prove that $(x)(y)[x + n(y) = x - y]$.
   (d) Prove that $(x)(y)[n(x)n(y) = xy]$.
   (e) Prove that $n(0) = 0$.
   (f) Prove that $(x)[n(x) = x \rightarrow x = 0]$.

   What is a reasonable interpretation of the correspondence n?

13. We define an assignment r so that for each $x \neq 0$ in $\mathfrak{U}$, $x \cdot r(x) = 1$.

   (a) Prove that r is a function with $\mathfrak{U} - \{0\}$ as domain.
   (b) Prove that r is a one-one correspondence. What is its inverse?
   (c) Prove that $(x)(y)[x \cdot r(y) = x/y]$.
   (d) Prove that $(x)(y)[r(x)r(y) = r(xy)]$.
   (e) Prove that $r(1) = 1$.
   (f) Prove that $(x)[r(x) = x \rightarrow x^2 = 1]$.

   What is a reasonable interpretation of the correspondence r?

14. Show that if $ba = a$, $dc = c$, $a \neq 0$, and $c \neq 0$, then $b = d$.

2 · INEQUALITIES AND ABSOLUTE VALUES

This section defines the conventional relations of inequality in a numerical universe $\mathfrak{U}$ and a function abs that assigns to each element of $\mathfrak{U}$ its absolute value.

To begin with, we suppose that $\mathfrak{U}$ contains 0, and that the operations of addition, multiplication, subtraction, and division are defined in $\mathfrak{U}$ and possess the properties $O1$–11, $O13$–21, and $O12'$. Then, as in Exercise 12, Section 1, we may define a function n so that

$$(x)[x + n(x) = 0]$$

is true. For each x, we call the value $n(x)$ the *negative of x* and denote it by $-x$. The properties developed in that exercise are:

$N1$. $(x)(y)[x = y \leftrightarrow -x = -y]$

$N2$. $(x)[-(-x) = x]$

$N3$. $(x)(y)[x + (-y) = x - y]$

$N4$. $(x)(y)[(-x)(-y) = xy]$

$N5$. $-0 = 0$

$N6$. $(x)[-x = x \rightarrow x = 0]$.

Furthermore, the function n has the property

$N7$. $(x)(y)[x(-y) = (-x)y = -(xy)]$.

Proof:

We prove first that $x(-y) = -(xy)$. All that is required is to show that

$$xy + [x(-y)] = 0$$

for then

$$x(-y) = n(xy) = -(xy)$$

by definition. We have

1. $xy + x(-y) = x[y + (-y)]$ by $O13$
2. $ = x0$ by definition
3. $ = 0$ by $O18$, $O6$.

The proof that $(-x)y = -(xy)$ is left to the reader.

In a number system $\mathfrak{U}$ in which a function n can be defined that has the properties $N1$–7 it is often convenient to define a partition by distinguishing some numbers as *positive* and others as *negative*. The number 0 is in a class by itself, being neither positive nor negative. If a predicate p is defined with the properties

$P1$. $\sim p(0)$

$P2$. $(x)[p(x) \leftrightarrow \sim p(-x)]$

$P3$. $(x)(y)[p(x) \wedge x = y \rightarrow p(y)]$

and interpreted so that for each x, $p(x)$ means "x is positive," then we may define a predicate q by the equivalence

P4. $(x)[q(x) \leftrightarrow p(-x)]$

such that $q(x)$ can be interpreted as "x is negative." Thus the elements of $\mathfrak{U}$ other than 0 are paired off by the correspondence n into pairs $(x, -x)$, and the predicates p and q are defined so that p assigns T to one element of each pair, and q assigns T to the other. For according to P4, if x is positive, then $-x$ is negative, and if $-x$ is positive, then x is negative. Using P2–4, we can prove

P5. $(x)[p(x) \leftrightarrow q(-x)]$

as well. Using P1–5, we can show that

P6. $\sim q(0)$.

The proofs are left to the reader. These properties assure us that the class of positive numbers, the class of negative numbers, and the class $\{0\}$ have no element in common. To have a partition of $\mathfrak{U}$ we must also know that each element of $\mathfrak{U}$ is in one of the three classes. This property is asserted by

P7. $(x)[x \neq 0 \to p(x) \lor q(x)]$

and is known as the *trichotomy* of arithmetic.

Using N1–7, P1–7, and the properties

P8. $(x)(y)[p(x) \land p(y) \to p(x + y)]$

P9. $(x)(y)[p(x) \land p(y) \to p(xy)]$

and the following theorems about sums and products can be proved:

P10. $(x)(y)[q(x) \land q(y) \to q(x + y)]$

P11. $(x)(y)[q(x) \land q(y) \to p(xy)]$

P12. $(x)(y)[p(x) \land q(y) \to q(xy)]$

P13. $(x)(y)[q(x) \land p(y) \to q(xy)]$.

Thus the usual relations hold. The sum and product of positive numbers and the product of negative numbers are positive, while the sum of two negative numbers and the product of a positive and a negative number are negative.

To prove P10, for example, we have

1. $(x + y) + [(-x) + (-y)]$

         $= [x + (y + (-y))] + (-x)$ by O5, O7
2. $= (x + 0) + (-x)$ by definition
3. $= x + (-x)$ by O17
4. $= 0$ by definition.

Thus,

$$5. \quad (-x) + (-y) = -(x + y) \qquad \text{by } N1$$
6. $q(x) \wedge q(y)$ — by assumption
7. $p(-x) \wedge p(-y)$ — by $P4$
8. $p((-x) + (-y))$ — by $P8$
9. $p(-(x + y))$ — by $P3$, from 5
10. $q(x + y)$ — by $P4$.

To prove $P12$, we have

1. $p(x) \quad q(y)$ — by assumption
2. $p(-y)$ — by $P4$
3. $p(x(-y))$ — by $P9$
4. $p(-(xy))$ — by $P3$, from $N7$
5. $q(xy)$ — by $P4$.

The proofs of other properties are left to the reader.

Intuitively, we think of the relation represented by $x < y$ to mean that a positive number must be added to x to obtain y. Thus we might define $x < y$ as

$$(\text{E } z)[p(z) \wedge x + z = y].$$

However, since the solution z of $x + z = y$ is defined as $y - x$ if it exists, we define "less than" by the equivalence

$D1. \quad (x)(y)[x < y \leftrightarrow p(y - x)].$

Thus, given two elements a and b of $\mathfrak{U}$, we have a definite test to determine whether or not $a < b$ is true. We ask simply whether $p(b - a)$ is true, for according to the definition, a is less than b if and only if $b - a$ is positive. In the rationals, for example, we can show that $(1/3) < (1/2)$ by noting that $(1/2) - (1/3) = 1/6$ is a positive number.

We proceed to show that the relation defined by $D1$ is a strict total order, as defined in Section 7, Chapter 1. To do this, we must prove that it has the following properties:

$S1. \quad (x)[x \not< x]$

$S2. \quad (x)(y)(z)[x < y \wedge y < z \rightarrow x < z]$

$S3. \quad (x)(y)[x < y \rightarrow y \not< x]$

$S4. \quad (x)(y)[x \neq y \rightarrow x < y \vee y < x].$

To prove $S1$, note that

1. $x - x = 0$ — by $N3$, definition
2. $\sim p(0)$ — by $P1$

3. $\sim p(x - x)$ by $P3$, from 1
4. $x \not< x$ by $D1$.

To prove $S2$, we have

1. $x < y \wedge y < z$ by assumption
2. $p(y - x) \wedge p(z - y)$ by $D1$
3. $z - x = (y - x) + (z - y)$ *
4. $p(z - x)$ by $P3$, from 3, and $P8$
5. $x < z$ by $D1$.

To prove $S3$, we have

1. $x < y$ by assumption
2. $p(y - x)$ by $D1$
3. $y - x = -(x - y)$ *
4. $p(-(x - y))$ by $P3$, from 3
5. $\sim p(x - y)$ by $P2$
6. $y \not< x$ by $D1$.

To prove $S4$, we have

1. $x \neq y$ by assumption
2. $x - y \neq 0$ *
3. $p(x - y) \vee p(-(x - y))$ by $P7$, $P4$
4. $-(x - y) = y - x$ *
5. $p(x - y) \vee p(y - x)$ by $P3$, from 4
6. $x < y \vee y < x$ by $D1$.

Proofs of the steps marked * are left to the reader.

In addition, we can establish the following monotonic and cancellation properties for $x < y$:

S5. $(x)(y)(z)[x < y \leftrightarrow x + z < y + z]$

S6. $(x)(y)(z)[p(z) \rightarrow (x < y \leftrightarrow xz < yz)]$

S7. $(x)(y)(z)[q(z) \rightarrow (x < y \leftrightarrow yz < xz)]$.

Note that $S7$ implies that multiplying both of two distinct numbers by the same negative number, reverses their order.

To establish $S5$, note only that

$$y - x = (y + z) - (x + z)$$

from which the result follows immediately by $P3$ and $D1$. The proofs of $S6$ and $S7$ depend similarly on the equation

$$xz - yz = (x - y)z.$$

If $p(z)$ is true, then $xz - yz$ is positive if and only if $x - y$ is positive. If $q(z)$ is true, then $yz - xz$ is positive if and only if $x - y$ is positive. In either case, the result follows by $P3$ and $D1$.

We leave it to the reader to prove

S8. $(x)[p(x) \leftrightarrow 0 < x]$

S9. $(x)[q(x) \leftrightarrow x < 0]$.

The converse of the relation represented by $x < y$ is another important arithmetic relation represented by $x > y$. It is interpreted to mean that "x is greater than y" and is defined by the equivalence

D2. $(x)(y)[x > y \leftrightarrow y < x]$.

Having established $S1$–9 for $x < y$, analogous properties hold for its converse, and their proofs consist in replacing statements of the form $x > y$ by $y < x$ and applying the properties already proved to these. Thus the relation $x > y$ is also a strict total order, with monotonic properties similar to those of $x < y$. We list these properties below:

T1. $(x)[x \not> x]$

T2. $(x)(y)(z)[x > y \wedge y > z \rightarrow x > z]$

T3. $(x)(y)[x > y \rightarrow y \not> x]$

T4. $(x)(y)[x \neq y \rightarrow x > y \vee y > x]$

T5. $(x)(y)(z)[x > y \leftrightarrow x + z > y + z]$

T6. $(x)(y)(z)[p(z) \rightarrow (x > y \leftrightarrow xz > yz)]$

T7. $(z)(y)(z)[q(z) \rightarrow (x > y \leftrightarrow yz > xz)]$

T8. $(x)[p(x) \leftrightarrow x > 0]$

T9. $(x)[q(x) \leftrightarrow 0 > x]$.

In most mathematical contexts we use $x < y < z$ as an abbreviation for the conjunction $x < y \wedge y < z$, and similarly for $x > y > z$.

A weak total order relation expressing "x is less than or equal to y" and represented by $x \leq y$ can be defined using connectives by the equivalence

D3. $(x)(y)[x \leq y \leftrightarrow x < y \vee x = y]$.

We shall see in the next section that this relation and its converse are useful in representing certain useful subsets of $\mathfrak{U}$ concisely by open statements.

The converse of this relation expresses that "x is greater than or equal to y" and is represented by $x \geq y$ and defined by the equivalence

D4. $(x)(y)[x \geq y \leftrightarrow y \leq x]$.

This relation too is a weak total order, and both satisfy the expected monotonic and cancellation properties. We list some of these properties below:

U1. $(x)[x \leq x]$

U2. $(x)(y)(z)[x \leq y \wedge y \leq z \rightarrow x \leq z]$

U3. $(x)(y)[x \leq y \wedge y \leq x \rightarrow x = y]$

U4. $(x)(y)[x \leq y \vee y \leq x]$

U5. $(x)(y)(z)[x \leq y \leftrightarrow x + z \leq y + z]$

U6. $(x)(y)(z)[\sim q(z) \rightarrow (x \leq y \leftrightarrow xz \leq yz)]$

U7. $(x)(y)(z)[\sim p(z) \rightarrow (x \leq y \leftrightarrow yz \leq xz)]$

U8. $(x)[\sim q(z) \leftrightarrow 0 \leq x]$

U9. $(x)[\sim p(z) \leftrightarrow x \leq 0]$.

The properties obtained by replacing each occurrence of "$\leq$" by "$\geq$" in U1–7 are also valid and are called V1–7. Analogues of U8–9 are

V8. $(x)[\sim q(x) \leftrightarrow x \geq 0]$

V9. $(x)[\sim p(x) \leftrightarrow 0 \geq x]$.

The statement $x \leq y \leq z$ is an abbreviation of the conjunction

$$x \leq y \wedge y \leq z.$$

Similarly for $x \geq y \geq z$, $x < y \leq z$, $x \leq y < z$, etc.

We now define a function that assigns to each element of each pair $(x, -x)$ of elements of $\mathfrak{u}$ the one that is not negative. We call this the *absolute value function* and denote it by *abs*. Its value $abs(x)$ for an argument x is denoted by $|x|$. Since $x \geq 0$ is equivalent to the statement that x is not negative and $x < 0$ is equivalent to the statement that x is negative, by V8 and S8, we may define *abs* as follows:

$$abs(x) = |x| = \begin{cases} x & \text{if } x \geq 0 \\ -x & \text{if } x < 0. \end{cases}$$

Note that if x is negative, then $-x$ is positive, so that no value of *abs* is negative.

The values of the function *abs* have the following properties:

A1. $|0| = 0$

A2. $(x)[|x| = 0 \rightarrow x = 0]$

A3. $(x)[-|x| \leq x \leq |x|]$

A4. $(x)(y)[y \geq 0 \rightarrow (|x| \leq y \leftrightarrow -y \leq x \leq y)]$

A5. $(x)(y)[y > 0 \rightarrow (|x| < y \leftrightarrow -y < x < y)]$

A6. $(x)(y)[|x + y| \leq |x| + |y|]$

A7. $(x)(y)[|x - y| \leq |x| + |y|]$

A8. $(x)(y)[|x + y| \geq ||x| - |y||]$

A9. $(x)(y)[|x - y| \geq ||x| - |y||]$

A10. $(x)(y)[|xy| = |x||y|]$

A11. $(x)(y)[0 < x < y \rightarrow |x| < |y|]$

A12. $(x)(y)[x < y < 0 \rightarrow |y| > |x|]$.

The proof of A1 is immediate from the definition. The proofs of other properties can be carried out by dividing the argument into cases which reflect those into which the definition of *abs* is divided.

To prove A2, let

$$|x| = 0 \qquad \text{by assumption.}$$

Case 1.

If $x > 0$, then $|x| = x > 0$, contradicting the assumption.

Case 2.

If $x < 0$, then $|x| = -x > 0$, contradicting the assumption. Since $x \not> 0$ and $x \not< 0$, we must have $x = 0$, by the trichotomy. The proof of A3 is left for the reader.

To prove A4, assume $y \geq 0$. To prove that

$$|x| \leq y \rightarrow -y \leq x \leq y$$

assume also $|x| \leq y$.

Case 1.

If $x \geq 0$, then $|x| = x$, so that $x \leq y$ follows by replacement. Since x is not negative, $-x \leq x$, so that $-x \leq y$ follows by T. Thus,

$$-y \leq x$$

by U7. Hence,

$$-y \leq x \leq y.$$

Case 2.

If $x < 0$, then $x < -x = |x|$, so that

$$-x \leq y \quad \text{and} \quad x \leq y.$$

From $-x \leq y$ it follows that $-y \leq x$, so that $-y \leq x \leq y$ holds in this case too.

To prove conversely that $-y \leq x \leq y \to |x| \leq y$, note in *Case 1* that $|x| = x$, so that $|x| \leq y$ follows from $x \leq y$ by replacement. In *Case 2*, $|x| = -x$ so that $x = -|x|$. Thus,

$$-y \leq -|x|$$

by replacement, and the conclusion follows by *U7*. The proof of *A5* is similar.

To prove *A6*, note that by *A3*

$$-|x| \leq x \leq |x|$$
$$-|y| \leq y \leq |y|$$

are both true. By monotonic properties, we have

$$-(|x| + |y|) \leq x + y \leq (|x| + |y|)$$

and the result follows by *A4*. *A6* is called the *triangle inequality* since it can be interpreted in some contexts to state the law that any side of a triangle has length no greater than the sum of the lengths of the other two sides.

The proofs of *A7–11* are left to the reader. To prove *A12*, note that

$$x < 0 \quad \text{and} \quad y < 0$$

so that

$$x = -|x| \quad \text{and} \quad y = -|y|.$$

From this and $x < y$ it follows that $-|x| < -|y|$, and the conclusion follows by *S7*.

EXERCISES

1. Prove that $(x)(y)[(-x)y = -(xy)]$.

2. Prove *P5* and *P6* using *N1–7* and *P1–4*.

3. Prove *P11* and *P13*, using *N1–7*, *P1–10*, and *P12*.

4. Complete the proofs of *S1–4* by proving the following statements.

   (a) $(x)(y)(z)[z - x = (y - x) + (z - y)]$
   (b) $(x)(y)[y - x = -(x - y)]$
   (c) $(x)(y)[x = y \leftrightarrow x - y = 0]$

5. Prove $S8$ and $S9$.

6. Using $D2$ and the properties $S1$–9, prove the properties $T1$–9.

7. Using $D3$ and the properties $S1$–9, prove the properties $U1$–9.

8. Prove properties $V1$–9.

9. Prove $A3$ and $A5$.

10. Prove $A7$–11.

11. For each element $x \neq 0$ of U, the value $r(x)$ of the function r defined in Exercise 13, Section 1, is called the *reciprocal* of x and denoted by $1/x$. Prove that the following properties hold for reciprocals.

$R1.$ $(x)[|1/x| = 1/|x|]$
$R2.$ $(x)(y)[0 < x < y \rightarrow 1/x > 1/y]$
$R3.$ $(x)(y)[x < 0 < y \rightarrow 1/x < 1/y]$
$R4.$ $(x)(y)[x < y < 0 \rightarrow 1/x > 1/y]$
$R5.$ $(x)[-(1/x) = 1/(-x)]$

3 · INTERVALS AND BOUNDED SETS

Let $\mathfrak{u}$ be a set of numbers over which the relations $x < y$ and $x \leq y$ are defined. If a and b are elements of $\mathfrak{u}$ with $a < b$, the solution set of the open statement $a < x < b$ is called the *open interval from a to b*, and is denoted by (a, b). If $a \leq b$, then the solution set of $a \leq x \leq b$ is called the *closed interval from a to b* and is denoted by $[a, b]$. A closed interval $[a, b]$ is the set whose elements are a, b, and all the numbers between them; the open interval (a, b) is that subset of $[a, b]$ consisting of all its elements except its *endpoints* a and b. In the universe $\mathcal{I}$ of integers, for example, we have

$$[-1, 3] = \{-1, 0, 1, 2, 3\}$$

while $(-1, 3) = \{0, 1, 2\}$. In the universe of rational numbers, there is no reasonable way to list the elements of an interval, because of the

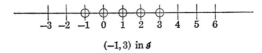

$(-1, 3)$ in $\mathcal{I}$

Figure 8

density of rational numbers, a property to be discussed below. In this universe, the interval $(-1, 3)$ consists of infinitely many elements, namely all rational numbers that are at the same time greater than -1 and less than 3. The interval notation is most useful in this case, as well as in the case of real numbers.

The graph of an interval is indicated as in Figures 8 and 9. In the universes $\mathfrak{N}$ and $\mathcal{I}$, its elements are sketched by marking appropriate points with circles, squares, or triangles, as before. In the universes $\mathcal{Q}$ and $\mathcal{R}$, the graph of an interval is indicated by a solid line segment, reflecting the density property of these sets. A closed interval is indicated by sketch-

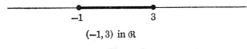

$(-1, 3)$ in $\mathcal{R}$

Figure 9

ing its endpoints with solid black dots, and an open interval is indicated by placing parentheses at the endpoints opening away from the interval.

If $a < b$, then the solution sets of $a < x \leq b$ and $a \leq x < b$ are half-open and half-closed intervals, since each contains one of its endpoints but not the other.

In many mathematical contexts it is convenient to have a function d of two arguments so that for any ordered pair (a, b) of elements of $\mathcal{u}$, $d(a, b)$ represents the distance traveled in passing from a to b. Here we regard $\mathcal{u}$ as a set of numbers that form a scale on a straight line along which motion occurs, and $d(a, b)$ as a number that denotes the distance through which the motion takes place *and* its direction. We define d here by the equation

$$d(a, b) = b - a.$$

Note that distance is positive when $a < b$, so that motion is to the right on the graph, and negative if $b < a$, so that motion is to the left. The number $d(a, b)$ is called the *directed distance from a to b*.

If it is unnecessary to distinguish direction of motion along a line, the *magnitude* of the distance, which is its absolute value, is used instead. Thus, if a and b are any elements of $\mathcal{u}$, then the magnitude of the distance from a to b is $|b - a|$. If $a \leq b$, this number is also called the *length* of the interval $[a, b]$. Similarly for other kinds of intervals. Thus, the distance from -3 to 4 is $4 - (-3) = 7$, the distance from 4 to -3 is -7, and the length of the interval $(-3, 4)$ is $|7| = 7$.

Note that the solution set of $|x| < a$ for some $a > 0$ is the same as that of $-a < x < a$, by $A4$, and so is the interval $(-a, a)$. We leave it to the reader to show that the solution set of $|x - b| < a$ for $a > 0$ is an interval whose center is b and whose length is $2a$.

A subset $\mathcal{a}$ of $\mathcal{u}$ is said to be *bounded above* if there is a number M in $\mathcal{u}$ such that

$$(x)(x \in \mathcal{a} \rightarrow x \leq M)$$

is true, and M is called an *upper bound* of α in this case. Similarly α is *bounded below* if there is a number m in $\mathfrak{u}$ such that $(x)(x \in \alpha \to m \leq x)$ is true, and m is called a *lower bound* of α in this case. If a set α is bounded both above and below, we say that α is *bounded* or is a *bounded set*. In this case there are two numbers m and $M \geq m$ such that α is a subset of the interval $[m, M]$.

We shall use the following properties of bounded sets:

*B*1. If M is an upper bound of α, and $M_1 \geq M$, then M_1 is an upper bound of α.

Proof:
Since M is an upper bound of α, $x \leq M$ for all elements x of α. But $M \leq M_1$, so that $x \leq M_1$ follows by $U2$. Thus, M_1 is an upper bound of α.

*B*2. If m is a lower bound of α, and $m_1 \leq m$, then m_1 is a lower bound of α.

Proof:
This proof is similar to the proof of $B1$ and is left to the reader.

*B*3. α is bounded if and only if there is a number M of $\mathfrak{u}$ such that $(x)(x \in A \to |x| \leq M)$ is true.

Proof:
If $|x| \leq M$ for some number $M > 0$ and all $x \in \alpha$, then by $A4$, $-M \leq x \leq M$, so that M is an upper bound of α and $-M$ is a lower bound. If $M = 0$, then $x = 0$. Thus, α is bounded in either case. Suppose now that α is bounded. Then there are numbers m_1 and m_2 such that

$$m_1 \leq x \leq m_2$$

for every $x \in \alpha$. Let M be the greater of the numbers $|m_1|$ and $|m_2|$. Consider three cases:

Case 1.
If $m_1 \geq 0$, then

$$|m_2| = m_2 \geq m_1 = |m_1|.$$

Thus, $M = m_2$ in this case. Since $-m_2 \leq 0$, we have $-M \leq x \leq M$, so that $|x| \leq M$ follows by $A4$.

Case 2.
If $m_2 \leq 0$, then

$$M = |m_1| = -m_1 \geq -m_2 = |m_2|$$

and again $-M \leq x \leq M$ for every $x \in \alpha$.

Case 3.

If $m_1 \leq 0 \leq m_2$, then

$$m_2 \leq M \quad \text{and} \quad m_1 = -|m_1| \geq -M$$

since $|m_1| \leq M$ by definition. Thus, $-M \leq x \leq M$, and the conclusion follows.

The property in $B3$ implies that every bounded set is a subset of an interval whose center is at 0.

Note that every interval as defined above is a bounded set whether it is open or closed. If M is any number greater than or equal to b it is an upper bound of (a, b). Similarly any number m less than or equal to a is a lower bound.

If α is bounded above by a number M, then according to $B1$, any larger number is an upper bound of α. Thus there is no largest upper bound of α, However, it may be that α has a smallest upper bound. Accordingly, we call a number B a *least upper bound* of α if

$M1$. B is an upper bound of α

$M2$. If C is any upper bound of α, then $B \leq C$.

For example, 7 is an upper bound of the interval $(-1, 3)$ and so are 5, 102, and 3. But 3 is a least upper bound, since no other upper bound can be smaller. There can be no more than one least upper bound to any set α, for if B_1 and B_2 are both least upper bounds of α, then $B_1 \leq B_2$ and $B_2 \leq B_1$ are both true by $M2$, so that $B_1 = B_2$ by $U3$. Thus we may call a number B satisfying $M1$–2 *the* least upper bound of α. We denote this number as $\mathrm{lub}(\alpha)$.

Similarly, if α is bounded below, we can ask if there is a *greatest lower bound* of α, and can prove that it is unique if it exists. It is a number *denoted by* $glb(\alpha)$ satisfying the properties

$M1$. b is a lower bound of α

$M2$. If c is any lower bound of α, then $c \leq b$.

If a set is not bounded above, then for every number M, no matter how large, there is some element x of the set such that $x > M$. An example of such a set is the solution set of the open statement $a < x$ for some number a, of which every number greater than a is an element. It is convenient to extend the notation of intervals to sets that are unbounded above and include all elements of U that are greater than a fixed number a. Thus we denote the solution set of the open statement $a < x$ (or $x > a$) for any element a of U by (a, ∞) and call it an *open upper infinite interval*. Since such a set has no upper bound, its graph consists of all points to the right of the point a, and we often use the briefer name *open upper halfline*.

A *closed upper halfline* consists of all numbers greater than or equal to a given number a. It is the solution set of $a \leq x$ (or $x \geq a$) and is denoted by $[a, \infty)$.

The symbol "∞" is called *infinity* and is used only to indicate that an interval is not bounded above. Since it is not an element of any universe that we shall consider, because it is not the name of a number, it is not a member of any solution set. Thus the notations $(a, \infty]$ and $[a, \infty]$ are not used.

If $\mathfrak{u}$ itself is not bounded below, then some of its subsets are not bounded below. The solution set of $x < a$ is called an *open lower halfline* and is denoted by $(-\infty, a)$ and the solution set of $x \leq a$ is called a *closed lower halfline* and is denoted by $(-\infty, a]$. In Figure 10 the graphs of $x < 3$, $x \leq -1$, $x > -2$, and $x \geq 5$ are sketched.

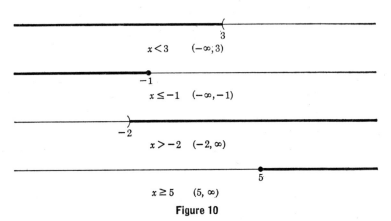

$$x < 3 \qquad (-\infty, 3)$$

$$x \leq -1 \qquad (-\infty, -1)$$

$$x > -2 \qquad (-2, \infty)$$

$$x \geq 5 \qquad (5, \infty)$$

Figure 10

We say that $\mathfrak{u}$ is *dense* if in every open interval (a, b) there is an element z of $\mathfrak{u}$. Using logical symbolism, $\mathfrak{u}$ is dense if and only if

$$(x)(y)\{x < y \rightarrow (\mathrm{E}\, z)(x < z < y)\}$$

is true in $\mathfrak{u}$. We prove that $\mathfrak{Q}$, the set of rational numbers, is dense in the following way. Suppose that $x < y$. Then

1. $2x < x + y$ by $S5$

and since $\frac{1}{2}$ is a rational number, we have

2. $x < \dfrac{x + y}{2}$ by $S6$.

Similarly,

3. $x + y < 2y$ by $S5$

and

4. $\dfrac{x + y}{2} < y$ by $S6$.

Thus,

$$x < \frac{x + y}{2} < y$$

so that $(E\ z)(x < z < y)$ follows by $L21$. Note that the proof is valid for the set $\mathfrak{R}$ of real numbers, since we can show there is a real number $\frac{1}{2}$. However this proof fails for natural numbers and for integers since neither set contains the number $\frac{1}{2}$. Recall that $\frac{1}{2}$ is the quotient of 1 by 2, or the unique solution of $2x = 1$. It can be shown that this equation has no solution either in $\mathfrak{N}$ or in $\mathcal{I}$.

In fact, we can show that neither the integers nor the natural numbers are dense, for there are open intervals in each set that contain no number in the set. An example is the interval $(1, 2)$.

If a set is dense, we can show that each open interval must contain infinitely many elements of the set. To show this, suppose that a set $\mathfrak{U}$ is dense and that a and b are elements of $\mathfrak{U}$ with $a < b$ and only a finite number (say n) of elements of $\mathfrak{U}$ in (a, b). If we call these $z_1, z_2, \ldots, z_n$ so that $z_1 < z_2 < \cdots < z_n$. Then the interval (z_1, z_2) contains no point of $\mathfrak{U}$, contrary to the assumption that $\mathfrak{U}$ is dense. Thus no such interval (a, b) can exist.

For the natural numbers and the integers it can be shown that every bounded interval (a, b) contains at most a finite number of elements of the universe. An ordered set for which this is true is said to be *discrete*.

In terms of the notions discussed in this section, a distinction between the integers and the natural numbers is that, while both sets are demonstrably unbounded above, the natural numbers are bounded below, and the integers are not.

An important distinction between the rational numbers and the real numbers can also be explained in these terms. We shall show later that every set of real numbers that is bounded above (or below) has a least upper bound (a greatest lower bound). The rational numbers do not enjoy this property, whose importance will concern us later. There are bounded sets of rational numbers having neither a rational least upper bound nor a rational greatest lower bound.

An example of such a set is the solution set of $x^2 < 2$ in the domain Q. If we compare this to the solution set of the open statement $x^2 < 9$, which is the interval $(-3, 3)$, we would expect it to be a bounded open interval symmetric about 0. Note that the interval $(-3, 3)$ is bounded for it is also the solution set of $|x| < 3$. This interval has least upper bound 3 and greatest lower bound -3. Note that both these numbers are solutions of $x^2 = 9$.

Now the solution set of $x^2 < 2$ is also bounded, for we can show that

$$(x)(x^2 < 2 \rightarrow |x| < 2)$$

which means that it is a subset of the interval $(-2, 2)$. However, if we try to locate a rational least upper bound and a rational greatest lower bound by solving the analogous equation $x^2 = 2$, we fail, for we can show that no rational number satisfies this equation.

To show this, assume on the contrary that p/q is a rational number that satisfies $x^2 = 2$ and that p and q have no common divisor other than 1. No generality is lost in the last assumption, since every rational number can be represented by a fraction of this kind. Then

 1. $\dfrac{p^2}{q^2} = 2$ by assumption

 2. $p^2 = 2q^2$ by $O10$.

Thus, p^2 is even, since $(E\ x)(p^2 = 2x)$ follows by $L21$. We leave it to the reader to show that therefore p is even. Thus, $(E\ u)(p = 2u)$ and

 3. $4u^2 = 2q^2$ by replacement
 4. $2u^2 = q^2$ by $O12$.

Thus, by a similar argument q^2, and therefore q, is even. But then p and q have 2 as a common factor, contradicting the choice of p and q. Thus the assumption must be abandoned and $x^2 = 2$ has no rational solution. Of course the real numbers $\sqrt{2}$ and $-\sqrt{2}$ are solutions of this equation.

EXERCISES

1. Express the solution sets in the universe of real numbers of the given open statements as intervals.

 (a) $2 \le x \le 7$ (e) $2 \ge x \ge 101$
 (b) $x > -4$ (f) $|x| < 7$
 (c) $x \le 2$ (g) $|x + 2| \le 4$
 (d) $-1 < x \le 5$ (h) $|2x - 3| \le 7$

2. Sketch the graph of each solution set of Exercise 1.

3. Express as a union of two intervals the solution set in the universe of real numbers of the given open statements.

(a) $(3 < x < 7) \wedge \sim(4 < x < 5)$
(b) $(-1 \leq x \leq 10) \wedge \sim(2 \leq x < 7)$
(c) $(2 < x \leq 8) \vee (10 < x \leq 15)$
(d) $|x| > 2$
(e) $|x + 3| \geq 5$
(f) $x^2 > 5$
(g) $2 < |x| \leq 7$
(h) $4 < x^2 < 9$

4. Express each of the following as a single interval.

(a) $[-1, 3) \cup (2, 4)$
(b) $(4, 7] \cup (6, 10)$
(c) $[3, 11) \cap (7, 12]$
(d) $(3, 11] \cap (7, 12)$
(e) $[3, 11) \cap [7, 12]$
(f) $(3, 11] - (4, 11]$
(g) $[3, 11] - [3, 5]$
(h) $(3, 11) - (4, 12)$

5. Find the length of each interval in Exercise 1.

6. If the results of Exercise 4 are interpreted to have the class $\mathcal{I}$ of integers as universe, express each of these results as a union of closed intervals.

7. Show that the solution set of

$$ax + b > 0 \quad (a \neq 0)$$

is the right halfline $(-b/a, \infty)$ if $a > 0$. What is the solution set if $a < 0$? Discuss the case of the open statements

$$ax + b < 0, \qquad ax + b \geq 0 \quad \text{and} \quad ax + b \leq 0$$

8. Show that the open statement

$$(ax + b)(cx + d) > 0 \quad (ac \neq 0)$$

is equivalent to the open statement

$$[(ax + b > 0) \wedge (cx + d > 0)] \vee [(ax + b < 0) \wedge (cx + d < 0)].$$

Conclude from this that the solution set is the union of the intersections of two pairs of halflines. Give examples to show that the intersection of two halflines could be:

(a) a halfline
(b) a bounded interval
(c) empty.

9. Use the result of Exercise 8 to find the solution sets of

    (a) $(x - 1)(x + 3) > 0$

    (b) $(2x + 5)(x - 7) > 0$

    (c) $(-4x + 1)(x + 4) > 0$

    (d) $(-x + 1)(2x - 5) > 0$.

10. Develop a technique similar to that described in Exercise 8 for arriving at the solution set of
$$(ax + b)(cx + d) < 0 \quad (ac \neq 0).$$

11. Show that if p and q are both numbers between $-b/a$ and $-d/c$ ($ac \neq 0$), then
$$(ap + b)(cp + d) \quad \text{and} \quad (aq + b)(cq + d)$$
have the same sign.

12. Show that the result of Exercise 11 is true if p and q are both smaller than the smaller of $-b/a$ and $-d/c$ or both larger than the larger of these two quotients.

13. Use the results of Exercises 8–12 to show that the inequality
$$(ax + b)(cx + d) > 0$$
can be solved in the following way:

    (1) Let p be any number in any of the intervals into which the numbers $-b/a$ and $-d/a$ partition the real numbers.

    (2) If p is a solution of the inequality, then every number in the interval is also a solution. If p is not a solution, then no point of the interval is a solution.

Use this technique to solve the inequalities of Exercise 6.

14. Extend the technique developed in Exercise 13 to inequalities involving products of any number of linear factors and to quotients of such products.

15. Use the techniques developed in Exercise 14 to solve the following.

    (a) $x^2 - 5x < 6$

    (b) $\dfrac{(x + 2)(x - 3)}{2x + 5} > 0$

    (c) $x < \dfrac{1}{x}$

    (d) $\dfrac{1}{x} > \dfrac{x}{3x - 2}$

    (e) $x + 5 > -\dfrac{6}{x}$

16. Discuss the solution of $ax^2 + bx + c > 0$ $(a \neq 0)$ in case

   (a) $b^2 - 4ac = 0$

   (b) $b^2 - 4ac > 0$

   (c) $b^2 - 4ac < 0$.

17. Prove $B2$.

18. Show that if a set α has a greatest lower bound, then it is unique.

19. For each of the solution sets in Exercise 1, name the least upper bound and the greatest lower bound, if they exist.

20. If α and $\mathcal{B}$ are sets of numbers, we defined their sum $\alpha + \mathcal{B}$ to be the set of all arithmetic sums $x + y$ for $x \in \alpha$ and $y \in \mathcal{B}$. Show that if M is an upper bound of α and N an upper bound of $\mathcal{B}$, then $M + N$ is an upper bound of $\alpha + \mathcal{B}$.

21. State and prove a property analogous to that of Exercise 20 for lower bounds.

22. Under the conditions established in Exercise 20 define $\alpha\mathcal{B}$ as the set of all arithmetic products xy for $x \in \alpha$ and $y \in \mathcal{B}$. Does the property analogous to that of Exercise 20 hold? Give reasons for your answer.

23. If lub $(\alpha) \in \alpha$ for any set α, we call it the *maximum element* of α. Similarly for minimum element. Name the maximum element and the minimum element if they exist of each solution set of Exercise 1.

24. Show that for each integer p, if p^2 is even, then p is even.

4 · NATURAL NUMBERS

It was shown in Section 8 of Chapter 1 that cardinal numbers, defined for counting finite sets of objects, satisfied five fundamental properties, listed there as 1–5. Here we shall show that these five properties, along with common properties of equality and common rules of logic allow us to establish the abstract laws for operating with nonnegative whole numbers. We show in particular that addition and multiplication are definable and satisfy properties $O1-12'$, 13 of Section 1. Proofs of these statements occupy this section and the next. We preface the number of a property with the letter "N" to emphasize that we are considering the set $\mathfrak{N}$ as the universe for all quantifiers in these sections.

The natural numbers are objects of a set $\mathfrak{N}$ which is the domain and contains the range of a function S and the universe over which a predicate $x = y$ is defined. The axioms for natural numbers are:

$AN1.$ $(E\,x)(x = 0)$

$AN2.$ $(x)(\text{E } y)(y = S(x))$

$AN3.$ $(x)(y)(S(x) = S(y) \leftrightarrow x = y)$

$AN4.$ $(x)(0 \neq S(x))$

$AN5.$ For any unary predicate p:

$$p(0) \wedge (x)[p(x) \to p(S(x))] \to (x)p(x)$$

According to $AN1$, there is at least one natural number—0, and $AN2$ provides a function S whose value for every natural number argument is a unique natural number. This uniqueness is explicitly included in the statement of $AN3$ which provides that S is a one-to-one correspondence. We call S the *successor function* and $S(x)$ the *successor of* x. So far there is no guarantee that 0 is not the only natural number, for $AN1$–3 would be satisfied if it were and if we define $S(0) = 0$. However, $AN4$ provides that $0 \neq S(x)$ for any x. This axiom guarantees infinitely many elements in $\mathfrak{N}$, for we shall prove that no element can equal its successor.

$AN5$ is called the *axiom of induction* and permits us to assert that every natural number x has a given property p if we can prove that

1. 0 has the property p, and
2. If any number x has the property p, then so does its successor.

The proof of 1 is called the *basis* of the induction, and the proof of 2 is called the *induction step*. In the induction step, we assume $p(x)$ as the *hypothesis of the induction* (HI) attempting to show that it implies $p(S(x))$, the so-called *conclusion of the induction*. The adoption of $AN5$ is justified partly by the order structure of natural numbers such that each number is either 0 or the successor of another number.

In addition to the axioms $AN1$–5, we use the properties R, S, and T of equality (see p. 50) and the logical rules of Sections 5–6 of Chapter 1.

We prove first that no number is equal to its successor.

$N1.$ $(x)(x \neq S(x))$

Proof:

We proceed by induction, using $AN5$. To do this, we must prove first the basis $0 \neq S(0)$. This follows from $AN4$ by $L23$. We assume for the induction step

$HI.$ $x \neq S(x)$

and must show that it implies

$CI.$ $S(x) \neq S(S(x))$.

But this follows from the contrapositive of one of the implications of $AN3$ which is true by $L12$. Hence the theorem is proved by $AN5$.

We define addition and multiplication for natural numbers using induction. Such a definition requires two statements: one to define the operation for 0 and the other to define it for $S(x)$, assuming that it has been defined already for x. Addition is defined first, since multiplication is defined in terms of it.

$DN1$. (a) $x + 0 = x$

(b) $x + S(y) = S(x + y)$

Having defined addition, the definition of multiplication is

$DN2$. (a) $x0 = 0$

(b) $x[S(y)] = xy + x$.

The remainder of this section is devoted to a demonstration that the properties $O1$–$12'$, 13 are theorems. Some of the proofs are left as exercises. We prove first that addition is well defined.

$NO1$. $(x)(y)(E\,z)[x + y = z]$

Proof:

We proceed by an induction on x. For the basis we must prove that

$$(y)(E\,z)[0 + y = z].$$

This we do by induction on y. First we have $0 + 0 = 0$ by $DN1$(a), so that

$$(E\,z)[0 + 0 = z]$$

is true by $L21$. Assuming $(E\,z)[0 + y = z]$ we must show that

$$(E\,z)[0 + S(y) = z].$$

Using the assumption, let

$$0 + y = u$$

Then $\qquad\qquad 0 + S(y) = S(0 + y) \qquad$ by $DN1$(b)

$$= S(u) \qquad\qquad \text{by } AN3.$$

Thus,

$$(E\,z)[0 + S(y) = z]$$

is true by $L22$, and the proof of the basis of the main induction is complete. Now assume

HI. $(y)(E\,z)[x + y = z]$

to prove

CI. $(y)(E\,z)[S(x) + y = z]$.

If by assuming HI true, we can prove that

1. $(y)[S(x) + y = S(x + y)]$

then if $x + y = u$, we have $S(x) + y = S(u)$ so that the theorem follows by $L15$. Hence the theorem now rests on a proof of 1. We proceed by induction on y. For the basis, we have

$$x + 0 = x \qquad \text{by } DN1(a)$$
$$S(x + 0) = S(x) \qquad \text{by } AN3$$
$$= S(x) + 0 \qquad \text{by } DN1(a).$$

Assuming

HI. $S(x) + y = S(x + y)$

we must prove

CI. $S(x) + S(y) = S(x + S(y))$.

We have

$$S(x) + S(y) = S[S(x) + y] \qquad \text{by } DN1(b)$$
$$= S[S(x + y)] \qquad \text{by } H1$$
$$= S(x + S(y)) \qquad \text{by } DN1(b), AN3$$

completing the proof of 1 and so of the theorem.

We leave for the reader the proof that multiplication is well defined.

$NO2$. $(x)(y)(E\ z)[xy = z]$

The uniqueness of sums and products depends on the fact that the first equation assigns a unique result in each definition, and the second uses only the successor function whose value is unique by $AN3$.

We prove now that addition is associative, leaving the proof for multiplication to the reader.

$NO7$. $(x)(y)(z)[(x + y) + z = x + (y + z)]$

$NO8$. $(x)(y)(z)[(xy)z = x(yz)]$

Proof of NO7:

We proceed by induction on z. For the basis, we have

$$(x + y) + 0 = x + y \qquad \text{by } DN1(a)$$
$$= x + (y + 0) \qquad \text{by } DN1(a).$$

Assume

HI. $(x + y) + z = x + (y + z)$.

Then

$$(x + y) + S(z) = S[(x + y) + z] \qquad \text{by } DN1(b)$$
$$= S[x + (y + z)] \qquad \text{by } H1$$
$$= x + S(y + z) \qquad \text{by } DN1(b)$$
$$(x + y) + S(z) = x + (y + S(z)) \qquad \text{by } DN1(b).$$

The last equation is CI, so the induction is complete.

The next two theorems give the commutative properties of addition and multiplication. We prove the second leaving the proof of the first to the reader.

$NO5.$ $(x)(y)[x + y = y + x]$

$NO6.$ $(x)(y)[xy = yx]$

Proof of NO6:

For the basis of an inductive proof on y we must show that $x0 = 0x$. Now $x0 = 0$ by $D2(a)$ so that we must prove that $0x = 0$, and this is accomplished by induction on x. The basis of this induction is $00 = 0$, which is true by $D2(a)$. Assume

$HI.$ $0x = 0$.

To prove

$CI.$ $0S(x) = 0$

we have

$$0S(x) = 0x + 0 \qquad \text{by } D2(b)$$
$$= 0 + 0 \qquad \text{by } H1$$
$$= 0 \qquad \text{by } D1(a)$$

so $(x)(0x = x0)$ follows by $AN5$. For the main induction step assume

$HI.$ $xy = yx$

to prove

$CI.$ $xS(y) = S(y)x.$

We have

$$xS(y) = xy + x \qquad \text{by } D2(b)$$
$$= S(y)x \qquad *$$

completing the proof. The proof of $S(y)x = xy + x$ at $*$ is part of the proof of $NO2$, which is an exercise.

$NO13.$ $(x)(y)(z)[x(y + z) = xy + xz]$

Proof:

Proceeding by induction on z, the basis is

$$x(y + 0) = xy + x0.$$

Now $y + 0 = y$ by $D1$(a), so that

$$x(y + 0) = xy.$$

However,

$$xy + x0 = xy + 0 \qquad \text{by } D2\text{(a)}$$
$$= xy \qquad \text{by } D1\text{(a)}$$

so the basis follows by properties of equality. We assume

$HI.\ x(y + z) = xy + xz$

to prove

$CI.\ x(y + S(z)) = xy + xS(z).$

We have

$$x(y + S(z)) = xS(y + z) \qquad \text{by } D1\text{(b)}$$
$$= x(y + z) + x \qquad \text{by } D2\text{(b)}$$
$$= (xy + xz) + x \qquad \text{by } HI$$
$$= xy + (xz + x) \qquad \text{by } NO7$$
$$= xy + xS(z) \qquad \text{by } D2\text{(b)}$$

and the theorem follows.

The monotonic properties for addition and multiplication are:

$NO9.\ (x)(y)(z)[x = y \rightarrow x + z = y + z]$

$NO10.\ (x)(y)(z)[x = y \rightarrow xz = yz].$

We prove $NO9$, leaving the proof of $NO10$ as an exercise.

Proof of NO9:

The basis of an induction on z is

$$x = y \rightarrow x + 0 = y + 0.$$

Assume

   1. $x = y$ assumption

then

$$x + 0 = x \qquad \text{by } D1\text{(a)}$$
$$= y \qquad \text{by } 1$$
$$= y + 0 \qquad \text{by } D1\text{(a)}$$

so the implication follows by *L2*. For the induction step assume

$HI.$ $x = y \rightarrow x + z = y + z$

to prove

$CI.$ $x = y \rightarrow x + S(z) = y + S(z)$.

Let

2. $x = y$ assumption

then

$x + z = y + z$ by HI and $L1$

and

3. $S(x + z) = S(y + z)$ by $AN3$.

Thus

$$x + S(z) = S(x + z) \quad \text{by } D1(b)$$
$$= S(y + z) \quad \text{by } 3$$
$$= y + S(z) \quad \text{by } D1(b)$$

so the theorem follows in the usual way.

Finally, the cancellation laws are:

$NO11.$ $(x)(y)(z)[x + z = y + z \rightarrow x = y]$

$NO12'.$ $(x)(y)(z)[z \neq 0 \wedge xz = yz \rightarrow x = y]$.

The proof of $NO11$ is left as an exercise.

Proof of NO12':

For the basis of an induction on x, we must show that

$$z \neq 0 \wedge 0z = yz \rightarrow 0 = y$$

is true. Assume that

1. $z \neq 0 \wedge 0z = yz$ assumption

Then

$$yz = 0z \quad \text{by } S$$
$$= z0 \quad \text{by } NO6$$
$$= 0 \quad \text{by } D2(a).$$

The proof of

$$(x)[xy = 0 \wedge x \neq 0 \rightarrow y = 0]$$

is left to the reader. From this it follows that

$$y = 0$$

so $0 = y$ and the basis is proved. For the induction step assume

$HI.$ $z \neq 0 \wedge xz = yz \rightarrow x = y$

to prove

$CI.$ $z \neq 0 \wedge S(x)z = yz \rightarrow S(x) = y.$

We prove CI by induction on z. In the basis

$$0 \neq 0 \wedge S(x)0 = y0 \rightarrow S(x) = y$$

the antecedent is false because of the clause $0 \neq 0$. Thus the conditional is true. Now assume CI as the hypothesis of the induction on z. Then the conclusion of this induction is

$CI_1.$ $S(z) \neq 0 \wedge S(x)S(z) = yS(z) \rightarrow S(x) = y.$

The first clause of the antecedent is true by $AN4$. Thus a proof of CI_1 rests on the truth of

2. $S(x)S(z) = yS(z) \rightarrow S(x) = y$

from the assumptions HI and CI. If we prove 2 by induction on y, the basis is

$$S(x)S(z) = 0S(z) \rightarrow S(x) = 0.$$

If

$$S(x)S(z) = 0S(z) = 0 \quad \text{and} \quad S(z) \neq 0$$

then by an argument previously left to the reader we have $S(x) = 0$. Of course this is a false statement, but then so is the antecedent of 2 which implies it. Thus the basis holds. Now assume 2 as the hypothesis of this induction. Then we must prove

$CI_2.$ $S(x)S(z) = S(y)S(z) \rightarrow S(x) = S(y).$

We have

$$S(x)S(z) = S(z)S(x) \qquad \text{by } NO10$$
$$= S(z)x + S(z) \qquad \text{by } D2(b).$$

Similarly

$$S(y)S(z) = S(z)y + S(z).$$

Thus, by properties of equality, we have

$$S(z)x + S(z) = S(z)y + S(z)$$

from which $S(z)x = S(z)y$ follows by $NO11$. It follows from this by HI that $x = y$, and by $AN3$ that $S(x) = S(y)$. Thus, CI_2 holds, completing the proof of CI_1, and so of CI and the theorem.

EXERCISES

1. Prove $NO2$.

2. Prove $NO8$.

3. Prove $NO5$.

4. Prove $NO10$.

5. Prove $NO11$.

6. We define the operation *exponentiation* for natural numbers as follows:

   DE. (a) $x^0 = 1$

   (b) $x^{S(y)} = x^y x$

   assuming that $1 = S(0)$. Prove that x^y is well-defined by proving the following theorems.

   $NE1.$ $(x)(y)(E\ z)[z = x^y]$
   $NE2.$ $(x)(y)(z)(w)[z = x^y \wedge w = x^y \to z = w]$

7. Using the definition DE, prove that the exponentiation operation has the following properties.

   $NE3.$ $(x)(y)(z)[x^y x^z = x^{y+z}]$
   $NE4.$ $(x)(y)(z)[(x^y)^z = x^{yz}]$
   $NE5.$ $(x)(y)(z)[x^z y^z = (xy)^z]$
   $NE6.$ $(x)(y)(z)[x = y \to x^z = y^z]$
   $NE7.$ $(x)(y)(z)[y = z \to x^y = x^z]$
   $NE8.$ $(x)(y)(z)[x^z = y^z \to x = y]$
   $NE9.$ $(x)(y)(z)[x^y = x^z \to y = z]$

8. Show that the exponentiation operation is neither associative nor commutative.

9. Use DE to express 4^3 as a product, where $3 = S(S(S(0)))$ and $4 = S(3)$.

10. Prove that $(x)(y)[x + S(y) \neq x]$.

11. Prove the generalized monotonic laws:

    $(x)(y)(z)(w)[x = y \wedge z = w \to x + z = y + w]$
    $(x)(y)(z)(w)[x = y \wedge z = w \to xz = yw]$
    $(x)(y)(z)(w)[x = y \wedge z = w \to x^z = y^w]$.

12. Define the predecessor function P so that for each natural number $x \neq 0$,

    $$P(x) = y \leftrightarrow x = S(y) \quad \text{and} \quad P(0) = 0$$

    Show that for each x, $P(x)$ is well defined.

13. Define the *difference operation* by induction as follows:

    DD. (a) $x - 0 = x$

    (b) $x - S(y) = P(x - y)$.

Prove that the following theorems hold.

*NE*1. $(x)(y)(\text{E }z)[z = x - y]$

*NE*2. $(x)(y)(z)(w)[z = x - y \wedge w = x - y \rightarrow z = w]$

*NE*3. $(x)(y)(z)[x - (y - z) = (x - y) + z]$

*NE*4. $(x)(y)(z)[x - (y + z) = (x - y) - z]$

*NE*5. $(x)(y)[x - (x + y) = 0]$

14. State and prove monotonic and cancellation laws for the difference operation.

5 · SUBTRACTION AND THE INEQUALITY RELATION

In Exercise 13 of Section 4, a subtraction operation was defined and it was shown that every pair of natural numbers had a difference. In Section 1, subtraction was defined in yet another way. Under this definition, we can show that if there is a number c such that $c + b = a$, then c is the difference $a - b$. Thus, for example, we have $4 = 7 - 3$, for it can be shown that $4 + 3 = 7$. The same may be true under the latter definition, since according to it

$$7 - 3 = 7 - S(2) \qquad \text{by definition}$$
$$= P(7 - 2) \qquad \text{by } DD(\text{b})$$
$$= P(7 - S(1)) \qquad \text{by definition}$$
$$= P(P(7 - 1)) \qquad \text{by } DD(\text{b})$$
$$= P(P(7 - S(0))) \qquad \text{by definition}$$
$$= P(P(P(7 - 0))) \qquad \text{by } DD(\text{b})$$
$$= P(P(P(7))) \qquad \text{by } DD(\text{a})$$
$$= P(P(6))$$
$$= P(5)$$
$$= 4 \qquad \text{by definition.}$$

Under the definition in Section 1, however, the difference $3 - 7$ is not a natural number for it can be shown that there is no natural number c for which $c + 7 = 3$. On the other hand, $3 - 7$ is defined by the latter definition, since

$$3 - 7 = 3 - (3 + 4) = 0$$

by *NE*5. Clearly the fact that *NE*5 is a theorem forces us to reject this latter definition since this property is foreign to what we expect of subtraction. Thus, we are left with the definition of Section 1 and with the fact that natural numbers are not closed under subtraction so defined. In the next sequence of theorems we characterize all ordered pairs (a, b) of natural numbers whose differences $a - b$ are not natural numbers. We are concerned here with finding all ordered pairs (a, b) for which $(\text{E } x)[x + a = b]$ is false. By logical properties, this is the same as those ordered pairs for which $(x)[x + a \neq b]$ is true.

NS1. $(x)(y)[x + S(y) \neq x]$

Proof:
The basis of an induction on x is $0 + S(y) \neq 0$ which is true since

$$0 + S(y) = S(y) \neq 0 \qquad \text{by } NO5, D1(a), \text{ and } AN4.$$

Assume for the induction step

HI. $x + S(y) \neq x$

to prove

CI. $S(x) + S(y) \neq S(x)$.

We have

$$S(x) + S(y) = S(x + S(y)) \qquad \text{by proof of } NO1$$
$$\neq S(x) \qquad \text{by } HI \text{ and } AN3$$

completing the proof.

We leave it to the reader to show that the following theorem holds.

NS2. $(x)(y)[x + S(y) \neq 0]$

According to NS2 the equation $x + b = 0$ has no solution if b is the successor of a number. Of course if $b = 0$, the only natural number that is not a successor, then the equation has the solution 0, by $D1(a)$.

The most general result is that $x + b = a$ has no solution if there is a number z for which $b = a + S(z)$. This result, which is proved below, implies that $x + 7 = 3$ has no solution since there is a z (namely 3) such that $7 = 3 + S(z)$.

NS3. $(x)(y)(z)[x + (y + S(z)) \neq y]$

Proof:
Suppose on the contrary that there are numbers x, y, and z such that

$$x + (y + S(z)) = y.$$

By commutative and distributive properties and $D1(a)$, we have

$$(x + S(z)) + y = y$$
$$= 0 + y$$

from which

$$x + S(z) = 0$$

follows by cancellation. But this contradicts *NS2*, so the theorem must hold.

We consider informally the case of ordered pairs (a, b) for which the difference $a - b$ is a natural number, that is, cases in which

$$(E\ x)(x + b = a)$$

is true. One such case is certainly $a = b$, for $0 + a = a$ for every number a. All other pairs whose differences are natural numbers have the form $(b + S(z), b)$, for

$$x + b = b + S(z)$$

obviously has $S(z)$ as a solution.

We have thus considered the equation

$$x + b = a$$

for all ordered pairs of natural numbers, or, what is the same thing, all differences $a - b$. We define a predicate for differences for two of the cases that we have considered. If $S(z)$ is a solution of $x + b = a$ for some number z, that is, if

$$(E\ z)[S(z) + b = a]$$

is true, we shall call $a - b$ a *positive* difference and denote this statement by $p(a - b)$. If $x + b = a$ has no solution, we call the difference *negative* and write $q(a - b)$. Thus we may define the predicates p and q by the equivalences:

$$(E\ z)[S(z) + b = a] \leftrightarrow p(a - b)$$

$$(z)[z + b \neq a] \leftrightarrow q(a - b).$$

Of course p and q are actually binary predicates. The first holds for an ordered pair (a, b) of natural numbers if and only if their difference is a successor, and the second holds if and only if the difference is not a natural number at all. A third case, in which the difference is zero, is also important to distinguish. If a, b, and the differences $a - b$ and $c - d$ are natural numbers, we leave it to the reader to show that the following relations are true:

ND1. $(a - b) + (c - d) = (a + c) - (b + d)$

ND2. $(a - b) - (c - d) = (a + d) - (b + c)$

ND3. $(a - b)(c - d) = (ac + bd) - (ad + bc).$

To prove $ND3$, for example, it must be shown that if

$$x + b = a \quad \text{and} \quad y + d = c$$

then

$$xy + (ad + bc) = ac + bd.$$

We define a unary operation of *negation* for differences such that the negative $-(a - b)$ of a difference $a - b$ is its converse $b - a$. Thus,

$ND4.$ $-(a - b) = b - a.$

We leave to the reader the proof of the following criterion for equality of differences:

$ND5.$ $a - b = c - d \leftrightarrow a + d = b + c.$

To prove this it must be shown that if

$$x + b = a \quad \text{and} \quad y + d = c$$

then $x = y$ if and only if $a + d = b + c$. According to $ND5$, for example, it can be shown that $a - a = b - b$ for any natural numbers a and b, and that

$$a - b = (a + c) - (b + c).$$

It can be proved that the properties $N1$–7 of Section 2 hold for negation of differences. We restate them here without quantifiers, paraphrasing them for the universe of differences we are considering.

$NN1.$ $(a - b) = (c - d) \leftrightarrow -(a - b) = -(c - d)$

$NN2.$ $-\{-(a - b)\} = a - b$

$NN3.$ $(a - b) + \{-(c - d)\} = (a - b) - (c - d)$

$NN4.$ $\{-(a - b)\}\{-(c - d)\} = (a - b)(c - d)$

$NN5.$ $-(a - a) = a - a$

$NN6.$ $-(a - b) = (a - b) \rightarrow a - b = c - c$

$NN7.$ $\{-(a - b)\}(c - d) = (a - b)\{-(c - d)\}$
$$= -\{(a - b)(c - d)\}$$

The proofs of $NN1$–7 are simple and are left, for the most part, to the reader. They depend on properties $ND1$–5. To prove $NN1$, for example, note that $a - b = c - d$ means by $ND5$ that

$$a + d = b + c.$$

On the other hand

$$-(a - b) = -(c - d)$$

means that

$$b - a = d - c \qquad \text{by } ND4$$

and this means by $ND5$ that $b + c = a + d$. But these conclusions are equivalent by the symmetry property of equality. For the last equality of $NN7$, note that

$$
\begin{aligned}
(a - b)\{-(c - d)\} &= (a - b)(d - c) & \text{by } ND4 \\
&= (ad + bc) - (ac + bd) & \text{by } ND3 \\
&= -\{(ac + bd) - (ad + bc)\} & \text{by } ND4 \\
&= -\{(a - b)(c - d)\} & \text{by } ND3.
\end{aligned}
$$

We show next that the properties $P1$–13 of Section 2 are valid for the predicates p and q of differences defined here. Since $P1$–4, 7–9 imply the others in this list, it suffices to prove these. We list them here paraphrased for differences, providing some of the proofs and leaving the rest to the reader.

$NP1.$ $\sim p(a - a)$

Proof:
By $NS1$,

$$S(z) + a = a + S(z) \neq a$$

for any number z. Thus, $x + a = a$ does not have a successor as a solution, so that $p(a - a)$ is false.

$NP2.$ $p(a - b) \leftrightarrow \sim p(-(a - b))$

Proof:
Assume $p(a - b)$ is true. Then

$$(\text{E } z)[S(z) + b = a]$$

If $p(-(a - b))$ were also true, then

$$p(b - a) \quad \text{and} \quad (\text{E } w)[S(w) + a = b]$$

would be true as well. But then

$$
\begin{aligned}
a &= S(z) + b \\
&= S(z) + S(w) + a \\
&= S(S(z) + w) + a
\end{aligned}
$$

so that

$$(\text{E } u)[a = S(u) + a]$$

contradicting $NS1$. Thus, $p(-(b - a))$ is false. The converse is proved similarly.

$NP3.$ $p(a - b) \wedge a - b = c - d \rightarrow p(c - d)$

Proof:

Assume

$$p(a - b) \quad \text{and} \quad a - b = c - d.$$

Then

$$(E\ z)[S(z) + b = a] \quad \text{and} \quad a + d = b + c.$$

We have

$$S(z) + d + b = S(z) + b + d$$
$$= a + d$$
$$= b + c$$
$$= c + b.$$

Thus, by cancellation $S(z) + d = c$ and $p(c - d)$ is true.

$NP4.$ $q(a - b) \leftrightarrow p(-(a - b))$

Proof:

Assume that $q(a - b)$ is true. Then $(z)[z + b \neq a]$. If $p(-(a - b))$ were false we would have $p(a - b)$ by $NP2$ and thus,

$$(E\ z)[S(z) + b = a]$$

would be true, contradicting the hypothesis. The converse is established by reversing the steps of the foregoing proof.

$NP7.$ $a - b \neq 0 \rightarrow p(a - b) \vee q(a - b)$

Proof:

Assume that $a - b \neq 0$. We must show that either $p(a - b)$ is true and that $S(z) + b = a$ for some number z or else that $q(a - b)$ is true and $z + b = a$ for no number z. Suppose that on the contrary both of these alternatives are false. Then $x + b = a$ has a solution that is not a successor. The only natural number that satisfies this condition is 0. But 0 is not the solution by hypothesis, so that the conclusion must follow from the premise.

We leave the paraphrases and proofs of properties $P8$–9 to the reader.

It follows that if we define the inequality predicate $x < y$ to mean that $p(y - x)$ is true, then the properties $S1$–9 of this predicate as listed in Section 2 hold. For the predicates $x > y$, $x \leq y$, $x \geq y$ as defined there, the properties $T1$–9, $U1$–9, $V1$–9 respectively hold as well.

This section concludes with a proof that the natural numbers are *well ordered*. This means that every nonempty set $\mathcal{A}$ of natural numbers has a smallest element—an element m such that

$$m \in \mathcal{A} \wedge (x)[x \in \mathcal{A} \rightarrow m \leq x].$$

To prove this, let α be any nonempty set of natural numbers and let $\mathcal{B}$ be the set of all lower bounds of α. Thus y is an element of $\mathcal{B}$ if

$$(x)[x \in \alpha \rightarrow y \leq x]$$

is true. We leave it to the reader to show that $0 \leq x$ for every natural number x. This implies that $\mathcal{B}$ must have at least one element—namely 0. Now $\mathcal{B}$ cannot contain all natural numbers, since if $x \in \alpha$, then

$$S(x) = x + 1 > x$$

so that $S(x) \notin \mathcal{B}$. There must be an element $c \in \mathcal{B}$ such that $S(c) \notin \mathcal{B}$. Since $c \in \mathcal{B}$, $c \leq x$ for every $x \in \alpha$. Furthermore, $c \in \alpha$. Were this not so, we would have $c < x$ for every $x \in \alpha$, so that $S(c) \leq x$ would be an element of $\mathcal{B}$ contrary to the way in which c was chosen.

The well-ordered property of natural numbers is not a property of other number systems we shall discuss. A set of integers unbounded below, and an open interval in the universe of rational numbers are examples of sets having no least element.

EXERCISES

1. Prove $NS2$.

2. Prove $ND1$–3.

3. Prove $ND5$.

4. Prove $NN2$–6.

5. State and prove properties analogous to $P8$–9 of Section 2 for differences of natural numbers.

6 · INTEGERS AND THEIR PROPERTIES

Having noted that the set $\mathcal{N}$ of natural numbers is not closed under subtraction, we approach the problem of defining a set $\mathcal{J}$ of integers for which subtraction can be defined. This means that in the new universe $\mathcal{J}$, the statements

$$(x)(y)(\text{E } z)[z + y = z]$$

and

$$(x)(y)(z)(u)[z + y = x \wedge u + y = x \rightarrow z = u]$$

are both true. But in defining such a set we should like to preserve certain properties of $\mathcal{N}$. For example, it is important that we be able to define addition and multiplication operations under which $\mathcal{J}$ is closed and which have properties similar to those that hold in $\mathfrak{N}$. Moreover, we would like to be able to define an inequality operation $x < y$ so that the usual order properties hold.

Not wishing to lose any of the language developed for natural numbers, we make another demand on our definition of $\mathcal{J}$. It is important that $\mathcal{J}$ contain a subset $\mathfrak{N}^*$ which is the domain of a one-one correspondence f having $\mathfrak{N}$ as range and having the following properties:

1. For any two integers a and b of $\mathfrak{N}^*$, $f(a + b) = f(a) + f(b)$.
2. For any two integers a and b of $\mathfrak{N}^*$, $f(ab) = f(a)f(b)$.
3. For any two integers a and b of $\mathfrak{N}^*$, $a < b \leftrightarrow f(a) < f(b)$.

If f has these properties, it is said to *preserve* sums, products, and order, and is called an *isomorphism* of $\mathfrak{N}^*$ on $\mathfrak{N}$. The existence of f assures us that a subset of $\mathcal{J}$ provides arithmetic of exactly the same form as the arithmetic of $\mathfrak{N}$ relative to sums, products, and order. Of course it turns out that the set $\mathfrak{N}^*$ is the set of nonnegative integers.

An example of an isomorphism between two finite sets is provided in the set $\mathcal{J}_4 = \{0, 1, 2, 3\}$ of integers modulo 4 and the set $\mathcal{C} = \{1, i, -1, -i\}$ of complex units with $i^2 = -1$. We define "product" for $\mathcal{J}_4$ as addition modulo 4 and for $\mathcal{C}$ as complex multiplication. Then the product tables for these two sets are

+	0	1	2	3
0	0	1	2	3
1	1	2	3	0
2	2	3	0	1
3	3	0	1	2

·	1	i	-1	$-i$
1	1	i	-1	$-i$
i	i	-1	$-i$	1
-1	-1	$-i$	1	i
$-i$	$-i$	1	i	-1

We define f with domain $\mathcal{J}_4$ and range $\mathcal{C}$ by the following equations: $f(0) = 1$, $f(1) = i$, $f(2) = -1$, and $f(3) = -i$. Of course f is a one-one correspondence. We leave it to the reader to check that it preserves products and is thus an isomorphism relative to products.

We could proceed to define $\mathcal{J}$ by a set of axioms as we did $\mathfrak{N}$. However, it is unnecessary to do so since we can use the principles of logic and sets to combine elements of $\mathfrak{N}$ in such a way that $\mathcal{J}$ can be defined from them. Then properties of operations over $\mathcal{J}$ will depend on properties of analogous operations over $\mathfrak{N}$. In order to define integers in terms of natural numbers, we take our first clues from the discussion of differences of natural numbers in the preceding section.

Recall that in that section we considered for each ordered pair (a, b) of natural numbers the equation $x + b = a$. We called (a, b) a positive difference if $a > b$, a negative difference if $a < b$, and the difference 0 if $a = b$. In the second case the equation had no solution. In each case, however, we denoted the ordered pair by $a - b$.

It may occur to the reader that we might define each difference as an integer. But this would cause trouble with the uniqueness of the solution of $x + b = a$. To be sure, $a - b$ is a solution, by definition. But there are differences $c - d$, distinct from $a - b$, that satisfy this equation. In fact according to $ND5$, any difference $c - d$ for which $a + d = b + c$ satisfies $x + b = a$. For example, $7 - 3$ is a solution of $x + 3 = 7$, but so are $5 - 1$, $4 - 0$, $110 - 106$, and so on. Thus we must define integers otherwise, for in order that subtraction be definable, the equation must have a unique solution.

The properties of differences developed in the preceding section serve to indicate appropriate ways to define the class $\mathcal{I}$ of integers. We begin by considering the class $\mathfrak{N}^2$ of ordered pairs of natural numbers, interpreting each pair as a difference, as in the preceding section. Using the property $ND5$ as a definition of the relation of equality in $\mathfrak{N}^2$, we have

$ID1.$ $(a, b) = (c, d) \leftrightarrow a + d = b + c$.

Note that the equality being defined is on the left of the biconditional. The equality on the right is the equality in the universe $\mathfrak{N}$ that was taken as a primitive relation. $ID1$ provides a test in the theory of natural numbers for deciding two ordered pairs are equal. We show first that the relation defined by $ID1$ is an equivalence relation.

First note that $a + a = a + a$ by the reflexive property of equality in $\mathfrak{N}$. Thus by $ID1$ $(a, a) = (a, a)$ demonstrating the reflexive property of equality in $\mathfrak{N}^2$. To prove the symmetric property, assume that $(a, b) = (c, d)$. Then by $ID1$ $a + d = b + c$. By the symmetric property of equality in N, we have $b + c = a + d$. Thus,

$$(c, d) = (a, b) \qquad \text{by } ID1$$

For the transitive property assume

$$(a, b) = (c, d) \quad \text{and} \quad (c, d) = (e, f)$$

so that by $ID1$

$$a + d = b + c \quad \text{and} \quad c + f = d + e.$$

Then

$$a + d + f = b + c + f$$
$$= b + d + e.$$

Thus, $a + f + d = b + e + d$, so that $a + f = b + e$ follows by cancellation. Thus, $(a, b) = (e, f)$ by $ID1$.

Since equality in $\mathfrak{N}^2$ is an equivalence relation, $\mathfrak{N}^2$ is partitioned into cells of mutually equivalent ordered pairs. We denote each cell by bold-faced letter, and the set of all cells by $\mathscr{I}$. Each cell is called an *integer*. Thus an integer is defined as a class of differences all of which satisfy the same equation $x + b = a$ or are converses of pairs that satisfy these equations.

We leave it to the reader to prove that the following properties of equality in $\mathfrak{N}^2$ hold:

$$(a, a) = (0, 0) \tag{7}$$

$$(a + c, b + c) = (a, b) \tag{8}$$

$$(a, b) = (0, 0) \rightarrow a = b. \tag{9}$$

Property (8) enables us to recognize quickly that two ordered pairs are equal by noting that one can be obtained from the other by adding the same natural number to both members. Properties (7) and (9) imply that there is an integer that contains for each natural number a the pair (a, a), and only such pairs. Note that all of these pairs arise from equations of the form $x + a = a$ of which the natural number 0 is the solution. Thus we call this set of pairs the *integer zero*. We denote particular integers by boldface numerals, and use the same numeral as for analogous natural numbers. Thus the integer zero is denoted by **0**.

For all pairs (a, b) other than those in **0** we have by $S4$ (for natural numbers) that either $a > b$ or $a < b$, but, by $S3$, not both. For these we can prove the following:

$$a > b \wedge (a, b) = (c, d) \rightarrow c > d \tag{10}$$

$$a > b \rightarrow (\text{E } c) \, [p(c) \wedge (a, b) = (c, 0)] \tag{11}$$

$$a < b \wedge (a, b) = (c, d) \rightarrow c < d \tag{12}$$

$$a < b \rightarrow (\text{E } c) \, [p(c) \wedge (a, b) = (0, c)]. \tag{13}$$

According to (10) if an integer contains an ordered pair (a, b) with $a > b$, then $c > d$ for every pair (c, d) that it contains. Such an integer must contain according to (13) a pair $(c, 0)$. In this case we denote the integer by **c**. Thus for every natural number c there is one and only one integer **c**, namely the one that contains $(c, 0)$. If **c** is such an integer it is said to be *positive* and we write $p(\mathbf{c})$.

Similarly if $a < b$ for any pair (a, b) in an integer then $c < d$ for every pair (c, d) that it contains. If **a** is an integer containing (a, b) for $a < b$, we say that **a** is *negative* and write $q(\mathbf{a})$. In this case there is a nonzero natural number c for which $(0, c) \in a$ and we denote **a** by $-\mathbf{c}$.

We leave it to the reader to verify that the predicates p and q defined for integers reflect the properties of analogous predicates defined for differences in the preceding section. This provides assurance that if subtraction is defined, the inequality relations discussed in Section 2 are definable for integers by the definitions given there and that they have the properties listed.

We prove (10) and (13) leaving proofs of the other two properties for the reader. For (10), assume that

$$a > b \quad \text{and} \quad (a, b) = (c, d)$$

Then

$$S(z) + b = a$$

for some z, and

$$a + d = b + c.$$

By monotonic properties,

$$S(z) + b + d = b + c$$

and by cancellation,

$$S(z) + d = c.$$

Thus $c > d$. For (13) note that $c = b - a$, for $(a, b) = (0, b - a)$. This is a positive number, since $a < b$ by hypothesis. Note also that for each a and b, c is unique.

Using the property $ND4$ as a motivation we define the operation of negation for integers as follows:

$ID2.$ $(a, b) \in \mathbf{a} \leftrightarrow (b, a) \in -\mathbf{a}.$

$ID2$ defines the unary operation negation in the sense that it assigns to each integer $\mathbf{a}$ another integer $-\mathbf{a}$, namely, the one containing the converses of all the pairs that a contains. We prove that negation is well defined by showing that any two pairs, members of the same integer, have converses that are both members of the same integer.

Much confusion sometimes arises in using the terms "negative integer" and "negative of an integer." The first of these terms denotes a kind of integer, in particular one that contains as members ordered pairs (a, b) of natural numbers with $a < b$. We denote negative integers by $\bar{\mathbf{c}}$. On the other hand what we usually call the negative of an integer $\mathbf{a}$ is the value $-\mathbf{a}$ that the negation function assigns to $\mathbf{a}$. It may happen that the negative of an integer is a negative integer, or it may happen that it is a positive integer or zero. For negation defined by $ID2$, we may prove the following properties listed in Section 2 as $N2$, $N5$, and $N6$.

$$-(-\mathbf{a}) = \mathbf{a} \tag{14}$$

$$-\mathbf{0} = \mathbf{0} \tag{15}$$

$$\mathbf{a} = -\mathbf{a} \rightarrow \mathbf{a} = \mathbf{0}. \tag{16}$$

In addition for $\mathbf{a}$ positive we have,

$$-\mathbf{a} = \bar{\mathbf{a}} \tag{17}$$

$$-\bar{\mathbf{a}} = \mathbf{a}. \tag{18}$$

To prove (14), let $(a, b) \in \mathbf{a}$. Then

$$(b, a) \in -\mathbf{a} \quad \text{and} \quad (a, b) \in -(-\mathbf{a}).$$

Since $\mathbf{a}$ and $-(-\mathbf{a})$ are equivalence classes that have an element in common, we have $-(-\mathbf{a}) = \mathbf{a}$. For (15) note that if $(a, b) \in \mathbf{0}$, then

$$a = b \quad \text{and} \quad (b, a) \in -\mathbf{0}.$$

But then

$$(a, b) = (a, a) = (b, a)$$

so $-\mathbf{0} = \mathbf{0}$. For (16), if $\mathbf{a} = -\mathbf{a}$, then $(a, b) = (b, a)$ for $(a, b) \in \mathbf{a}$. Thus,

$$a + a = b + b \quad \text{by } ID1$$

so that $a = b$, by monotonic properties. Thus,

$$(a, b) = (a, a) \in \mathbf{0}.$$

The proofs of (17) and (18) are left to the reader.

EXERCISES

1. Show that f is an isomorphism from $\mathcal{I}_4$ to $\mathcal{C}$. Define g from $\mathcal{I}_4$ to $\mathcal{C}$ so that $g(0) = 1$, $g(1) = -i$, $g(2) = -1$, and $g(3) = i$. Prove that g is an isomorphism relative to products that is different from f.

2. Prove (7)–(9).

3. Prove (11) and (12).

4. Prove (17) and (18).

5. Prove that the predicates p and q possess the properties $P1$–13 listed in Section 2. Why can we not yet define $x < y$ over $\mathcal{I}$?

6. Let a and b be two integers. Define their *sum* $\mathbf{a} + \mathbf{b}$ as the class containing the pair $(a + c, b + d)$ whenever $(a, b) \in \mathbf{a}$ and $(c, d) \in \mathbf{b}$. Show that $\mathbf{a} + \mathbf{b}$ is well defined by showing that:

   (a) for each $\mathbf{a}$ and $\mathbf{b}$, the above definition determines at least one integer $\mathbf{a} + \mathbf{b}$, and

   (b) for each $\mathbf{a}$ and $\mathbf{b}$ at most one integer $\mathbf{a} + \mathbf{b}$ is determined.

[Hint: for (b) show that if $(a, b) \in \mathbf{a}, (a', b') \in \mathbf{a}, (c, d) \in \mathbf{b}$, and $(c', d') \in \mathbf{b}$, then $(a + c, b + d) = (a' + c', b' + d')$.]

7. Let $\mathfrak{N}^*$ be the set of nonnegative integers. Show that $\mathfrak{N}^*$ and $\mathfrak{N}$ are isomorphic relative to sums. [Hint: for Exercises 7, 9, and 11 use the correspondence f for which $f(\mathbf{c}) = c$.]

8. Let $\mathbf{a}$ and $\mathbf{b}$ be integers. Define their *product* $\mathbf{ab}$ as the class containing the pair $(ac + bd, ad + bc)$ whenever $(a, b) \in \mathbf{a}$ and $(c, d) \in \mathbf{b}$. Show that $\mathbf{ab}$ is well defined.

9. Show that $\mathfrak{N}^*$ and $\mathfrak{N}$ are isomorphic relative to products.

10. Let $\mathbf{a}$ and $\mathbf{b}$ be integers. Define their *difference* $\mathbf{a} - \mathbf{b}$ as the sum $\mathbf{a} + (-\mathbf{b})$. Show that for each pair $(\mathbf{a}, \mathbf{b})$ of integers, $\mathbf{a} - \mathbf{b}$ is the unique solution of $\mathbf{x} + \mathbf{b} = \mathbf{a}$ in the universe $\mathscr{I}$. Is $\mathbf{a} - \mathbf{b}$ well defined?

11. Define the predicate $\mathbf{x} < \mathbf{y}$ for integers so that

$$\mathbf{x} < \mathbf{y} \leftrightarrow p(\mathbf{y} - \mathbf{x})$$

as in Section 2. Show that $\mathfrak{N}^*$ and $\mathfrak{N}$ are isomorphic relative to inequalities.

7 · OPERATIONS ON INTEGERS

The sum, product, and difference of ordered pairs of integers are defined in Exercises 6, 8, and 10 respectively of Section 6. The reader is asked there to show that these operations are well defined. This is the requirement that the properties O1–2, O3–4, and O14–15 of Section 1 are true in the universe of integers. In this section we prove that other properties of sums, products, and differences listed in Section 1 hold in the universe $\mathscr{I}$ of integers. The present section concludes with a discussion of division as an operation over $\mathscr{I}$. As before, we use italics for natural numbers and boldface for integers. To recapitulate the definitions, for two integers $\mathbf{a}$ and $\mathbf{b}$, containing ordered pairs (a, b) and (c, d) respectively, we define the *sum* $\mathbf{a} + \mathbf{b}$ as the class that contains the pair $(a + c, b + d)$, and the *product* $\mathbf{ab}$ as the class that contains the pair $(ac + bd, ad + bc)$. Note that these definitions reflect the properties *ND1* and *ND3* of natural numbers given in Section 5. Assuming that it has been shown that these operations are well defined we proceed to investigate other properties of sums and products.

The procedure followed in the proofs of these properties demonstrates that their validity rests solely on the validity of analogous properties of similar operations over natural numbers. This is because the result of adding or multiplying two integers is completely determined by combining in the way indicated in the definition an ordered pair of natural numbers for each integer. We prove first the commutative property of sums.

105. $(x)(y)[x + y = y + x]$

Proof:

Suppose that

$$(a, b) \in \mathbf{x} \quad \text{and} \quad (c, d) \in \mathbf{y}.$$

Then by the definition of sum

$$(a + c, b + d) \in \mathbf{x} + \mathbf{y}$$

and

$$(c + a, d + b) \in \mathbf{y} + \mathbf{x}.$$

However,

$$(a + c, b + d) = (c + a, d + b) \qquad \text{by } ID1$$

since

$$(a + c) + (d + b) = (c + a) + (b + d)$$

follows from associative and commutative properties of natural number addition. Since $\mathbf{x} + \mathbf{y}$ and $\mathbf{y} + \mathbf{x}$ are equivalence classes having an element in common, we conclude that they are equal. Thus, $\mathbf{x} + \mathbf{y} = \mathbf{y} + \mathbf{x}$. Note that the "=" sign is used three times in this proof, and each time with a different meaning. The first use is as equality of ordered pairs as introduced by $ID1$, the second as equality of natural numbers, a relation taken as primitive, and the third as equality of sets. Similarly, the "+" sign is used in two senses: to indicate natural number sums and integer sums. Similar remarks hold true in the proof to follow.

We leave to the reader the proof of the next two properties, and provide a proof for the third.

106. $(x)(y)[xy = yx]$

107. $(x)(y)(z)[(x + y) + z = x + (y + z)]$

108. $(x)(y)(z)[(xy)z = x(yx))$

Proof:

Suppose that

$$(a, b) \in \mathbf{x}, \qquad (c, d) \in \mathbf{y}, \quad \text{and} \quad (e, f) \in \mathbf{z}.$$

Then, by definition of integer product, we have

$$(ce + df, cf + de) \in \mathbf{yz}$$
$$(a(ce + df) + b(cf + de), a(cf + de) + b(ce + df)) \in \mathbf{x(yz)}$$
$$(ac + bd, ad + bc) \in \mathbf{xy}$$

and

$$((ac + bd)e + (ad + bc)f, (ac + bd)f + (ad + bd)e) \in \mathbf{(xy)z}.$$

Using properties of natural number addition we can show by $ID1$ that

$$(a(ce + df) + b(cf + de), a(cf + de) + b(ce + df))$$
$$= ((ac + bd)e + (ad + bc)f, (ac + bd)f + (ad + bc)e)$$

for they are both equal to

$$(ace + adf + bcf + bde, acf + ade + bce + bdf).$$

Hence $(\mathbf{xy})\mathbf{z} = \mathbf{x}(\mathbf{yz})$.

$IO9.$ $(x)(y)(z)[x = y \rightarrow x + z = y + z]$

Proof:

Suppose $\mathbf{x} = \mathbf{y}$ and let

$$(a, b) \in \mathbf{x}, \quad (c, d) \in \mathbf{y}, \quad \text{and} \quad (e, f) \in \mathbf{z}$$

Then

$$a + d = b + c, \quad (a + e, b + f) \in \mathbf{x} + \mathbf{z},$$
$$\text{and} \quad (c + e, d + f) \in \mathbf{y} + \mathbf{z}.$$

Using monotonic properties of natural number sums we have

$$a + d + e + f = b + c + e + f$$

so that

$$(a + e) + (d + f) = (b + f) + (c + e)$$

and

$$(a + e, b + f) = (c + e, d + f) \qquad \text{by } ID1.$$

Thus,

$$\mathbf{x} + \mathbf{z} = \mathbf{y} + \mathbf{z}$$

We leave the proof of the following to the reader:

$IO10.$ $(x)(y)(z)[x = y \rightarrow xz = yz]$

$IO11.$ $(x)(y)(z)[x + z = y + z \rightarrow x = y].$

The proof of the cancellation law of multiplication follows:

$IO12'.$ $(x)(y)(z)[z \neq 0 \land xz = yz \rightarrow x = y].$

Proof:

Let

$$(a, b) \in \mathbf{x} \quad \text{and} \quad (c, d) \in \mathbf{y}.$$

Assuming that $\mathbf{z} \neq \mathbf{0}$, either $\mathbf{z}$ is positive or $\mathbf{z}$ is negative. Accordingly we consider two cases:

Case 1: $\mathbf{z} > \mathbf{0}$. Then there is a natural number $e \neq 0$ such that

$$(e, 0) \in \mathbf{z} \quad \text{and} \quad (ae, be) \in \mathbf{xz} \quad \text{and} \quad (ce, de) \in \mathbf{yz}.$$

Since $\mathbf{xz} = \mathbf{yz}$, we have by $ID1$ that $ae + de = be + ce$. Thus,

$$(a + d)e = (b + c)e.$$

Since $e \neq 0$, $a + d = b + c$, so that

$$(a, b) = (c, d) \quad \text{and} \quad \mathbf{x} = \mathbf{y}.$$

Case 2: $\mathbf{z} < \mathbf{0}$. Then there is a natural number $e \neq 0$ such that $(0, e) \in \mathbf{z}$. Then

$$(be, ae) \in \mathbf{xz} \quad \text{and} \quad (de, ce) \in \mathbf{yz}.$$

Since $\mathbf{xz} = \mathbf{yz}$, we have

$$be + ce = ae + de \quad \text{or} \quad (a + d)e = (b + c)e$$

and the conclusion follows as before.

We leave the proof of the distributive law to the reader.

$IO13.$ $(x)(y)(z)[x(y + x) = xy + xz)$

The result of Exercise 10 of the preceding section shows that if the difference $\mathbf{a} - \mathbf{b}$ is defined so that

$$\mathbf{a} - \mathbf{b} = \mathbf{a} + (-\mathbf{b})$$

then the properties $O14$–16 of Section 2 are fulfilled. We prove finally two properties of the integer $\mathbf{0}$ and a property of the integer $\mathbf{1}$.

$IO17.$ $(x)[x + \mathbf{0} = x]$

Proof:

Let $(a, b) \in \mathbf{x}$. Since $(0, 0) \in \mathbf{0}$, we have

$$(a + 0, b + 0) \in \mathbf{x} + \mathbf{0}.$$

However,

$$(a + 0, b + 0) = (a, b)$$

so that $\mathbf{x} + \mathbf{0} = \mathbf{x}$.

$IO18.$ $(x)[x\mathbf{0} = \mathbf{0}]$

Proof:

Let $(a, b) \in \mathbf{x}$. Since $(0, 0) \in \mathbf{0}$, we have

$$(a0 + b0, b0 + a0) \in \mathbf{x0}.$$

Since $(a0 + b0, b0 + a0) = (0, 0)$, we have $\mathbf{x0} = \mathbf{0}$.

$IO21.$ $(x)[\mathbf{1x} = \mathbf{x}]$

Proof:

Let $(a, b) \in \mathbf{x}$. Since $(1, 0) \in \mathbf{1}$, we have $(a1 + b0, a0 + b1) \in \mathbf{1x}$.

However,
$$(a1 + b0, b1 + a0) = (a, b)$$
so that $1\mathbf{x} = \mathbf{x}$.

We turn now to properties of positive and negative integers relative to sums and products as listed in Section 2. Since the distinction between positive and negative integers is seen in the fact that the first kind contains a pair $(a, 0)$ and the second a pair $(0, a)$ for some $a \neq 0$, this distinction can be used to derive the desired results. Consider in particular

IP8. $(x)(y)[p(x) \wedge p(y) \rightarrow p(x + y)]$

IP9. $(x)(y)[p(x) \wedge p(y) \rightarrow p(xy)]$.

Proofs:

Assume $p(\mathbf{x})$ and $p(\mathbf{y})$. Then there are natural numbers $a \neq 0$ and $b \neq 0$ such that
$$(a, 0) \in \mathbf{x} \quad \text{and} \quad (b, 0) \in \mathbf{y}.$$
Then
$$(a + b, 0 + 0) \in \mathbf{x} + \mathbf{y} \quad \text{and} \quad (ab + 00, a0 + b0) \in \mathbf{xy}.$$
But these pairs are equal to $(a + b, 0)$ and $(ab, 0)$ respectively so that $p(\mathbf{x} + \mathbf{y})$ and $p(\mathbf{xy})$ follow.

Even though $P10$–13 follow from these properties as in Section 2 it is interesting to construct proofs of these properties based only on the definition of positive and negative integers.

The situation of the integers with respect to quotients is analogous to that of natural numbers with respect to differences. Thus for a given ordered pair $(\mathbf{a}, \mathbf{b})$ of integers, the equation $\mathbf{xb} = \mathbf{a}$ sometimes has a unique solution and sometimes not. We saw in Section 2 that if $\mathbf{b} = \mathbf{0}$, then this equation cannot have a unique solution, for if $\mathbf{a} = \mathbf{0}$, uniqueness fails, since by $O18$ every integer is a solution, while if $\mathbf{a} \neq \mathbf{0}$, there is no solution by $O18$. Thus if any set of numbers contains an element $\mathbf{0}$ satisfying $O18$, we must be content to define division only for ordered pairs $(\mathbf{a}, \mathbf{b})$ with $\mathbf{b} \neq \mathbf{0}$.

Our discontent with the integers lies in the fact that even for the limited set of pairs, the quotient is not always an integer. To be sure the equation $\mathbf{x2} = \mathbf{6}$ has the solution $\mathbf{3}$ and $\mathbf{x5} = \mathbf{30}$ has the solution $\mathbf{6}$, yet it can be shown that the equations $\mathbf{x7} = \mathbf{3}$ and $\mathbf{x1} = \mathbf{5}$ have no solution. To prove this requires a development of the well-known theory of divisibility, into which we shall not enter here.

In order to have a set of numbers under which every equation $xb = a$ ($b \neq 0$) has a solution, we form another extension, this time extending $\mathscr{I}$

to the set Q of rational numbers. The procedure is outlined in the next section and is similar to the extension just completed. That is, a rational number is defined as an equivalence class of ordered pairs (a, b) of integers with $b \neq 0$. Q is closed under division except for division by 0, and contains a subset $\mathcal{J}^*$ isomorphic to $\mathcal{J}$ relative to sums, products, differences, and order.

To indicate how the equivalence relation, sum, product, difference, and inequality relations are best defined in Q, we state here a number of properties of quotients of integers, leaving their proofs to the reader. As before, we shall denote the solution of $\mathbf{xb} = \mathbf{a}$ when it exists by $\mathbf{a/b}$. We assume that, in each fraction $\mathbf{a/b}$, $\mathbf{b} \neq \mathbf{0}$.

   1. $(\mathbf{a/b}) = (\mathbf{c/d}) \leftrightarrow \mathbf{ad} = \mathbf{bd}$
   2. $\mathbf{0/b} = \mathbf{0}$
   3. $\mathbf{c} \neq \mathbf{0} \rightarrow \mathbf{ac/bc} = \mathbf{a/b}$
   4. $(\mathbf{a/b}) + (\mathbf{c/d}) = (\mathbf{ad} + \mathbf{bc})/\mathbf{cd}$
   5. $(\mathbf{a/c}) + (\mathbf{b/c}) = (\mathbf{a} + \mathbf{b})/\mathbf{c}$
   6. $(\mathbf{a/b})(\mathbf{c/d}) = \mathbf{ac/bd}$
   7. $(\mathbf{a/c}) - (\mathbf{b/d}) = (\mathbf{ad} - \mathbf{bc})/\mathbf{bd}$
   8. $\mathbf{a/1} = \mathbf{a}$
   9. $\mathbf{bd} > \mathbf{0} \rightarrow (\mathbf{a/b} < \mathbf{c/d} \leftrightarrow \mathbf{ad} < \mathbf{bc})$
 10. $\mathbf{bd} < \mathbf{0} \rightarrow (\mathbf{a/b} < \mathbf{c/d} \leftrightarrow \mathbf{ad} > \mathbf{bc})$
 11. $\mathbf{a/(-1)} = -\mathbf{a}$

EXERCISES

1. Prove $I O6$ and $I O7$.

2. Prove $I O10$ and $I O11$.

3. Prove $I O13$.

4. Prove properties $P10$–13 using the definitions of positive and negative integers given in the present section.

5. Verify that the properties 1–11 at the end of the present section hold for quotients that are integers.

6. Extend the definition DE of exponentiation given for natural numbers in Exercise 6 of Section 4 to the largest possible subset of $\mathcal{J}^2$ so that the properties given in Exercise 7 of Section 4 remain valid. Thus, for example, if $\mathbf{a} > \mathbf{0}$ and $\mathbf{b} > \mathbf{0}$, define $\mathbf{a^b}$ as the integer containing $(a^b, 0)$. If $\mathbf{a} < \mathbf{0}$ and $\mathbf{b} > \mathbf{0}$ define $\mathbf{a^b}$ separately when $\mathbf{b}$ is even and when $\mathbf{b}$ is odd. When is $\mathbf{a^b}$ definable if $\mathbf{b} \leq \mathbf{0}$ so that the properties of Example 7 of Section 4 hold?

8 · RATIONAL NUMBERS

The extension from integers to rational numbers is sketched in this section. It is left as a project for the reader to supply the details of this procedure, which is similar to the extension just completed in many ways. Recall that the fundamental motivation for this extension is to provide a set of numbers for which division, except by zero, is definable, as well as addition, subtraction, and multiplication. The extension is accomplished so that the set $\mathbb{Q}$ of rational numbers has a subset $\mathscr{I}^*$ isomorphic to $\mathscr{I}$ under the last three operations. Further we wish to define an inequality relation which is preserved under this isomorphism.

We denote integers by italics in what follows, and rational numbers by boldface letters. Consider the set $\mathscr{I} \times (\mathscr{I} - \{0\})$ of all ordered pairs (a, b) of integers with $b \neq 0$. Each such pair determines an equation $xb = a$ with universe $\mathscr{I}$. For such equations that have solutions (a, b) denote the quotients a/b. We use these pairs and the others as the basic elements in terms of which to define rational numbers. Of course it is undesirable to call each pair a rational number because two distinct equations of the above form may have the same solution. Using the first property in the list at the end of the preceding section, we define a relation of equivalence that identifies pairs of ordered pairs as follows:

QD1. $(a, b) = (c, d) \leftrightarrow ad = bc.$

It must be shown first that this relation is an equivalence relation. Thus, $\mathscr{I} \times (\mathscr{I} - \{0\})$ is partitioned into cells by this relation containing mutually equivalent ordered pairs of integers. Each cell is called a *rational number* and the set of all cells is denoted by $\mathbb{Q}$. We can prove

$$c \neq 0 \rightarrow (ac, bc) = (a, b)$$

which is a cancellation law for pairs.

Now the structure of certain cells of this partition can be investigated. Thus, we can prove that

$$(0, a) = (0, c)$$

and

$$(0, a) = (b, c) \rightarrow b = 0$$

hold for all integers except that $a \neq 0$ and $c \neq 0$. This means that there is a rational that contains all pairs $(0, a)$ and only those. This we call the *rational number zero* and denote it by **0**.

We can show next that every rational number different from zero contains a unique pair (a, b) such that $b > 0$ and a and b have no common factor greater than 1. For each rational number different from 0 we call this pair the *simplest form* of the number. The rational number itself is denoted by $\mathbf{a}/\mathbf{b}$, where (a, b) is its simplest form. In practice we denote a rational number by a/b for *any* pair (a, b) that it contains, but will adhere in this section to using $\mathbf{a}/\mathbf{b}$ as the name of a nonzero rational number only if (a, b) is its simplest form.

A rational number $\mathbf{a}/\mathbf{b}$ is said to be *positive* if $a > 0$ and *negative* if $a < 0$. The *negation* of the rational number a/b is the number $(-\mathbf{a})/\mathbf{b}$. The following list of properties given in Section 2 may now be proved: $N1, 2, 5, 6, P1\text{-}4, 7\text{-}9$.

Of the properties listed at the end of Section 7, we may use 4, 6, and 7 to motivate definitions of sum, product, and difference of rational numbers. Accordingly, let $\mathbf{a}/\mathbf{b}$ and $\mathbf{c}/\mathbf{d}$ be rational numbers. We define their *sum* as the rational containing the pair $(ad + bc, bd)$, their *product* as the rational containing the pair (ac, bd), and their *difference* as the rational containing the pair $(ad - bc, bd)$.

With these definitions we can prove properties $N3, 4$, and 7 of Section 2, thus assuring ourselves that the appropriate inequality relations are definable as in Section 2. The properties of these operations as listed in Section 1 can now be proved also.

Consider the class $\mathscr{I}^*$ of all rationals of the form $\mathbf{a}/\mathbf{1}$ called *rational integers*. Denote $\mathbf{a}/\mathbf{1}$ also by $\mathbf{a}$. It can be shown that $\mathscr{I}^*$ is isomorphic to $\mathscr{I}$ relative to the operations and relations defined.

Finally, if $\mathbf{c} \neq \mathbf{0}$, define the *quotient* of $\mathbf{a}/\mathbf{b}$ and $\mathbf{c}/\mathbf{d}$ to be the rational containing the pair (ad, bc). The properties of quotients listed in Section 1 can now be proved. In particular every equation $\mathbf{xb} = \mathbf{a}$ in the universe $\mathbb{Q}$ with $\mathbf{b} \neq \mathbf{0}$ has a unique solution.

PROJECT

Complete the extension outlined in this section, arranging definitions and theorems in appropriate order and providing proofs of the theorems.

EXERCISE

Define $\mathbf{a}^{\mathbf{b}}$ for the largest subset of $\mathbb{Q}^2$ for which the properties of Exercise 7 of Section 4 hold.

9 · RATIONAL SEQUENCES AND LIMITS

It was shown in Section 2 that a set of numbers, such as $\mathbb{Q}$, that is closed under division is *dense*. This means that for every pair of distinct numbers *a* and *b* there is a number *c*, distinct from both, contained in the interval between them. It follows from this that every interval of positive length contains infinitely many numbers, and that given any number *a* one may find another number *b* as close to *a* as he likes. Thus, if a set of numbers is closed under division, no interval, no matter how short, is free of a number of the set. The considerations concerning the density of number systems lead to procedures involving approximation.

It will become clear in later sections that approximation procedures lie at the very basis of the study of real numbers and functions of real arguments. Indeed the nature of real numbers is such that operating with them effectively in applications of mathematics *requires* that approximations be made during calculations. If approximation is unavoidable in a computation then there is some obligation to keep track of the maximum possible error committed, and it is desirable to find some way in which this error can be reduced if necessary. In this section we introduce notions concerned with approximation procedures with rational numbers.

Given any number *a*, any open interval having *a* as an interior point (not an endpoint) is called a *neighborhood* of *a*. If the neighborhood has *a* as its midpoint and extends *c* units ($c > 0$) to either side of *a*, we call it a *c-neighborhood* of *a*. We say that *b* *approximates a to within c* if *b* is interior to the *c*-neighborhood of *a*. Thus, .333 approximates $\frac{1}{3}$ to within .001, since it lies interior to the interval $(\frac{1}{3} - .001, \frac{1}{3} + .001)$ as in Figure 11.

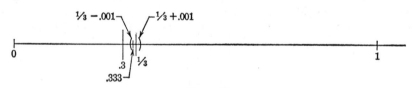

Figure 11

Given $c > 0$ and *a*, the *c*-neighborhood of *a* is the interval $(a - c, a + c)$ and every number in this interval approximates *a* to within *c*. This interval is the common solution set of the open statements

$$a - c < x < a + c \quad \text{and} \quad |x - a| < c.$$

Given a set $\mathfrak{a}$ of numbers, a number *a* is called an *accumulation point* of $\mathfrak{a}$ if every neighborhood of *a* contains a member of $\mathfrak{a}$ distinct from *a* in its interior. Thus, for *every* $c > 0$ there is an element *t* of $\mathfrak{a}$ such that $0 < |t - a| < c$. This means that $\mathfrak{a}$ contains numbers that approximate *a* to within any positive number we choose. In approximation procedures we are naturally interested that this positive number be small.

For example, the interval $(-1, 3)$ has all its members as accumulation points, and the numbers -1 and 3 as well. The set $\{1, \frac{1}{2}, \frac{1}{3}, \frac{1}{4}, \ldots\}$ of reciprocals of positive integers has 0 as its only accumulation point. To show that a is an accumulation point of a set we must show that every neighborhood of a contains at least one point of the set distinct from a. To show that a *is not* an accumulation point of the set, it is sufficient to exhibit a single neighborhood of a containing no points of the set.

Note that the definition insists that if a is an accumulation point of $\mathcal{C}$ then every neighborhood of a contains a point b of $\mathcal{C}$ *distinct from a.* The requirement that $b \neq a$ enables us to prove that no finite set can have an accumulation point. Indeed if $\mathcal{C}$ is finite and a is any number not in $\mathcal{C}$, a neighborhood of a can be found that excludes all members of $\mathcal{C}$. If $a \in \mathcal{C}$, then a neighborhood of a can be found that excludes all points of $\mathcal{C}$ other than itself. Of course we could have relaxed the requirement that $b \neq a$, which would allow us to prove that every member of a finite set is an accumulation point of the set. Clearly this does not describe situations that interest us here, since in such cases the approximation coincides with the accumulation point in each neighborhood.

In most cases approximations to a given number are presented in a given temporal order rather than being simply elements of a set $\mathcal{C}$ in which no order of this kind is provided. Rather than consider a set $\mathcal{C}$ of approximations to a given number a that is its accumulation point, we consider instead a *sequence* of approximations to a. We might think of the approximations as discrete numbers listed one after the other by a computing machine that can keep running as long as we wish. To have a sequence of numbers it is essential that the members of the sequence be arranged in a linear order, and that the sequence have infinitely many members.

Both linear order and the infinite property are available in the positive integers. If f is a function that has the positive integers as domain and some set $\mathcal{C}$ of rational numbers as range, we call the pair $(\mathcal{C}, f)$ an *infinite sequence of rationals* or, briefly, a *sequence.* The numbers in $\mathcal{C}$ are arranged by the natural order of the domain of f so that we may say that the member $f(1)$ is the *first* element, $f(2)$ is the *second* element, $f(3)$ the *third* element of the sequence, and so on. Usually the terms of the sequence are listed in this order between parentheses and $f(n)$ is abbreviated f_n. Thus if f is a function that assigns a rational number f_n to each positive integer n, the sequence defined is denoted $(f_1, f_2, \ldots, f_n, \ldots)$. When no ambiguity results, we abbreviate this notation (f_n). Often it is possible to present a sequence by providing a formula that allows the computation of f_n for each n once n is known. Thus, if $f_n = 1/n$ for each n, we have the sequence $(1, \frac{1}{2}, \frac{1}{3}, \ldots, 1/n, \ldots)$, or briefly $(1/n)$. The sequence defined by the formula $f_n = 1/2^{n+1}$ is $(\frac{1}{4}, \frac{1}{8}, \frac{1}{16}, \ldots)$. The function f can be defined in other ways. Thus,

$$f_n = \begin{cases} 1 & \text{if } n \text{ is odd} \\ 1/n & \text{if } n \text{ is even} \end{cases}$$

defines the sequence $(1, \frac{1}{2}, 1, \frac{1}{4}, 1, \frac{1}{6}, \ldots)$.

We say that a is an *accumulation point of the sequence* (f_n) if every neighborhood of a contains infinitely many terms of (f_n). Note that here we do not require that these terms be distinct from a. If we did, the sequence $(3, 3, 3, \ldots)$, for example, would have no accumulation point. In this case it would be contrary to the purpose we want sequences to serve, for clearly, if every term of a sequence is 3, then the error committed by approximating 3 by the sequence is always zero. This convenient situation is destroyed if we are not allowed to distinguish 3 as an accumulation point of the sequence.

Consider now the sequences:

$$(1, \tfrac{1}{2}, \tfrac{1}{3}, \tfrac{1}{4}, \ldots, 1/n, \ldots)$$

$$(1, \tfrac{1}{2}, 1, \tfrac{1}{4}, 1, \tfrac{1}{8}, \ldots, 1, 1/2^{n/2}, \ldots)$$

$$(0, 1, 2, 0, 1, 2, \ldots, 0, 1, 2, \ldots)$$

$$(1, \tfrac{1}{2}, 1, \tfrac{2}{3}, 1, \tfrac{3}{4}, \ldots).$$

It can be shown that 0 is the only accumulation point of the first sequence, 0 and 1 are accumulation points of the second, 0, 1, and 2 are accumulation points of the third, and 1 is the only accumulation point of the fourth.

Our major concern is with sequences that provide successively more accurate approximations to some unique number a. Thus we wish to consider primarily sequences (f_n) for which there is one accumulation point a having the property that every neighborhood of a contains *all but a finite number* of terms of (f_n). This is a stronger condition than the requirement that each neighborhood of a contain infinitely many terms of the sequence. Under the weaker condition there could be a number $c > 0$ for which infinitely many terms of (f_n) fail to approximate a to within c. Under the stronger condition no matter how small c is chosen, only a finite number of terms of (f_n) fail to approximate a to within c. If such an accumulation point of (f_n) exists, we can show that it is unique, and we call it the *limit* of (f_n). The limit of (f_n) is denoted by $\lim f_n$.

Thus, $a = \lim f_n$ means that every neighborhood of a contains all but a finite number of terms of (f_n). This means that for every $c > 0$ there is some positive integer N so that for each term f_n with $n > N$ we must have $|f_n - a| < c$. In symbolic terms

$$(c)\{c > 0 \to (E\ N)(n)(n > N \to |f_n - a| < c).$$

To prove that the limit, if it exists, is unique, consider two limits a and b of (f_n). If $a \neq b$, there is a c-neighborhood of a and a d-neighborhood of b that are disjoint from one another. But it is clearly impossible for both to contain all but a finite number of terms of (f_n). Hence $a = b$, and the limit is unique if it exists. Of course there are many sequences (f_n) for which $\lim (f_n)$ does not exist. The second and third of the sequences listed above are examples.

Let us prove that the first sequence in that list has limit 0. Thus we wish to prove the statement that $\lim (1/n) = 0$ or

$$(c)\{c > 0 \to (E\ N)(n)(n > N \to |(1/n) - 0| < c)\}.$$

Given $c > 0$ we must find a number $N > 0$ such that

$$|(1/n) - 0| = 1/n < c$$

for $n > N$. But to obtain the conclusion $1/n < c$ it is sufficient to have $n > 1/c$ by R2 of Exercise 11, Section 2. Hence for any $c > 0$ we can let N be the greatest integer in $1/c$, and if $n > N$, we will have $1/n < c$.

To show that the limit of the fourth sequence is 1, we must show that for any $c > 0$ there is an N so that if $n > N$, then $|f_n - 1| < c$, where

$$f_n = \begin{cases} 1 & \text{if } n \text{ is odd} \\ n/(n + 2) & \text{if } n \text{ is even.} \end{cases}$$

However,

$$|f_n - 1| = |1 - 1| = 0 < c$$

for all odd n. For even n we have

$$|n/(n + 2) - 1| = \frac{2}{n + 2}.$$

If this is $<c$ for some $c > 0$, then we have

$$\frac{n + 2}{2} > \frac{1}{c}$$

$$n + 2 > \frac{2}{c}$$

$$n > \frac{2}{c} - 2$$

so that if N is chosen as the greatest integer in $(2/c) - 2$, the conclusion holds since the steps above are reversible.

Suppose that we want to show that a particular number k is not the limit of a sequence. All that is necessary is to show that there is an interval about k that excludes an infinite number of terms of the sequence. This denies the statement that every neighborhood contains all but a finite number of terms. Consider the second sequence in the list above. We show that 1 is not its limit by noting that the .1-neighborhood of 1 excludes all terms in sequence except those that are 1. The procedure is illustrated in Figure 12.

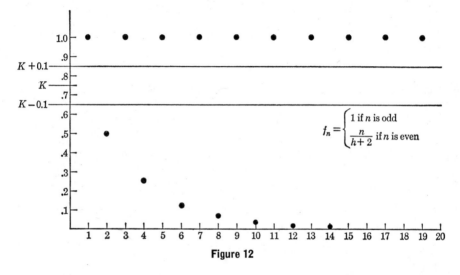

Figure 12

Actually, this sequence has no limit, but to prove this could require infinitely many proofs of the kind in the last paragraph. Of course since 1 and 0 are accumulation points of this sequence, and the only ones, and since we know that if a limit exists it must be unique, it is sufficient in this case to prove that neither 0 nor 1 is the limit. The proof that 0 is not the limit is left to the reader.

This section closes with a number of theorems about sequences that are useful in proving properties to be considered in the next section. We have already shown that the limit of a sequence is unique. We record this as follows:

Q1. If $\lim f_n = a$ and $\lim f_n = b$, then $a = b$.

We next prove that if a sequence has a limit, then the set of its terms is bounded.

Q2. If $\lim f_n = a$, then there is a number $M > 0$ such that $|f_n| \leq M$ for each n.

Proof:

Assume $\lim f_n = a$. Then for any $c > 0$ all but a finite number of terms of (f_n) are in the interval $(a - c, a + c)$. Let $c = 1$ and let N be the number of terms outside the interval $(a - 1, a + 1)$. If M_1 is the greater of the numbers $|a - 1|$ and $|a + 1|$ then

$$-M_1 < f_n < M_1$$

whenever $n > N$. Let M be the greatest of the numbers in the list:

$$M_1, |f_1|, |f_2|, \ldots, |f_n|.$$

Then

$$|f_n| \leq M$$

for $n > N$, since

$$|f_n| \leq M_1.$$

For other n, $|f_n| \leq M$ by definition of M.

We show now that if the limit of a sequence exists but is not 0, then all but a finite number of its terms lie outside some neighborhood of 0.

Q3. If $\lim f_n$ exists but does not equal 0, then there are numbers $m > 0$ and N so that $|f_n| \geq m$ for $n > N$.

Proof:

Suppose on the contrary that for every $m > 0$ and N there is an $n > N$ such that $|f_n| < m$. This means that every neighborhood of 0 has terms of the sequence in its interior. Thus every such neighborhood contains infinitely many terms of the sequence. If

$$\lim f_n = a \neq 0$$

one can find a neighborhood of a and a neighborhood of 0 disjoint from one another each containing infinitely many terms of (f_n). But this is impossible since every neighborhood of a contains all but a finite number of these terms.

Finally we consider a property of sequences that have limits according to which terms approximate not only the limit, but also each other to within any positive number c. This consequence of existence of a limit is called the *Cauchy convergence criterion*, and any sequence that satisfies the conclusion of this theorem is said to be *Cauchy convergent*.

Q4. If $\lim f_n = a$ exists, then given $c > 0$ there is an integer $N > 0$ such that $|f_m - f_n| < c$ whenever $m > N$ and $n > N$.

Proof:

Suppose $\lim f_n = a$. Then, by definition of limit, if $c_1 > 0$ is any number then $N > 0$ can be found so that if $n > N$ and $m > N$ then

$$|f_n - a| < c_1 \quad \text{and} \quad |f_m - a| < c_1.$$

But then

$$\begin{aligned} |f_m - f_n| &= |f_n - a + a - f_n| \\ &\leq |f_m - a| + |f_n - a| \\ &< 2c_1 \quad \text{by } A7. \end{aligned}$$

Given any $c > 0$, let $c_1 = c/2$. Then the desired conclusion holds.

The property of Cauchy convergence of a sequence given in the conclusion of $Q4$ is one that is naturally expected of sequences that have limits. For if all but a finite number of terms of sequence are to be found in any c-neighborhood of the limit, then each of these terms is within a $2c$-neighborhood of each of the others. A property that one is led to expect from considerations such as these is the converse of $Q4$: If a sequence is Cauchy convergent then it must have a limit. It is reasonable to expect that if it can be shown that the terms of a sequence "condense," so to speak, so that the difference of all pairs of terms, except for finitely many, can be made as small as one wishes, then there is some single number about which they must condense. However, we can show that the converse of $Q4$ does not hold for rational numbers: there are Cauchy convergent rational sequences whose limit is not a rational number.

We define a sequence (f_n) by induction as follows:

$$f_1 = 1$$
$$f_n = f_{n-1} + (x_n/10^{n-1}) \qquad (n > 1)$$

where for each $n > 1$, x_n is the greatest integer for which

$$f_n^2 \leq 2.$$

It is easy to check that $f_2 = 1.4, f_3 = 1.41, f_4 = 1.414, \ldots$. The sequence (f_n) can be generated by the familiar arithmetic procedure for extracting the square root of a number. As each new decimal digit is found (the number x_n in the definition) the entire number f_n is an approximation to one more decimal place than the previous approximation. Note that the sequence defined is strictly increasing: every term is greater than terms with smaller subscripts. Notice also that the sequence is bounded above, for $f_n^2 < 2 < 4$, so that $|f_n| < 2$. We show that (f_n) is Cauchy convergent by proving the following theorem:

Q5. If (f_n) is such that $f_n < f_{n+1}$ for all positive integers n and if there is a number $M > 0$ such that $|f_n| \leq M$ for all n, then (f_n) is Cauchy convergent.

Proof:

Let (f_n) be bounded and strictly increasing as in the hypothesis. Suppose on the contrary that (f_n) is not Cauchy convergent. Then there is a $c > 0$ such that

$$f_{n+1} - f_n = |f_{n+1} - f_n| \geq c$$

for infinitely many n. Let $N = 2M/c$. Consider any N differences $f_{n+1} - f_n$ that are distinct and $\geq c$. Their sum is greater than or equal to $Nc = 2M$. This means that the interval that these terms occupy has length greater than or equal to $2M$. This contradicts the boundedness property, since according to it all terms occupy an interval of length less than $2M$.

The conclusion continues to hold if the hypotheses are weakened: replace $f_n < f_{n+1}$ by $f_n \leq f_{n+1}$ and $|f_n| \leq M$ by $f_n \leq M$. A similar result holds when the terms of sequence are nonincreasing and are bounded below. Thus the sequence defined above is Cauchy convergent by Q5. Since $\lim f_n^2 = 2$, we can show also that $(\lim f_n)^2 = 2$, using properties to be developed in the next section. Thus, $\lim f_n$ is a number whose square is 2, and we showed in Section 3 that such a number is not rational.

We can prove other relations between Cauchy convergence and boundedness:

Q6. If (f_n) is Cauchy convergent, then it is bounded. That is, there is an $M > 0$ such that for each n, $|f_n| \leq M$.

Q7. If (f_n) is a Cauchy convergent sequence that has no rational limit, then there are numbers m and N such that if $n > N$ then $|f_n| \geq m$.

The proofs are left to the reader. Q3 and Q7 together imply that every Cauchy convergent sequence whether or not it has a limit has all but a finite number of its terms outside some neighborhood of 0 just as long as the limit, if it exists, is not zero.

EXERCISES

1. Show that in any set of numbers containing with each pair (a, b) of its elements the element $(a + b)/2$, and ordered by the relation $x < y$:
   (a) Every interval $[a, b]$ contains an element of the set.
   (b) Every interval $[a, b]$ contains infinitely many points of the set.
   (c) Every neighborhood of every element of the set contains a point of the set distinct from itself.

(d) Every neighborhood of every element of the set contains infinitely many distinct elements of the set.

2. Show that if b approximates a to within c, then b approximates a to within d for any $d > c$.

3. Show that if b approximates a to within c then a approximates b to within c.

4. Show that a approximates a to within c for any $c > 0$.

5. If $c > 0$ is fixed, is the relation represented by "x approximates y to within c" an equivalence relation?

6. For each of the sequences below, guess a formula for f_n and prove that it is correct.

   (a) $(2, \frac{3}{2}, \frac{5}{4}, \frac{9}{8}, \frac{17}{16}, \ldots)$
   (b) $(2, \frac{1}{2}, \frac{5}{4}, \frac{7}{8}, \frac{17}{16}, \ldots)$
   (c) $(2, \frac{1}{2}, \frac{5}{4}, \frac{1}{8}, \frac{17}{16}, \frac{1}{32}, \frac{65}{64}, \frac{1}{128}, \ldots)$
   (d) $(0, 1, 2, 3, 1, 2, 3, 1, 2, 3, \ldots)$
   (e) $(1, \frac{1}{4}, \frac{1}{9}, \frac{1}{16}, \ldots)$
   (f) $(1, \frac{1}{4}, \frac{8}{9}, \frac{1}{16}, \frac{24}{25}, \frac{1}{36}, \ldots)$

7. What are the accumulation points (if any) of the sequences in Exercise 6? What are the limits?

8. Prove that 0 is the limit of the sequence in Exercise 6(e).

9. Prove that the sequence in Exercise 6(c) has no limit.

10. Prove that 1 is the limit in Exercise 6(a).

11. Show that the weaker hypotheses $f_n \leq f_{n+1}$ and $f_n < M$ imply the conclusion of $Q5$.

12. Prove $Q6$ and $Q7$.

13. Prove that if $a > 0$ and $b > 0$ and x approximates a to within c and y approximates b to within d, then $x + y$ approximates $a + b$ to within $c + d$. Are the hypotheses $a > 0$ and $b > 0$ necessary?

10 · PROPERTIES OF LIMITS

In this section we consider some of the properties of limits of sequences of rational numbers. On the one hand these properties serve as a pattern for a theory of limits that will be developed in other contexts later, on the other hand, the validity of these properties serves to motivate the extension to be undertaken in the next section to the set $\mathcal{R}$ of real numbers. In this section we assume that all the sequences we consider have limits, unless we state otherwise.

Let us attempt to find first a criterion for deciding under what conditions two sequences have the same limit. Certainly if for any $c > 0$ terms of (f_n) and (g_n) are to be found in a common c-neighborhood of some number L when n is large enough, then we could expect that $|f_n - L|$, $|g_n - L|$, and $|f_n - g_n|$ are all quantities that we can make as small as we like by choosing n large enough. For the first two differences this means that

$$\lim f_n = L = \lim g_n$$

and for the third difference this means that

$$\lim (f_n - g_n) = 0.$$

We can show that these two conditions are equivalent.

Q8. $\lim f_n = \lim g_n = L \leftrightarrow \lim (f_n - g_n) = 0$

Proof:

Suppose $\lim f_n = \lim g_n = L$. Then given $c > 0$ there are numbers N_1 and N_2 such that if $n > N$, then

$$|f_n - L| < \frac{c}{2} \quad \text{and} \quad |g_n - L| < \frac{c}{2}.$$

But then if $N > N_1$ and $N > N_2$

$$\begin{aligned}
|(f_n - g_n) - 0| &= |f_n - g_n| \\
&= |(f_n - L) - (g_n - L)| \\
&\leq |f_n - L| + |g_n - L| \qquad \text{by } A7 \\
&< \frac{c}{2} + \frac{c}{2} = c
\end{aligned}$$

for $n > N$. Thus, $\lim (f_n - g_n) = 0$. Conversely, suppose

$$\lim (f_n - g_n) = 0 \quad \text{and} \quad \lim f_n = L.$$

Then given $c > 0$ there are numbers N_1 and N_2 such that if $n > N$ then

$$|f_n - g_n| < \frac{c}{2} \quad \text{and} \quad |f_n - L| < \frac{c}{2}.$$

To show also that $\lim g_n = L$, if $N > N_1$ and $N > N_2$, we have

$$\begin{aligned}
|g_n - L| &= |f_n - L - (f_n - g_n)| \\
&\leq |f_n - L| + |f_n - g_n| \\
&< \frac{c}{2} + \frac{c}{2} = c
\end{aligned}$$

for $N > N$.

The proof of the following consequence of Q8 is left to the reader:

*Q*9. If $\lim f_n$ does not exist and $\lim (f_n - g_n) = 0$ then $\lim g_n$ does not exist.

Let (f_n) and (g_n) be sequences having limits L and M respectively, and let k be a rational number. Then the sequence (kf_n) is formed by multiplying each term of (f_n) by k, the nth term of each of the sequences $(f_n + g_n)$, $(f_n - g_n)$, $(f_n g_n)$, and (f_n/g_n) is formed by taking respectively the sum, difference, product, and quotient of the nth terms of (f_n) and (g_n). The next theorems establish a relation between sequences defined thus, from (f_n) and (g_n) and the limits L and M.

If $\lim f_n = L$ and $\lim g_n = M$, and if k is a rational number, then

*Q*10. $\lim (kf_n) = k \lim f_n = kL$

*Q*11. $\lim (f_n + g_n) = \lim f_n + \lim g_n = L + M$

*Q*12. $\lim (f_n - g_n) = \lim f_n - \lim g_n = L - M$

*Q*13. $\lim (f_n g_n) = (\lim f_n)(\lim g_n) = LM$.

*Q*14. $\lim (f_n/g_n) = (\lim f_n)/(\lim g_n) = L/M$,
provided further that $M \neq 0$ and for each n, $g_n \neq 0$.

The last condition is necessary to be sure that f_n/g_n is defined for each n.

Proofs:

For each theorem assume that for any numbers $c_1 > 0$ and $c_2 > 0$ there are numbers N_1 and N_2 such that

$$|f_n - L| < c_1 \quad \text{whenever } n > N_1 \text{ and}$$

$$|g_n - M| < c_2 \quad \text{whenever } n > N_2.$$

For each of the theorems we let c be any positive number and show that we can determine N so that a certain absolute difference is less than c whenever $n > N$. To do this we impose conditions on the choice of c_1 and c_2 which determine N_1 and N_2. Then N is determined from these.

To prove *Q*10 we must determine N so that $|kf_n - kL| < c$ whenever $n > N$. But we have

$$|kf_n - kL| = |k||f_n - L|.$$

Now given $c > 0$, if $k \neq 0$ choose $c_1 = c/|k|$. Let $N = N_1$. Then if

$$n > N = N_1$$

$$|f_n - L| < c_1 = c/|k|$$

so that

$$|kf_n - kL| = |k||f_n - L| < |k|(c/|k|) = c.$$

The proof for $k = 0$ is left to the reader.

To prove $Q11$ we must show that

$$|(f_n + g_n) - (L + M)| < c$$

whenever $n > N$. Choose $c_1 = c_2 = c/2$ and let N be the larger of N_1 and N_2. If $n > N$, then $n > N_1$, and $n > N_2$. Thus,

$$\begin{aligned} |(f_n + g_n) - (L + M)| &= |(f_n - L) + (g_n - M)| \\ &\leq |f_n - L| + |g_n - M| \\ &< \frac{c}{2} + \frac{c}{2} = c. \end{aligned}$$

The proof of $Q12$ is left to the reader.

To prove $Q13$, we note first that by $Q2$ there are numbers N_3 and K so that $|f_n| \leq K$ whenever $n > N_3$. Now

$$\begin{aligned} |f_n g_n - LM| &= |f_n g_n - f_n M + f_n M = LM| \\ &\leq |f_n||g_n - M| + |M||f_n - L| \\ &< Kc_2 + |M|c_1 \end{aligned}$$

in n is greater than the largest of N_1, N_2, and N_3. Now given any $c > 0$, if $M \neq 0$ let

$$c_1 = c/2|M| \quad \text{and} \quad c_2 = c/2K.$$

Then $|f_n g_n - LM| < c$, so that the theorem holds. The proof for $M = 0$ is left to the reader.

To prove $Q14$ note that by $Q3$ there are numbers N_3 and m so that $|g_n| \geq m$ whenever $n > N_3$. Then

$$\begin{aligned} \left|\frac{f_n}{g_n} - \frac{L}{M}\right| &= \frac{|f_n M - g_n L|}{|g_n M|} \\ &= \frac{|f_n M - LM - (g_n L - LM)|}{|g_n||M|} \\ &\leq \frac{1}{|g_n|} |f_n - L| + \frac{|L|}{|g_n||M|} |g_n - M| \\ &< \frac{1}{m} c_1 + (|L|/|g_n||M|)c_2 \end{aligned}$$

if n is greater than the largest of N_1, N_2, and N_3. Now given $c > 0$ let

$$c_1 = mc/2 \quad \text{and} \quad c_2 = |g_n||M|/2|L|.$$

Then

$$\left|\frac{f_n}{g_n} - \frac{L}{M}\right| < c.$$

This list of theorems assures us that if a single operation is performed consistently on corresponding terms of two sequences that have limits, then the result of the same operation on the limits is the limit of the new sequence.

The next set of theorems relates bounds of sequences to their limits. Let $\lim f_n = L$.

Q15. If there are numbers N and K such that $f_n \leq K$ whenever $n > N$, then $L \leq K$.

Q16. If there are numbers N and K such that $f_n \geq K$ whenever $n > N$, then $L \geq K$.

To prove Q15, suppose that $L > K$. Then there is a neighborhood of L that excludes K. Since $L = \lim f_n$ this neighborhood contains all but a finite number of f_n. But this contradicts the hypothesis that $f_n \leq K$ for all but a finite number of arguments n. The proof of Q16 is similar.

Q17. If $\lim f_n = L$ and $\lim g_n = M$ and if there is a number N such that $f_n \leq g_n$ whenever $n > N$ then $L \leq M$.

Proof:

Let $h_n = f_n - g_n$. If $f_n \leq g_n$ for all but a finite number of arguments, then $h_n \leq 0$ for those arguments. Thus, by Q15 $\lim h_n \leq 0$. However,

$$
\begin{aligned}
L - M &= \lim f_n - \lim g_n \\
&= \lim (f_n - g_n) \qquad \text{by Q12} \\
&= \lim h_n \\
&\leq 0.
\end{aligned}
$$

Hence $L \leq M$.

The following theorem follows easily from Q17 and its proof is left to the reader:

Q18. If there is a number N such that $f_n \leq g_n \leq h_n$ whenever $n > N$ and if $\lim f_n = \lim h_n = L$, then $\lim g_n = L$.

The property in Q18 is that if the terms of a sequence are between corresponding terms of sequences having the same limit, then that sequence must have the same limit as well.

If a sequence (f_n) is unbounded then for any positive number M, no matter how large, there is at least one term f_j for which $|f_j| > M$. This means that either there are terms in the sequence that are arbitrarily large or terms that are arbitrarily small, or both. For example, the sequence $(1, -1, 2, -2, \ldots)$ such that $f_{2n+1} = n$ and $f_{2n} = -n$ for each positive integer n is unbounded. There is special interest in unbounded sequences of two kinds.

Suppose that given any number M not only could one show that some term of (f_n) is greater than M, but that *all but a finite number of terms* of (f_n) are greater than M. Then for any M no matter how large, a term in the sequence can be determined after which every term exceeds M. This means that for any point on the graph of the rationals, all but a finite number of points of the graph of the sequence lie to the right of the point, as in Figure 13. We describe this situation by saying that the *limit of* (f_n)

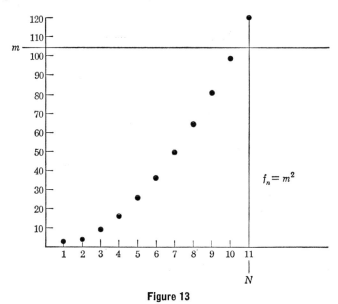

$$f_n = m^2$$

Figure 13

is *plus infinity* or simply infinity, and denote this by writing $\lim f_n = \infty$. Note that this means that (f_n) has no limit, and that it is unbounded and so cannot even be Cauchy convergent. But in a sense its unboundedness is consistent. The terms are unbounded above and for certain large terms, those that follow it are larger. Using logical symbolism we define $\lim f_n = \infty$ to mean that

$$(M)(E\ N)(n)[n > N \rightarrow f_n > M]$$

is true.

Similarly, we define $\lim f_n = -\infty$ ("minus infinity") to mean that

$$(M)(E\ N)(n)[n > N \rightarrow f_n < M]$$

is true. This means that for any number M, no matter how small, all but a finite number of terms of (f_n) are smaller. Thus, if we say that $\lim f_n = \infty$

we are interested in the fact that the terms of (f_n) are large for large n, and if we say that $\lim f_n = -\infty$ we are interested in the fact that the terms of (f_n) are small for large n.

We now consider some properties of infinite limits.

Q19. $\lim n = \infty$

Q20. $\lim (-n) = -\infty$

Q21. If $\lim f_n = \lim g_n = \infty$, then $\lim (f_n + g_n) = \lim (f_n g_n) = \infty$.

Q22. If k is a positive integer and $\lim f_n = \infty$, then $\lim (kf_n) = \lim (f_n^k) = \infty$.

Q23. If k is a positive integer, then $\lim n^k = \infty$.

Q24. If $\lim f_n = \infty$, then $\lim (1/f_n) = 0$.

Q25. Let p and q be positive integers and a_i $(i = 0, 1, \ldots, p)$ and b_j $(j = 0, 1, \ldots, q)$ be rational numbers with $a_p \neq 0$ and $b_q \neq 0$. Then

$$\lim \frac{a_p n^p + a_{p-1} n^{p-1} + \cdots + a_1 n + a_0}{b_q n^q + b_{q-1} n^{q-1} + \cdots + b_1 n + b_0} = \begin{cases} \infty & \text{if } p > q \text{ and } a_p b_q > 0 \\ -\infty & \text{if } p > q \text{ and } a_p b_q < 0 \\ a_p/b_q & \text{if } p = q \\ 0 & \text{if } p < q. \end{cases}$$

We prove Q21 and Q25 leaving the other proofs to the reader.

Proof of Q21:

Assume that $\lim f_n = \lim g_n = \infty$. Then given any number M_1 there are numbers N_1 and N_2 so that $f_n > M_1$ whenever $n > N_1$ and $g_n > M_1$ whenever $n > N_2$. Now let N be the greater of N_1 and N_2. If $n > N$, we have

$$f_n + g_n > M_1 + M_1 = 2M_1.$$

If M is any number, choose $M_1 = M/2$. Thus, $f_n + g_n > M$ whenever $n > N$.

For the product, note that if $n > N$, $f_n g_n > M_1^2$. Given M, choose M_1 to be any number whose square is greater than M. Thus, $f_n g_n > M$ whenever $n > N$.

To prove Q24 note that

$$\frac{a_p n^p + a_{p-1} n^{p-1} + \cdots + a_1 n + a_0}{b_q n^q + b_{q-1} n^{q-1} + \cdots + b_1 n + b_0}$$

$$= \frac{n^p}{n^q} \frac{a_p + (a_{p-1}/n) + \cdots (a_1/n^{p-1}) + (a_0/n^p)}{b_q + (b_{q-1}/n) + \cdots (b_1/n^{q-1}) + (b_0/n^q)}.$$

The limit of the second of these fractions is a_p/b_q. Using Q23–Q24 we find that

$$\lim (n^p/n^q) = \begin{cases} \infty & \text{if } p > q \\ 1 & \text{if } p = q \\ 0 & \text{if } p < q. \end{cases}$$

The result then follows properties of limits proved earlier and from the following extension of Q22: if $\lim f_n = \infty$ and k is a rational number, then $\lim (kf_n) = \infty$ if $k > 0$, $\lim (kf_n) = 0$ if $k = 0$, and $\lim (kf_n) = -\infty$ if $k < 0$. The proof of this is left to the reader.

Theorem Q25 is useful if the formula for f_n is a fractional expression with a polynomial in n in both numerator and denominator. Then $\lim f_n$ depends on the relative sizes of p and q and on the fraction a_p/b_q of leading coefficients. Thus,

$$\lim \frac{n+1}{2n-1} = \frac{1}{2}$$

since $p = q = 1$ and $a_p = 1$ and $b_q = 2$. Also

$$\lim \frac{n^2+1}{1-n} = -\infty$$

since $p = 2 > 1 = q$ and $a_p/b_q = 1/(-1) < 0$.

EXERCISES

1. Prove Q12.

2. Use Q15–16 to prove that if $f_n = k$ for each n then $\lim f_n = k$.

3. Use Q10–14 and the fact that $\lim (1/n) = 0$ to prove each of the following:

   (a) $\lim \left[\dfrac{1}{n^2} - \dfrac{2}{n} + 7 \right] = 7$

   (b) $\lim \dfrac{4 - (5/n)}{3n - (2/n^2)} = 0$

   (c) $\lim \left[\dfrac{4}{n^7} - 2 \right] = -2$.

4. Prove Q16.

5. Prove Q18.

6. Prove Q19 and Q20.

7. Prove Q22–24.

8. Find examples of sequences (f_n) such that $\lim f_n = 0$ and

    (a) $\lim (1/f_n) = \infty$

    (b) $\lim (1/f_n) = -\infty$

    (c) $\lim (1/f_n)$ does not exist.

9. Prove that if a sequence has limit $\pm\infty$, then it is not Cauchy convergent.

10. If $\lim f_n = \infty$, what can be said of $\lim kf_n$?

11 · DEFINITION OF THE REAL NUMBERS

We have noted that the set Q of rational numbers is dense, and that a consequence of this density property is that rational numbers may be used for systematic approximation procedures. An important mathematical notion related to the problem of approximation is that of sequence. We have found that if a sequence has a limit, in the sense defined above, then we can consider this limit to be the number approximated by the terms of the sequence. That is, if L is the limit of a sequence, then for any positive number c, all but a finite number of terms of the sequence lie in the interval $(L - c, L + c)$. If a sequence does have a limit, we can show it must be Cauchy convergent, for all but a finite number of its terms must approximate each other to within any positive number. One of the limitations of the rational numbers is that the converse of this property is not true. There are Cauchy convergent sequences of rational numbers having no rational limit. This situation, which is described by saying that the rational numbers are *incomplete* in the Cauchy sense, seems inadequate for a number of reasons.

One of the most important of these reasons is an intuitive conviction that if a sequence of numbers can be shown to have terms that are to be found as close together as we wish, then there must be a single number that they have as limit. This is similar (and, as we can show, logically equivalent) to the demand that if a sequence of closed intervals $\mathcal{I}_n = (n = 1, 2, \ldots)$ is such that $\mathcal{I}_{n+1} \subset \mathcal{I}_n$ for all n, then they must have at least one point in common. A sequence of intervals having the inclusion property is said to be *nested*, and the property that most concerns us here is: If for each n, m_n is the length of $\mathcal{I}_n$, if the closed intervals $\mathcal{I}_n$ are nested, and if $\lim m_n = 0$, then the intervals $\mathcal{I}_n$ have exactly one point in common. Figure 14 illustrates this property.

We shall show below that this nested interval property is equivalent to the completeness property, so that the rational numbers do not have this property either.

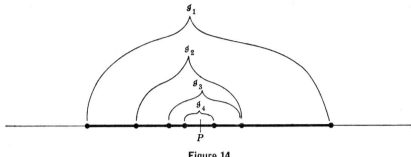

Figure 14

*R*1. A set $\mathcal{S}$ of numbers for which the operations and relations of Sections 1 and 2 can be defined is complete if and only if $\mathcal{S}$ has the nested interval property.

Proof:

We shall show first that if the nested interval property holds, then every Cauchy convergent sequence must have a limit. Let (f_n) be a Cauchy convergent sequence of elements of $\mathcal{S}$. Then there is a number M such that $|f_n| \leq M$ for all n, by Q6. Let $\mathcal{I}_1$ be the closed interval $[-M, M]$. Consider the two halves $[-M, 0]$ and $[0, M]$ of $\mathcal{I}_1$. At least one of these has infinitely many terms of (f_n) as elements, for if both had only a finite number, there could not be infinitely many terms of the sequence. If both have infinitely many terms of (f_n), then $0 = \lim f_n$ and the proof is complete. For let c be any positive number, we can show that $(-c, c)$ must contain all but a finite number of terms of (f_n), if both halves of $\mathcal{I}_1$ have infinitely many terms of (f_n). Consider a contrary case as in Figure 15 in which $[-M, -c]$ contains infinitely many terms

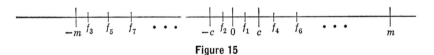

Figure 15

of (f_n). Since $[0, M]$ also has infinitely many terms, the condition of Cauchy convergence cannot hold, contradicting the hypothesis. Other contrary cases can be eliminated in a similar way.

Suppose now that only one of the intervals $[-M, 0]$ and $[0, M]$ has infinitely many terms of (f_n). Call this interval $\mathcal{I}_2$ and consider the two halves of $\mathcal{I}_2$. If both halves contain infinitely many terms of (f_n), then we can show that the midpoint of $\mathcal{I}_2$ is $\lim f_n$. If only one half contains infinitely many terms, call it $\mathcal{I}_3$ and repeat the same argument.

If we continue in this way, then we either locate $\lim f_n$ in a finite number of steps (and complete the proof) or the procedure continues indefinitely, producing an infinite sequence $(\mathcal{I}_n)$ of nested intervals whose lengths have limit 0. In this case, by the nested interval property, there is a unique number L common to all the intervals $\mathcal{I}_n$. We can show that $\lim f_n = L$. Note that the length of $\mathcal{I}_1$ is $2M$, the length of $\mathcal{I}_2$ is $2M/2 = M$, and in general, the length of $\mathcal{I}_n$ is $M/2^{n-2}$. Choose any number $c > 0$ and choose n so that $M/2^{n-2} < c$. Then $\mathcal{I}_n$ is a subset of the interval $(L - c, L + c)$. But only a finite number of terms of (f_n) lie outside $\mathcal{I}_n$, so that $(L - c, L + c)$ contains all but a finite number of terms of the sequence.

To prove the converse, suppose that every Cauchy convergent has a limit and let $(\mathcal{I}_n)$ be a nested sequence of intervals whose lengths have limit 0. Let (l_n) and (r_n) be, respectively, sequences whose terms are the left and right hand endpoints of the intervals $\mathcal{I}_n$. Then the sequence (l_n) is nondecreasing and bounded above by r_1, as in Figure 16. Thus it is a

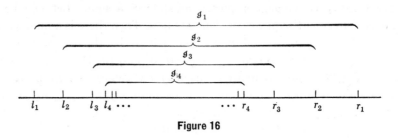

Figure 16

Cauchy convergent sequence by $Q5$. By similar reasoning (r_n) is Cauchy convergent. By hypothesis, both $L = \lim l_n$ and $M = \lim r_n$ exist. Since $r_n - l_n$ is the length of the interval $\mathcal{I}_n$, we have $\lim (r_n - l_n) = 0$. Thus, by $Q8$, $L = M$. We leave it to the reader to show that L is common to all intervals $\mathcal{I}_n$, thus concluding the proof of the theorem.

Aside from the limitations of rational numbers evidenced by the lack of Cauchy completeness and the nested interval property, another limitation noted earlier is that not every set bounded above has a least upper bound, and analogously for greatest lower bounds. We leave it to the reader to show that together these two properties, which we name *bound completeness*, are equivalent to Cauchy completeness and the nested interval property. Further, all these properties are equivalent to the *accumulation point property*: every bounded infinite set has an accumulation point.

To summarize, rational numbers lack the four desirable properties listed below, and these properties are equivalent to each other in any universe $\mathcal{S}$ of numbers having relations and operations with properties as in Sections 1 and 2:

1. Cauchy completeness: Every Cauchy convergent sequence has a limit.
2. Nested interval property: If $(\mathcal{I}_n)$ is a sequence of intervals whose lengths have limit 0 and if for each n, $\mathcal{I}_{n+1} \subset \mathcal{I}_n$, then there is a unique element $L \in \mathcal{S}$ common to all intervals $\mathcal{I}_n$ in the sequence.
3. Bound completeness: Every nondecreasing sequence bounded above and every nonincreasing sequence bounded below has a limit.
4. Accumulation point property: Every bounded infinite set has an accumulation point.

A result of the equivalence of these four properties is that if a set $\mathcal{S}$ has any one of them, it must have the others. In the remainder of this section and the next, we define a set $\mathcal{R}$ of real numbers so that: (1) $\mathcal{R}$ is Cauchy complete, and (2) the operations and relations defined for $\mathcal{Q}$ can be extended to $\mathcal{R}$ so that some subset $\mathcal{R}^*$ of $\mathcal{R}$ is isomorphic to $\mathcal{Q}$ with respect to these.

We begin by considering the set $\mathcal{C}$ of all Cauchy convergent sequences of rational numbers, and designate an element of $\mathcal{C}$ by (a_n), (b_n), and so on. If the element (a_n) has a limit, we denote this limit by a, and similarly for other letters used as names for rational numbers. By $Q8$, if $\lim a_n = a$ and $\lim b_n = b$, then

$$a = b \text{ if and only if } \lim (a_n - b_n) = 0.$$

We extend this notion of equality to all elements of $\mathcal{C}$, whether or not they have limits by the following definition.

$DR1.$ $(a_n) = (b_n) \leftrightarrow \lim (a_n - b_n) = 0$

We can show that the equality relation of $DR1$ is an equivalence relation over $\mathcal{C}$. The relation is reflexive, since

$$\lim (a_n - a_n) = \lim 0 = 0$$

so that $(a_n) = (a_n)$. The relation is symmetric, for suppose that $(a_n) = (b_n)$. Then

$$\lim (a_n - b_n) = 0$$

so

$$\lim (b_n - a_n) = \lim -(a_n - b_n) = - \lim (a_n - b_n) = 0$$

and

$$(b_n) = (a_n).$$

The relation is transitive, for suppose that

$$(a_n) = (b_n)$$

and

$$(b_n) = (c_n).$$

Then

$$\lim (a_n - b_n) = \lim (b_n - c_n) = 0$$

so that

$$\lim (a_n - c_n) = \lim (a_n - b_n + b_n - c_n)$$
$$= \lim (a_n - b_n) + \lim (b_n - c_n)$$
$$= 0 + 0 = 0$$

and

$$(a_n) = (c_n).$$

The relation defined in $DR1$ thus partitions $\mathfrak{C}$ into equivalence classes. Each of these classes is called a *real number,* and here denoted by a lower case letter in boldface. One of these classes contains the sequence (0), and contains a sequence (a_n) if and only if $\lim a_n = 0$, for, as the reader may prove, we have the following theorem:

$R2.$ $(a_n) = (0) \leftrightarrow \lim a_n = 0$.

We call this class the *real number zero* and denote it by $\mathbf{0}$. Let $(a_n) \neq (0)$. Then by $Q6$, there is a number $M > 0$ such that $|a_n| \geq M$ for all but at most a finite number of terms. For these sequences, it can be shown that for all but at most a finite number of terms, either

$$a_n \geq M \quad \text{or} \quad a_n \leq -M$$

but not both. If both of these relations fail to hold, then $|a_n| < M$ for infinitely many a_n contradicting the hypothesis that $(a_n) \neq (0)$. Also if M is such that both

$$a_n \geq M \quad \text{and} \quad a_n \leq -M$$

hold for all but a finite number of terms, then we could show that $M = 0$ and thus contradict the fact that $M > 0$ by hypothesis.

If $\mathbf{a} \neq \mathbf{0}$ then there is a sequence $(a_n) \in \mathbf{a}$ such that for some number $M > 0$, either

1. $a_n \geq M$ for all but a finite number of a_n, or
2. $a_n \leq -M$ for all but a finite number of a_n.

In *Case 1*, we say that **a** is *positive* and denote this by writing $p(\mathbf{a})$. In *Case 2*, we say that **a** is *negative* and denote this by writing $q(\mathbf{a})$.

In addition we may define a negation function n whose value $n(\mathbf{a})$ for a real number **a** we denote by $-\mathbf{a}$, as follows:

DR2. $(a_n) \in \mathbf{a} \leftrightarrow (-a_n) \in -\mathbf{a}$.

To show that for each **a** the number $-\mathbf{a}$ exists, we must show that if (a_n) is Cauchy convergent, then so is $(-a_n)$. But this is true because

$$\left|(-a_n) - (-a_m)\right| = \left|a_m - a_n\right| = \left|a_n - a_m\right|$$

so that if this last difference can be made as small as we please, then so can the first. The negation function is well defined, for if $(a_n) = (b_n)$ then

$$(-a_n) = (-b_n)$$

so that the negatives of all sequences in one cell are in a common cell.

We define the binary algebraic operations for real numbers **a** and **b** as follows. Let

$$(a_n) \in \mathbf{a} \quad \text{and} \quad (b_n) \in \mathbf{b}.$$

Then $\mathbf{a} + \mathbf{b}$, $\mathbf{a} - \mathbf{b}$, and $\mathbf{ab}$ are real numbers such that

$$(a_n + b_n) \in \mathbf{a} + \mathbf{b}$$
$$(a_n - b_n) \in \mathbf{a} - \mathbf{b}$$
$$(a_n b_n) \in \mathbf{ab}.$$

If $\mathbf{b} \neq \mathbf{0}$ then we can show that there is a sequence $(b_n) \in \mathbf{b}$ with $b_n \neq 0$ for each n. Assuming (b_n) above to be such a sequence, we define the quotient $\mathbf{a}/\mathbf{b}$ for $\mathbf{b} \neq \mathbf{0}$ so that

$$(a_n/b_n) \in \mathbf{a}/\mathbf{b}.$$

To prove the assertion, note that if $\mathbf{b} \neq \mathbf{0}$ then for any sequence $(b_n') \in \mathbf{b}$ there are positive numbers N and M such that $|b_n'| \geq M$ for $n > N$. Let $b_n = 1$ for $n \leq N$, and $b_n = b_n'$ otherwise. Then

$$(b_n) = (b_n') \in \mathbf{b}$$

and no term of (b_n) is 0.

We demonstrate below some of the properties of the predicates and operations defined that are listed in Sections 1 and 2, leaving other proofs to the reader.

Note first, however, that if **a** contains a sequence (a_n) that has a rational limit a, then every element of **a** has the same limit. Let $\mathfrak{R}^*$ be the set of real numbers whose elements have rational limits. Then $\mathfrak{R}^*$ is isomorphic to ℚ with respect to the operations and predicates just defined under the correspondence f such that for each $a \in$ ℚ, $f(a)$ is that element of ℜ* containing the sequence (a) all of whose terms are a.

In proving results about properties of operations and predicates on real numbers, the properties $Q10$–14 of the preceding section are of special importance, for they often permit us to reduce the problem of establishing a property of real numbers to an analogous property of rationals that has been established already. Thus, for example, to show that the commutative property of addition holds, we need note only that

$$(a_n + b_n) \in \mathbf{a} + \mathbf{b}$$
$$(b_n + a_n) \subset \mathbf{b} + \mathbf{a}$$

and

$$a_n + b_n = b_n + a_n.$$

Thus,

$$\mathbf{a} + \mathbf{b} \quad \text{and} \quad \mathbf{b} + \mathbf{a}$$

contain a sequence in common, so they must coincide, since they are equivalence classes.

We take as another example the proof that the product is well defined for real numbers. To prove this we must show first that if

$$(a_n) \in \mathbf{a} \quad \text{and} \quad (b_n) \in \mathbf{b}$$

then there is a class $\mathbf{ab}$ containing $(a_n b_n)$. This requires that we show that:

1. If (a_n) and (b_n) are Cauchy convergent, then $(a_n b_n)$ is Cauchy convergent.

Next we must show that for any sequence (a_n) in $\mathbf{a}$ and any sequence (b_n) in $\mathbf{b}$ then $(a_n b_n)$ is always in the same class $\mathbf{ab}$. This requires a proof of

2. If $(a_n) = (a_n')$ and $(b_n) = (b_n')$, then $(a_n b_n) = (a_n' b_n')$.

To prove 1, note that

$$|a_n b_n - a_m b_m| = |a_n b_n - a_n b_m + a_n b_m - a_m b_m|$$
$$\leq |a_n||b_n - b_m| + |b_m||a_n - a_m|.$$

Since (a_n) and (b_n) are Cauchy convergent, then for m and n large enough,

$$|a_n| < M, \quad |b_m| < M, \quad |a_n - a_m| < \frac{c}{2M}$$

and

$$|b_n - b_m| < \frac{c}{2M}$$

for some number M and any number $c > 0$. But then

$$|a_n b_n - a_m b_m| < c$$

and $(a_n b_n)$ is Cauchy convergent.

To prove 2, we assume

$$\lim (a_n - a'_n) = \lim (b_n - b'_n) = 0$$

and we must show that

$$\lim (a_n b_n - a'_n b'_n) = 0.$$

Note that

$$0 \le |a_n b_n - a'_n b'_n| = |a_n b_n - a_n b'_n + a_n b'_n - a'_n b'_n|$$

$$\le |a_n||b_n - b'_n| + |b'_n||b_n - b'_n|.$$

By reasoning similar to that in the paragraph above, the last expression has limit 0. Thus, by $Q15$–16,

$$\lim |a_n b_n - a'_n b'_n| = 0$$

so that the desired result follows if

$$\lim |f_n| = 0 \to \lim f_n = 0.$$

The proof of this is left to the reader.

Proofs of other properties in Sections 1 and 2 require similar constructions, and some are assigned as exercises.

EXERCISES

1. Enumerate and consider other contrary cases in the first part of the proof of $R1$. In each case show how the hypothesis is contradicted.

2. Show that the number L obtained at the end of the second part of the proof of $R1$ is common to all intervals $\mathcal{I}_n$ of the constructed sequence.

3. Of the four properties given on page 139, show that:

   (a) 1 and 3 are equivalent
   (b) 2 and 4 are equivalent.

4. Prove $R2$.

5. Prove properties $N1$–7 of negation for real numbers as they are listed in Section 2.

6. Prove properties $P1$–13 for the predicates p and q defined in this section. These properties are given in Section 2.

7. Prove that properties $O1$–11, 12′, 13 as listed in Section 1 hold for sums and products of real numbers.

8. Prove properties $O14$–21 as listed in Section 1 hold for differences and quotients of real numbers.

9. Extend the definition of exponentiation to the universe of real numbers so that the characteristic properties of this operation are preserved.

10. Define $\mathbf{a} > \mathbf{b}$ for real numbers $\mathbf{a}$ and $\mathbf{b}$ to mean that $p(\mathbf{a} - \mathbf{b})$ is true. Prove that if $\mathbf{a} > \mathbf{b}$, $(a_n) \in \mathbf{a}$ and $(b_n) \in \mathbf{b}$, then there is a number $N > 0$ such that $a_n > b_n$ whenever $n > N$.

11. Prove that if $\lim |f_n| = 0$, then $\lim f_n = 0$.

12 · COMPLETENESS OF THE REAL NUMBERS

In this section we consider the notions of limit and Cauchy convergence for sequences of real numbers, and prove that every Cauchy convergent sequence of real numbers has a limit. The definitions of these notions are exactly the same as for rationals.

DR3. A *real sequence* is an ordered pair $(\mathcal{C}, f)$, where $\mathcal{C}$ is a set of real numbers and f is a function with positive integers as domain and $\mathcal{C}$ as range. We denote a sequence by $(\mathbf{f_1}, \mathbf{f_2}, \ldots)$ as before, or briefly as $(\mathbf{f_n})$. The terms of a sequence are denoted by boldfaced letters to distinguish them from rational numbers that may enter the exposition to follow.

DR4. The real number $\mathbf{L}$ is the *limit* of the real sequence $(\mathbf{f_n})$ if given $\mathbf{c} > \mathbf{0}$ there is a number N so that $|\mathbf{f_n} - \mathbf{L}| < \mathbf{c}$ whenever $n < N$. In this case we write $\lim \mathbf{f_n} = \mathbf{L}$.

DR5. The real sequence $(\mathbf{f_n})$ is *Cauchy convergent* if given $\mathbf{c} > \mathbf{0}$ there is a number N such that $|\mathbf{f_n} - \mathbf{f_m}| < \mathbf{c}$ whenever $n > N$ and $m > N$.

From these definitions it follows as before that if a sequence has a limit, then the limit is unique and the sequence is Cauchy convergent. The properties $Q1$–25 of Sections 8 and 9 hold by proofs similar to those carried out there.

Before attempting to prove that every Cauchy convergent real sequence has a real limit we shall consider some preliminary properties of such sequences. Since each term of a real sequence $(\mathbf{f_n})$ is a real number, it is a class of Cauchy convergent rational sequences equivalent to each other in the sense of $DR1$. Let us denote any rational sequence belonging to the term f_j of the sequence (f_n) by (f_{jn}). Thus, if a rational number is represented by a letter with two subscripts, the second subscript refers to its position in a rational sequence and the first subscript refers to the position in a real sequence of the real number to which that rational sequence belongs. For example, f_{45} stands for a rational number that is the fifth term of some rational sequence chosen as some element of a real number f_4 that is the fourth term of some real sequence (f_n).

Every real sequence (f_n) gives rise to a great number of doubly infinite arrays such as

$$
\begin{array}{cccc}
f_{11} & f_{12} & f_{13} & \cdots \\
f_{21} & f_{22} & f_{23} & \cdots \\
f_{31} & f_{32} & f_{33} & \cdots \\
\cdots & \cdots & \cdots & \cdots
\end{array}
$$

where the numbers in the first row are terms of a rational sequence chosen from f_1, those of the second row are terms of a rational sequence chosen from f_2, and so on. The number of possible arrays is great because for any j, the numbers in the jth row may be terms of *any* rational sequence chosen from f_j. Having chosen one such array, we consider the rational sequence (d_n) such that for each n, $d_n = f_{nn}$. Since the terms of this sequence lie on a diagonal of the array, we call it a *diagonal sequence*. Every real sequence (f_n) gives rise to a great number of rational diagonal sequences, one for each distinct array. We establish two results for diagonal sequences.

$R4$. If (f_n) is a Cauchy convergent real sequence, then all of its rational diagonal sequences are Cauchy convergent.

Proof:

Let (d_n) be a diagonal sequence of (f_n). Then for each n, $d_n = f_{nn}$, a diagonal element of some doubly infinite array as above. We wish to show that if c is any positive number, then a number N can be found so that $|d_n - d_m| < c$ whenever $n > N$ and $m > N$. Now

$$|d_n - d_m| = |d_n - f_{mn} + f_{mn} - d_m| \leq |d_n - f_{mn}| + |f_{mn} - d_m|.$$

Thus, in the array

$$
\begin{array}{cccc}
d_1 & f_{12} & f_{13} & \cdots \\
f_{21} & d_2 & f_{23} & \cdots \\
f_{31} & f_{32} & d_3 & \cdots \\
\cdots & \cdots & \cdots & \cdots
\end{array}
$$

the difference of two diagonal terms is bounded by the sum of a difference $|d_n - f_{mn}|$ of two terms in the same column and a difference $|f_{mn} - d_m|$ of two terms in the same row. Suppose $c > 0$ is given. Since $(\mathbf{f}_n)$ is Cauchy convergent $|\mathbf{f}_n - \mathbf{f}_m| < \mathbf{c}/2$ if m and n are large enough. Since $|d_n - f_{mn}|$ is a term in a rational sequence belonging to $|\mathbf{f}_n - \mathbf{f}_m|$, this too must be less than $c/2$. Two terms in the same row are terms of the same Cauchy convergent rational sequence. Hence if n and m are large enough we have

$$|f_{mn} - d_m| < \frac{c}{2}.$$

Thus,

$$|d_n - d_m| < c$$

and the theorem is proved.

$R5.$ If (d_n) and (d_n') are two diagonal sequences of a Cauchy convergent real sequence $(\mathbf{f}_n)$, then $\lim (d_n - d_n') = 0$.

Proof:

Note that for each n, d_n and d_n' are corresponding terms of rational sequences that are elements of the same real number $\mathbf{f}_n$. The details of the proof are left to the reader.

According to $R4$–5 there is a unique real number $\mathbf{d}$ that contains all diagonal rational sequences of a Cauchy convergent real sequence $(\mathbf{f}_n)$. In the next theorem we show that $\lim \mathbf{f}_n = \mathbf{d}$, thus proving completeness.

$R6.$ Let $\mathbf{d}$ be the real number containing all diagonal sequences of a Cauchy convergent real sequence $(\mathbf{f}_n)$. Then $\lim \mathbf{f}_n = \mathbf{d}$.

Proof:

We must show that we can make $|\mathbf{f}_n - \mathbf{d}|$ as small as we wish for large n. A rational sequence that is an element of $|\mathbf{f}_n - \mathbf{d}|$ is $(|f_{nm} - d_m|)$. By an argument similar to that in the proof of $R4$, this sequence has limit 0. Thus,

$$\lim (\mathbf{f}_n - \mathbf{d}) = 0$$

and the theorem follows. The details of the proof are left to the reader.

We close with a discussion of two important properties of real numbers. Even though a definition of a positive real number in terms of the sequences it contains has been given, it is interesting that we are able to characterize positive real numbers in another useful way. We shall show that every positive number is a perfect square, and, since it is simple to show that every nonzero square is positive, we have the following property:

$$p(\mathbf{a}) \leftrightarrow (\text{E } \mathbf{b})(\mathbf{b} \neq 0 \wedge \mathbf{a} = \mathbf{b}^2).$$

For negative numbers we have

$$q(\mathbf{a}) \leftrightarrow (E\ \mathbf{b})(\mathbf{b} \neq \mathbf{0} \wedge \mathbf{a} = -\mathbf{b}^2).$$

Naturally we define $\mathbf{b}^2$ to be equal to $\mathbf{bb}$.

Using these properties, some of the usual properties of positives and negatives are immediate. Thus, for example

$$(-\mathbf{m}^2)(-\mathbf{n}^2) = (-\mathbf{mn})^2$$

proves that the product of two negative numbers is a positive number.

To show that every positive real number is the square of a number distinct from 0, let $\mathbf{p} > \mathbf{0}$ be a real number. Choose $\mathbf{b}_1 \in \mathfrak{R}^*$ so that

$$0 \leq \mathbf{b}_1^2 - \mathbf{p} < 1.$$

Choose $\mathbf{b}_2$ so that

$$0 \leq \mathbf{b}_2^2 - \mathbf{p} < \frac{1}{10}.$$

For each n, choose $\mathbf{b}_n$ so that

$$0 \leq \mathbf{b}_n^2 - \mathbf{p} < \frac{1}{10^{n-1}}.$$

Of course there are a variety of ways in which the sequence $(\mathbf{b}_n)$ may be chosen. One way is to choose $\mathbf{b}_n$ for each n so that it is the smallest number whose square is not less than $\mathbf{p}$ and differs from $\mathbf{p}$ by more than $1/10^{n-1}$. Of course the procedure of choosing some or all of the terms of (b_n) to be below p is also acceptable. What we must show is that each of the sequences (b_n) obtained in this way is Cauchy convergent and that all of the sequences belong to the same nonzero real number. Then we have a real number $b \neq 0$ such that whenever $(b_n) \in \mathbf{b}$, then $(b_n^2) \in \mathbf{p}$, so that $\mathbf{p} = \mathbf{b}^2$.

Now apparently $\lim \mathbf{b}_n^2 = \mathbf{p}$ by construction, so that (b_n^2) is a Cauchy convergent sequence. Since $b_n^2 > p$, $(b_n^2) \not\in \mathbf{0}$. It follows that $(b_n) \not\in \mathbf{0}$. But this means that there is a number M such that, for n large enough, $b_n > M$. Then $b_n + b_m > 2M$ when m and n are large enough. Now

$$|b_n - b_n| = \frac{|b_n^2 - b_m^2|}{|b_n + b_m|} < \frac{1}{2M} |b_n^2 - b_m^2|$$

which can be made as small as we please for large m and n, since (b_n^2) is Cauchy convergent.

Now let $(\mathbf{b}_n)$ and $(\mathbf{b}_n')$ be any two sequences constructed as above. Then

$$\lim \mathbf{b}_n^2 = \lim \mathbf{b}_n'^2 = \mathbf{p} \quad \text{and} \quad \lim (\mathbf{b}_n + \mathbf{b}_n') \neq \mathbf{0}$$

as before. Thus,

$$\lim (\mathbf{b}_n - \mathbf{b}'_n) = \frac{\lim (\mathbf{b}_n^2 - \mathbf{b}_n'^2)}{\lim (\mathbf{b}_n + \mathbf{b}'_n)} = 0$$

so that (b_n) and (b'_n) belong to the same real number.

Another important property of real numbers that follows from their completeness (in addition to those listed in Section 10) is the Heine-Borel *covering property*. Given any set $\mathcal{C}$, we say that a collection $\{\mathcal{I}_1, \mathcal{I}_2, \ldots\}$ of open intervals *covers* $\mathcal{C}$ if every element of $\mathcal{C}$ belongs to at least one interval in the collection. For example the interval $[0, 1]$ is not covered by the collection $\{(0, \frac{1}{2}), (\frac{1}{2}, 1)\}$ because in particular the numbers 0, $\frac{1}{2}$, and 1 are in neither of these open intervals. But $[0, 1]$ is covered by $\{(-\frac{1}{2}, .1), (0, .7), (.69, 1.1)\}$ and by the single interval $(-5, 5)$. See Figure 17.

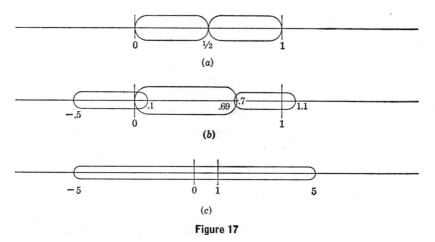

(a)

(b)

(c)

Figure 17

We shall use the Heine-Borel covering property later in the following form:

If a closed interval $[\mathbf{a}, \mathbf{b}]$ is covered by a collection $\mathcal{I}$ of open intervals, then a finite subcollection of $\mathcal{I}$ covers $[\mathbf{a}, \mathbf{b}]$.

We prove that this property follows from the nested interval property. Suppose a closed interval $[\mathbf{a}, \mathbf{b}]$ is given and is covered by a collection $\mathcal{I}$ of open intervals. If $\mathcal{I}$ is finite, then the proof is complete. Suppose, contrary to what must be proved, that $\mathcal{I}$ is infinite and that no finite subcollection of $\mathcal{I}$ covers $[\mathbf{a}, \mathbf{b}]$. If $[\mathbf{a}, \mathbf{b}]$ is bisected, at least one of its halves cannot be covered by a finite subcollection from $\mathcal{I}$. Call such a closed half interval of $[\mathbf{a}, \mathbf{b}]$ $\mathcal{I}_1$. In a similar way one of the halves of $\mathcal{I}_1$ cannot be covered by a finite subcollection taken from g. Call it g_2. Continue indefinitely, generating an infinite sequence (g_n) of closed nested intervals whose lengths have limit 0.

The intervals g_n are chosen so that no one of them can be covered by a finite subcollection from g. But by the nested interval property, there is a point $\mathbf{p}$ common to all of them. We have shown earlier that $\mathbf{p}$ is the limit of the sequence of right endpoints and of the sequence of left endpoints of the intervals g_n. Thus every neighborhood of $\mathbf{p}$ contains all but a finite number of intervals in the sequence (g_n). But $\mathbf{p}$ is an element of $[\mathbf{a}, \mathbf{b}]$ and so must be covered by some interval in the collection g. Call this interval g^*. Choose a neighborhood of $\mathbf{p}$ lying wholly within g^*. Then g^* covers all but a finite number of terms of (g_n) since it covers a neighborhood of $\mathbf{p}$. This contradicts the choice of (g_n) and proves the covering property.

EXERCISES

1. Complete the proof of $R5$.

2. Complete the proof of $R6$.

3. Show that for every real number $\mathbf{a}$, $q(\mathbf{a}) \leftrightarrow (\mathrm{E}\ \mathbf{b})(\mathbf{b} \neq 0 \wedge \mathbf{a} = -\mathbf{b}^2)$ is true.

4. Show that if $\mathbf{a} = \mathbf{b}^2$ and $\mathbf{b} \neq 0$, then $p(\mathbf{a})$ is true.

5. Using $(\mathrm{E}\ \mathbf{b})(\mathbf{b} \neq 0 \wedge \mathbf{a} = \mathbf{b}^2)$ as a definition of the predicate $p(\mathbf{a})$, prove that properties $P1$–13 of Section 2 hold.

6. Prove that if $(b_n^2) \not\subseteq 0$ then $(b_n) \not\subseteq 0$.

7. Show in the following way that the Heine-Borel property fails for open intervals.

   (a) Show that the collection of intervals $\{(0, 1),\ (0, \frac{3}{2}),\ (0, \frac{7}{4}),\ \ldots,$ $(0, (2 - \frac{1}{2}^{n-1}, \ldots,))\}$ covers $(0, 2)$.

   (b) No finite subcollection covers $(0, 2)$.

8. Show that the point $\mathbf{p}$ obtained at the end of the proof of the covering property must belong to the interval $[\mathbf{a}, \mathbf{b}]$.

BIBLIOGRAPHY

Dantzig, Number, *The Language of Science*, Macmillan 1959 (4th ed.).

Kerschner, Wilcox, *The Anatomy of Mathematics*, Ronald 1950.

Landau, *Foundations of Analysis*, Chelsea 1951.

Wilder, *Foundations of Mathematics*, Wiley 1952.

CHAPTER 3

Functions of One Real Argument

1 · THE ALGEBRA OF FUNCTIONS

In this chapter we examine some notions that relate to functions that have the set $\mathcal{R}$ of real numbers as image space and some subset $\mathcal{D}$ of $\mathcal{R}$ as domain. We shall denote such functions by letters and numerals in boldface type to distinguish them from real numbers and from variables in the universe $\mathcal{R}$. The present section investigates properties of operations and relations on the class $\mathcal{F}$ of functions of this type. Section 2 is concerned with graphs of functions, and with their symmetries, and Sections 3 and 4 introduce and examine limits of function values. Derivatives are investigated in Section 5 and definite integrals in Section 6. Section 7 deals with proofs that the definite integral of a function exists, and Section 8 considers antiderivatives, indefinite integrals and the fundamental theorem of calculus.

We begin with a new definition of the notion of function for purposes of this chapter.

*DF*1. Given a subset $\mathcal{D}$ of the set $\mathcal{R}$ of real numbers, a *real function* **f** with domain $\mathcal{D}$ is an assignment to each number in $\mathcal{D}$ of a unique number in $\mathcal{R}$. Each element of $\mathcal{D}$ is called an *argument* of **f** and each assigned number of $\mathcal{R}$ is a *value* of $\mathbf{f}$. The set $\mathcal{C}$ of all values of $\mathbf{f}$ is called the *range* or *image set* of $\mathbf{f}$. Given an argument a of $\mathbf{f}$, the value that $\mathbf{f}$ assigns to a is denoted by $\mathbf{f}(a)$.

A real function $\mathbf{f}$ may be defined by any device which permits us to check for a given ordered pair (a, b) whether or not $b = \mathbf{f}(a)$. One such device is a list of ordered pairs determined in this way by the function $\mathbf{f}$ being defined. Since for each argument a to value $\mathbf{f}(a)$ is unique, any such list must also satisfy the condition that (a, b) and (a, c) are in the list if and only if $b = c$.

Another device for defining functions is an open statement in the universe $\mathcal{R}^2$ of ordered pairs of real numbers. If a single function is to be defined this way, then (a, b) and (a, c) are in the solution set of the open statement if and only if $b = c$. When this is not the case the open statement is said to define several functions *implicitly*. Thus the equation $y^2 = x$ defines several functions implicitly since, for example, $(1, 1)$ and $(1, -1)$ are both in its solution set and $1 \neq -1$. However, $y^3 = x + 1$ defines a single function implicitly since

$$y_1^3 = y_2^3 \rightarrow y_1 = y_2$$

for all y_1 and y_2. If the open statement has the form $y = p(x)$, where $p(x)$ is an expression involving x as its only variable, then we say it defines a function *explicitly* since it provides a formula for computing the value that the function assigns to any one of its arguments a. Thus,

$$y = x^{1/2} \quad \text{and} \quad y = -x^{1/2}$$

define explicitly two of the functions defined implicitly by $y^2 = x$, and

$$y = \begin{cases} x^{1/2} & \text{on } [0, 4] \\ -x^{1/2} & \text{on } (4, \infty) \end{cases}$$

defines another. The equation $y = (x + 1)^{1/3}$ defines explicitly the function defined implicitly by $y^3 = x + 1$.

In the exposition to follow we use yet another device for defining functions, whose advantage is that it eliminates the need to use variables in the definitions and in operations to be defined for functions. Not all functions can be defined this way. However, we are satisfied to confine our attention to those that can, and among these are the explicitly definable algebraic functions. This device consists in defining certain basic functions outright and then providing operations on functions that can be used to define others. In order to define the basic functions we must specify their domains, and for each function provide a *mapping rule* that allows the determination of the value assigned to each argument.

DF2. We define the *identity function* **x** with domain $\Re$ to have the mapping rule: $(a)[\mathbf{x}(a) = a]$.

DF3. For each real number c, we define the *constant function* **c** with domain $\Re$ to have the mapping rule: $(a)[\mathbf{c}(a) = c]$.

DF4. We define the *absolute value* function **abs** with domain $\Re$ to have the mapping rule $(a)[\mathbf{abs}(a) = |a|]$.

DF5. We define the *greatest integer function* **int** with domain $\Re$ so that for each a, $\mathbf{int}(a) = [a]$, where $[a]$ is the greatest integer $n \leq a$.

We define a relation of equality for functions as follows:

DF6. If **f** and **g** are functions, then **f** *equals* **g** if and only if **f** and **g** have the same domain and, for each argument a, $\mathbf{f}(a) = \mathbf{g}(a)$. In this case we write $\mathbf{f} = \mathbf{g}$.

Note that **x** assigns every argument to itself as value. For each real number c, **c** assigns c to every argument. Thus, its range consists of the single number c. The function **abs** assigns to each argument its absolute value as value. For every integer n, the function **int** assigns n as value to each argument in the interval $[n, n + 1)$.

It may happen that two functions are equal on a subset of the common part of their domains. If, for example, **f** and **g** assign the same value to each argument of an interval (a, b), we write $\mathbf{f} = \mathbf{g}$ on (a, b). Note that

$$\mathbf{abs} = \begin{cases} \mathbf{x} & \text{on} \quad [0, \infty) \\ -\mathbf{x} & \text{on} \quad (-\infty, 0) \end{cases}$$

and

$$\mathbf{int} = \begin{cases} \cdots \\ -\mathbf{3} & \text{on } [-3, -2 \\ -\mathbf{2} & \text{on } [-2, -1 \\ -\mathbf{1} & \text{on } [-1, 0) \\ \mathbf{0} & \text{on } [0, 1) \\ \mathbf{1} & \text{on } [1, 2) \\ \mathbf{2} & \text{on } [2, 3) \\ \cdots \end{cases}$$

In defining operations on functions we must specify both how the domain of the result of the operation depends on the domains of the arguments of the operation and how the value for a given argument of the result is related to the values of the functions operated on. In what follows we denote the domain of a function $\mathbf{f}$ by $\mathfrak{D}_f$. Let $\mathbf{f}$ and $\mathbf{g}$ be functions and p be a real number.

DF7. The *sum* $\mathbf{f} + \mathbf{g}$ has domain $\mathfrak{D}_{f+g} = \mathfrak{D}_f \cap \mathfrak{D}_g$ and mapping rule

$$(\mathbf{f} + \mathbf{g})(a) = \mathbf{f}(a) + \mathbf{g}(a)$$

for each a in $\mathfrak{D}_{f+g}$.

DF8. The *difference* $\mathbf{f} - \mathbf{g}$ has domain $\mathfrak{D}_{f-g} = \mathfrak{D}_f \cap \mathfrak{D}_g$ and mapping rule

$$(\mathbf{f} - \mathbf{g})(a) = \mathbf{f}(a) - \mathbf{g}(a)$$

for each a in $\mathfrak{D}_{f-g}$.

DF9. The *product* $\mathbf{f} \cdot \mathbf{g}$ has domain $\mathfrak{D}_{fg} = \mathfrak{D}_f \cap \mathfrak{D}_g$ and mapping rule

$$(\mathbf{f} \cdot \mathbf{g})(a) = \mathbf{f}(a)\mathbf{g}(a)$$

for each a in $\mathfrak{D}_{fg}$.

DF10. The *quotient* $\mathbf{f}/\mathbf{g}$ has domain

$$\mathfrak{D}_{f/g} = (\mathfrak{D}_f \cap \mathfrak{D}_g) - \{a \,|\, \mathbf{g}(a) = 0\}$$

and mapping rule

$$(\mathbf{f}/\mathbf{g})(a) = \mathbf{f}(a)/\mathbf{g}(a)$$

for each a in $\mathfrak{D}_{f/g}$.

DF11. The *p-th multiple* $p\mathbf{f}$ has domain $\mathfrak{D}_{pf} = \mathfrak{D}_f$ and mapping rule

$$(p\mathbf{f})(a) = p[\mathbf{f}(a)]$$

for each a in $\mathfrak{D}_{pf}$.

DF12. The *p-th power* $\mathbf{f}^p$ has as domain $\mathfrak{D}_{f^p}$ the set of all arguments a of $\mathbf{f}$ for which $[\mathbf{f}(a)]^p$ is a real number, and mapping rule

$$(\mathbf{f}^p)(a) = [\mathbf{f}(a)]^p$$

for each a in $\mathfrak{D}_{f^p}$.

DF13. The *composition* $\mathbf{f}[\mathbf{g}]$ has as domain $\mathfrak{D}_{f[g]}$ the set of all arguments a of $\mathbf{g}$ for which $\mathbf{g}(a)$ is an argument of $\mathbf{f}$ and mapping rule

$$(\mathbf{f}[\mathbf{g}])(a) = \mathbf{f}(\mathbf{g}(a))$$

for each a in $\mathfrak{D}_{f[g]}$.

Note that from the domain of the quotient we exclude those arguments a of $\mathbf{g}$ for which $\mathbf{g}(a) = 0$ and that from the domain of $\mathbf{f}^p$ those arguments a of $\mathbf{f}$ for which $[\mathbf{f}(a)]^p$ is not defined. Thus, $\mathbf{abs}/\mathbf{x}$ cannot have 0 in its domain, since $\mathbf{x}(0) = 0$. Since 0 is the only exclusion, its domain is $(-\infty, 0) \cup (0, \infty)$. Note also that -5, for example, is not in the domain of $(2\mathbf{x} + 1)^{1/2}$, for $(2\mathbf{x} + 1)(-5) = -9$, and $(-9)^{1/2}$ is not a real number. Actually any number a for which $2a + 1 < 0$ is excluded from the domain of $(2\mathbf{x} + 1)^{1/2}$ for this reason. The set of all such numbers a is $(-\infty, -\frac{1}{2})$, so that the domain of this function is $[-\frac{1}{2}, \infty)$.

Note that the function $(-\mathbf{abs})^{1/2}$ has only 0 in its domain, since if $a \neq 0$,

$$-\mathbf{abs}(a) = -|a|$$

is negative and $(-\mathbf{abs}(a))^{1/2}$ is not a real number. The function $(-\mathbf{x}^2 - 1)^{1/2}$ has an empty domain. The limitations imposed on the domain of the result of a composition can be determined in a similar way.

Since these operations allow the construction of a great variety of functions from the basic functions at hand, it is not surprising that some of them should be equal. Thus, we can show that if $\mathbf{f}$ is any function, then

$$\mathbf{x}[\mathbf{f}] = \mathbf{f}[\mathbf{x}] = \mathbf{f}$$

for

$$(\mathbf{x}[\mathbf{f}])(a) = \mathbf{x}(\mathbf{f}(a)) = \mathbf{f}(a)$$
$$(\mathbf{f}[\mathbf{x}])(a) = \mathbf{f}(\mathbf{x}(a)) = \mathbf{f}(a)$$

using $DF2$ and $DF13$. We leave it to the reader to show that the domains of these three functions coincide. It can also be shown that for every real number p and real function $\mathbf{f}$,

$$\mathbf{f}^p = \mathbf{x}^p[\mathbf{f}]$$
$$p\mathbf{f} = p\mathbf{x}[\mathbf{f}]$$

and if p is a positive integer, then

$$\mathbf{f}^p = \mathbf{f}\cdot\mathbf{f}\cdot\mathbf{f}\cdots\mathbf{f} \quad \text{to} \quad p \text{ factors}$$
$$p\mathbf{f} = \mathbf{f} + \mathbf{f} + \mathbf{f} + \cdots + \mathbf{f} \quad \text{to} \quad p \text{ terms.}$$

An interesting class of functions among those defined above is the class of *polynomial functions* (with real coefficients). This class may be defined inductively as follows:

(a) $\mathbf{x}$ is a polynomial function
(b) for each real number c, $\mathbf{c}$ is a polynomial function
(c) If $\mathbf{f}$ and $\mathbf{g}$ are polynomial functions, then $\mathbf{f} + \mathbf{g}$ and $\mathbf{f}\cdot\mathbf{g}$ are polynomial functions.

Thus the class of polynomial functions may be thought of as the smallest class of functions closed under addition and multiplication and containing the identity function and all constant functions. A result of the properties above is that every polynomial function is equal to one of the form

$$c_n\mathbf{x}^n + c_{n-1}\mathbf{x}^{n-1} + \cdots + c_1\mathbf{x} + \mathbf{c_0}$$

with n a nonnegative integer, $c_1, c_2, \ldots, c_n$ real numbers, $c_n \neq 0$, and $\mathbf{c_0}$

a constant function. The integer n is called the *degree* of the polynomial function. If $n = c_n = 0$, then the polynomial is the function $\mathbf{0}$ and is assigned no degree. Polynomial functions of degree zero are constant functions, those of degree one, together with constant functions, are called *linear functions* and have the form $a\mathbf{x} + \mathbf{b}$ with $a \neq 0$. Polynomial functions of degree two are called *quadratic functions*. These have the standard form $a\mathbf{x}^2 + b\mathbf{x} + \mathbf{c}$, with $a \neq 0$.

If $b^2 - 4ac \geq 0$, then the quadratic function $a\mathbf{x}^2 + b\mathbf{x} + \mathbf{c}$ can be written as a product of two factors, both of which are linear functions. For, since $a \neq 0$, we have

$$a\mathbf{x}^2 + b\mathbf{x} + \mathbf{c} = a\left(\mathbf{x}^2 + \frac{b\mathbf{x}}{a} + \frac{\mathbf{c}}{a}\right)$$

$$= a\left[\mathbf{x}^2 + \frac{b}{a}\mathbf{x} + \frac{\mathbf{b}^2}{4a^2} - \left(\frac{\mathbf{b}^2}{4a^2} - \frac{\mathbf{c}}{a}\right)\right]$$

$$= a\left[\left(\mathbf{x} - \frac{\mathbf{b}}{2a}\right)^2 - \frac{(\mathbf{b}^2 - 4\mathbf{ac})}{4a^2}\right]$$

$$= a\left[\mathbf{x} - \frac{-\mathbf{b} + (\mathbf{b}^2 - 4\mathbf{ac})^{1/2}}{2a}\right]$$

$$\cdot \left[\mathbf{x} - \frac{-\mathbf{b} - (\mathbf{b}^2 - 4\mathbf{ac})^{1/2}}{2a}\right].$$

If $b^2 - 4ac < 0$, then its square root is not a real number so the factorization is not possible in the universe $\mathfrak{R}$. In this case we say that the quadratic is *prime*.

A real number a is called a *zero* of a function $\mathbf{f}$ if $\mathbf{f}(a) = 0$. A nonzero constant function has no zeros. Every first degree linear function $a\mathbf{x} + \mathbf{b}$ ($a \neq 0$) has one real zero, namely $-b/a$. If $b^2 - 4ac \geq 0$, then the quadratic $a\mathbf{x}^2 + b\mathbf{x} + \mathbf{c}$ ($a \neq 0$) has zeros that coincide with those of its linear factors, namely

$$\frac{-b \pm (b^2 - 4ac)^{1/2}}{2a}$$

and these are equal when $b^2 - 4ac = 0$. If $b^2 - 4ac < 0$, then the quadratic function has no real zeros.

Let $\mathbf{q}$ be any polynomial function of degree greater than one. Then in some domain not including a real number a,

$$\frac{\mathbf{q}}{\mathbf{x} - \mathbf{a}} = \mathbf{r} + \frac{\mathbf{q}_1}{\mathbf{x} - \mathbf{a}}$$

where $\mathbf{r}$ and $\mathbf{q}_1$ are polynomials. Here $\mathbf{r}$ is the quotient and $\mathbf{q}_1$ the remainder on dividing $\mathbf{q}$ by $\mathbf{x} - \mathbf{a}$. It follows that

$$\mathbf{q} = (\mathbf{x} - \mathbf{a})\mathbf{r} + \mathbf{q}_1$$

is also true in this domain. We shall show later that this equation holds at a as well. Thus at a, $\mathbf{q}(a) = \mathbf{q}_1(a)$, so that if a is a zero of $\mathbf{q}$, then $\mathbf{q}_1(a) = 0$ and $(\mathbf{x} - \mathbf{a})$ is a factor of $\mathbf{q}$. Obviously, if $\mathbf{x} - \mathbf{a}$ is a factor of $\mathbf{q}$, then $\mathbf{q}(a) = 0$. Hence a is a zero of $\mathbf{q}$, if and only if $\mathbf{x} - \mathbf{a}$ is a factor of $\mathbf{q}$.

If $(\mathbf{x} - \mathbf{a})^r$ for some positive integer r is a factor of a polynomial $\mathbf{q}$, but $(\mathbf{x} - \mathbf{a})^{r+1}$ is not a factor, we say that r is the *multiplicity* of the zero a and of the factor $\mathbf{x} - \mathbf{a}$ in $\mathbf{q}$. Every polynomial may be expressed in a unique way as a product containing a factor $(\mathbf{x} - \mathbf{a})^r$ for every zero a of multiplicity r in $\mathbf{q}$. Thus, if a polynomial is represented in factored form it is immediately apparent what are its zeros and their multiplicities.

If $\mathbf{p}$ and $\mathbf{q}$ are polynomial functions of degrees m and n respectively, then $\mathbf{p}/\mathbf{q}$ is called a *rational function*. It can be shown that rational functions are closed under sums, differences, products, quotients, and compositions, and that each rational function $\mathbf{p}/\mathbf{q}$ is equal to one of the form $\mathbf{r} + (\mathbf{p}_1/\mathbf{q})$, where $\mathbf{r}$ is a polynomial function of degree $m - n$ if $m > n$, a constant function if $m = n$, and $\mathbf{0}$ otherwise, and $\mathbf{p}_1$ is a polynomial of degree less than n.

Thus, for example, we have

$$\frac{\mathbf{x}^3 - 2\mathbf{x}^2 + \mathbf{x} - 6}{\mathbf{x}^2 + 4} = \frac{\mathbf{x}^3 + 4\mathbf{x} - 2(\mathbf{x}^2 + 4) - 3\mathbf{x} + 2}{\mathbf{x}^2 + 4}$$

$$= \mathbf{x} - 2 + \frac{-3\mathbf{x} + 2}{\mathbf{x}^2 + 4}.$$

This can be verified by long division.

EXERCISES

1. Define each of the functions $\mathbf{x}$, $\mathbf{c}$, $\mathbf{abs}$, and $\mathbf{int}$ by describing a list of ordered pairs and by an open statement in the universe $\mathfrak{R}^2$.

2. Which of the following functions are equal: $5, 55, 5 \cdot 5, 5[5]$? Give reasons for your answer.

3. What is the domain of each of the following functions?

   (a) $\mathbf{x} + (1/\mathbf{x})$
   (b) $\mathbf{x} - (\mathbf{x} + 1)^{1/2}$
   (c) $(2\mathbf{x} + 1)^{1/3} - (1/\mathbf{abs})$
   (d) $(\mathbf{x}^2)^{1/2}$

(e) $(\mathbf{x}^{1/2})^2$

(f) $(3\mathbf{x} + 1)^{1/2}$

(g) $1/(3\mathbf{x} + 1)^{1/2}$

4. Find the largest domain in which the following equalities are true:

(a) $\mathbf{abs}/\mathbf{x} = 1$

(b) $\mathbf{abs}/\mathbf{x} = -1$

(c) $\mathbf{x}/\mathbf{x} = 1$

(d) $(\mathbf{x}^2)^{1/2} = \mathbf{x}$

(e) $(\mathbf{x}^{1/2})^2 = \mathbf{x}$

(f) $(\mathbf{x}^2)^{1/2} = \mathbf{abs}$

(g) $(\mathbf{x}^2)^{1/2} = -\mathbf{x}$

(h) $\mathbf{int} = 105$

(i) $(\mathbf{x}^2 - 4)/(\mathbf{x} + 2) = \mathbf{x} - 2$.

5. Prove that for any function $\mathbf{f}$ and any real number p, $\mathbf{x}^p[\mathbf{f}] = \mathbf{f}^p$ and $p\mathbf{x}[\mathbf{f}] = p\mathbf{f}$.

6. Prove that if p is a positive integer and $\mathbf{f}$ is any function, then $p\mathbf{f} = \mathbf{f} + \mathbf{f} + \cdots + \mathbf{f}$ (to p terms) and $\mathbf{f}^p = \mathbf{f} \cdot \mathbf{f} \cdots \mathbf{f}$ (to p terms).

7. Show that the class of polynomial functions is closed under sums, products, differences, multiples, positive integer powers, and compositions.

8. Show that the domain of every polynomial is $\mathfrak{R}$.

9. Show that the class of rational functions is closed under sums, products, differences, quotients, multiples, all integer powers, and compositions.

10. If $\mathbf{p}/\mathbf{q}$ is any rational function and $\mathfrak{z}$ is the set of zeros of $\mathbf{q}$, then the domain of $\mathbf{p}/\mathbf{q}$ is $\mathfrak{R} - \mathfrak{z}$.

11. We say that a function $\mathbf{f}$ is *positive* and write $\mathbf{f} > 0$ if $\mathbf{f}(a) > 0$ for every argument a, and that $\mathbf{f}$ is *negative* ($\mathbf{f} < 0$) if $\mathbf{f}(a) < 0$ for every argument a. Give an example of a function that is

(a) positive

(b) negative

(c) neither positive nor negative.

12. Show that the function $a\mathbf{x} + b$ is positive in $(-b/a, \infty)$ and negative in $(-\infty, -b/a)$ if $a > 0$. Describe the situation if $a < 0$.

13. Show that if $a\mathbf{x}^2 + b\mathbf{x} + \mathbf{c}$ ($a \neq 0$) is a prime quadratic, then it is positive if $a > 0$ and negative if $a < 0$.

14. Show that if $a\mathbf{x}^2 + b\mathbf{x} + \mathbf{c}$ ($a \neq 0$) has a single zero M of multiplicity two, then it is positive on $(-\infty, M) \cup (M, \infty)$ if $a > 0$, and negative there if $a < 0$.

15. Describe the situation in a way similar to Exercises 13 and 14 for a quadratic polynomial that has two distinct zeros.

16. Use procedures similar to those in Exercises 13–15 to develop a technique for determining domains in which $\mathbf{f} > 0$ and $\mathbf{f} < 0$ in case

   (a) $\mathbf{f}$ is any polynomial function
   (b) $\mathbf{f}$ is any rational function.

17. Use the result of Exercise 16 to find domains in which the following inequalities are true:

   (a) $\mathbf{x}^2 - 3\mathbf{x} + 2 > 0$
   (b) $\mathbf{x} - (1/\mathbf{x}) < 0$
   (c) $\mathbf{x} + 3/(\mathbf{x} + 4) > 0$
   (d) $\dfrac{(\mathbf{x} - 1)^2(\mathbf{x} + 5)}{\mathbf{x}^3(\mathbf{x} - 3)^4} < 0.$

2 · GRAPHS OF FUNCTIONS

Given a coordinate system with two axes, we define the *graph* of a function as the set of points with coordinates $(a, \mathbf{f}(a))$ on the plane determined by the two axes, where a is any argument of $\mathbf{f}$. Since the horizontal scale is the graph of arguments and the vertical scale the graph of values of $\mathbf{f}$, we call the first the *domain axis* and the second the *range axis* and label them as D and R, respectively, as in Figure 18. The important property

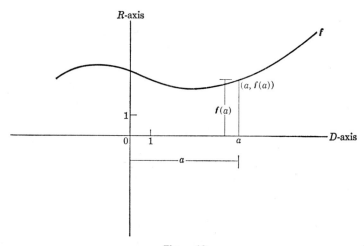

Figure 18

that distinguishes graphs of functions from graphs of open statements is that the graph of a function must cross no vertical line more than once. This is because each vertical line in the plane that determines an argument also determines a unique value. If a vertical line crossed a graph more than once, say in the points (a, b) and (a, d), then

$$b = \mathbf{f}(a) = d$$

which is impossible if the points are distinct.

If the graph of a function crosses no horizontal line more than once, a similar argument shows that no value is assigned to more than one argument. Such a function is a one-one correspondence, and there is a function that is its inverse. Figure 19 illustrates these possibilities.

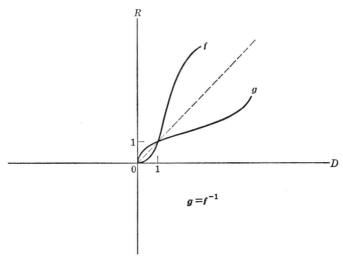

Figure 19

The graphs of **x**, **3**, **abs**, and **int** are illustrated in Figure 20. Of course one may always attempt to sketch the graph of a function by plotting a number of its points and joining these with a smooth curve. This method works for many simple functions, but is not always reliable. In this section we consider general properties of functions that enable us to feel more certain that the graphs we obtain are correct.

The principal purpose for sketching the graph of a function is to obtain at a glance a great number of helpful bits of information about the behavior of the function. For one thing, we might be interested in whether a function reproduces the pattern of its values in some interval in a related way in another interval. This question is related to *symmetry* of a graph. Our interest may be in whether the values of a function at arguments near a given number get arbitrarily close to some number, or arbitrarily large or small. We can also become interested in whether the

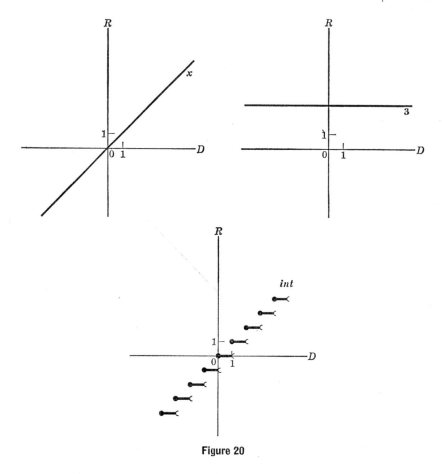

Figure 20

graph of a function has breaks in it and what kinds of breaks these are, or whether the graph of a function always stays between two given horizontal lines.

Let us note first, from the definition of sum of two functions, that if the graphs of **f** and **g** are known, then the graph of **f** + **g** may be sketched easily. This is because

$$(\mathbf{f} + \mathbf{g})(a) = \mathbf{f}(a) + \mathbf{g}(a)$$

so the distance from the D-axis to the **f** + **g** graph at any argument is the sum of the distances to the **f** and **g** curves separately. Thus, if the graphs of **f** and **g** are sketched on the same set of axes, as in Figure 21, points on the graph of **f** + **g** can be determined at several arguments and the curve connecting them can be fairly accurately sketched by

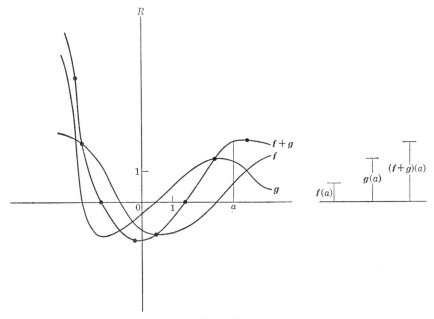

Figure 21

noting characteristics of **f** and **g**. We illustrate this by sketching graphs of **x + abs**, **x − int**, and **x² − x** in Figure 22. Note that among the most interesting arguments are those at which the graphs of **f** and **g** cross, or at which either of them crosses the *D*-axis. Note also that if **f** > **0**, then the graph of **f + g** lies above the graph of **g**.

This principle has an important consequence if **g** is a constant function, for in this case, the graphs of **f** and **f + g** can be made to coincide by moving either graph |g| units toward the other. Figure 23 illustrates this in sketches of **x²** and **x² + 2**. Thus the graph of **f + c** is congruent to the graph of **f** and *c* units above it if *c* > 0 and −*c* units below it if *c* < 0.

Another function whose graph is similarly related to the graph of a function **f** is **f[x + c]**, for some constant function *c*. We have

$$(\mathbf{f[x + c]})(a - c) = \mathbf{f}(a - c + c) = \mathbf{f}(a)$$

so that the graph of **f[x + c]** at *a* − *c* has the same height as that of the graph of **f** at *a*. This means that the graph of **f[x + c]** is congruent to the graph of **f** and *c* units to the left of it if *c* > 0 and −*c* units to the right of it if *c* < 0.

We can illustrate these principles by sketching the graph of **x² + 4x + 9**. We might consider this function first as the sum of **x²**

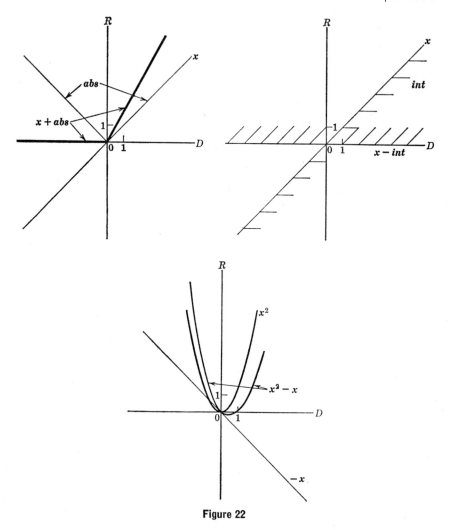

Figure 22

and $4\mathbf{x} + \mathbf{9}$, graphing these and adding ordinates as in Figure 24. On the other hand, let us note that

$$\mathbf{x}^2 + 4\mathbf{x} + \mathbf{9} = (\mathbf{x} + \mathbf{2})^2 + \mathbf{5}$$

so that the graph of this function is found by moving the graph of $\mathbf{x}^2$ two units to the left to get the graph of $(\mathbf{x} + \mathbf{2})^2$ and then five units up. The order of these translations can be reversed.

Other useful relations between graphs of functions are called *symmetries*, of which we consider two kinds:

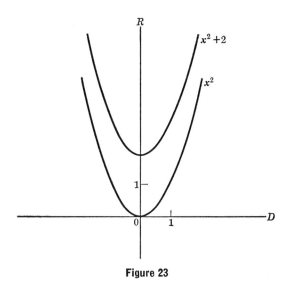

Figure 23

1. Two graphs are symmetric in a line l if every perpendicular to l cuts the graph in points on opposite sides of and equally far from l, provided it cuts either graph.

2. Two graphs are symmetric in a point p if every line through p cuts

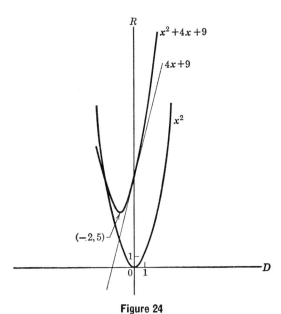

Figure 24

the graphs in points on opposite sides of and equally far from p, provided it cuts either graph.

Let $\mathbf{f}$ and $\mathbf{g}$ be functions. Then their graphs are symmetric in the D-axis if and only if $\mathbf{f} = -\mathbf{g}$, for in this case the value $\mathbf{f}(a) = -\mathbf{g}(a)$ for each argument a and the points of the two graphs on a vertical line lie on opposite sides and equally far from the D-axis.

In a similar way one may show that the graphs of $\mathbf{f}$ and $\mathbf{g}$ are symmetric in the R-axis if and only if

$$\mathbf{f} = \mathbf{g}[-\mathbf{x}]$$

for then

$$\mathbf{f}(a) = \mathbf{g}(-a)$$

for every argument a. The condition for symmetry in the origin is that $\mathbf{f} = -\mathbf{g}[-\mathbf{x}]$.

We say that a graph is symmetric in a line or a point if it is symmetric to itself in that line or point. If the graph of a function $\mathbf{f}$ is to be symmetric in the D-axis, then $\mathbf{f} = -\mathbf{f}$ must be true. But then $2\mathbf{f} = \mathbf{0}$ or $\mathbf{f} = \mathbf{0}$, since $\mathbf{2}$ never takes the value $\mathbf{0}$. Thus the only function whose graph is symmetric in the D-axis is the function $\mathbf{0}$.

If the graph of $\mathbf{f}$ is to be symmetric in the R-axis, we must have $\mathbf{f} = \mathbf{f}[-\mathbf{x}]$ true. Any such function is said to be *even* since examples are the functions $\mathbf{x}^n$, where n is an even integer. For note that

$$\mathbf{x}^n(-a) = (-a)^n = a^n$$

when n is even, so that

$$\mathbf{x}^n[-\mathbf{x}] = \mathbf{x}^n.$$

Even functions have the property that the portion of their graph to the left of the R-axis is the mirror image of the portion to the right.

If the graph of $\mathbf{f}$ is to be symmetric in the origin, we must have $\mathbf{f} = -\mathbf{f}[-\mathbf{x}]$ true. Any such function is said to be *odd* since examples are the functions $\mathbf{x}^n$ with n an odd integer. Properties of even and odd functions are explored in the exercises.

We consider now some relations between linear functions and their graphs. If a straight line through the origin is nonvertical, then it can be characterized by its slope, a number that indicates the number of units of vertical change in traversing the line from any point to a point one horizontal unit away. Let m be the slope of a nonvertical line through the origin. Since this line crosses no vertical more than once it is the graph of some function $\mathbf{f}$. Let $t \neq 0$ be an argument of $\mathbf{f}$. Then we must have

$$\mathbf{f}(t)/t = m$$

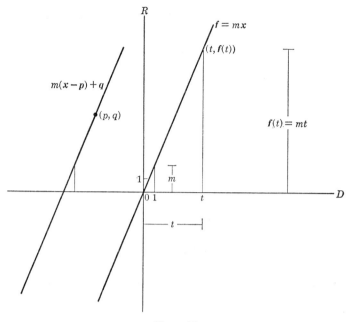

Figure 25

if $(t, \mathbf{f}(t))$ is to lie on the line, using similar triangles as in Figure 25. Then $\mathbf{f}(t) = mt$, and since the line goes through the origin, this equation is true even when $t = 0$. Thus, if a line through the origin has slope m, then it is the graph of $m\mathbf{x}$.

Consider now a line through the point (p, q) having slope m. This line may be obtained by translating the graph of $m\mathbf{x}$ $|p|$ units to the right if $p > 0$ and to the left if $p < 0$ and $|q|$ units up if $q > 0$ and down if $q < 0$. Hence this line is the graph of

$$m(\mathbf{x} - \mathbf{p}) + \mathbf{q}.$$

Given a function $\mathbf{f}$ we might ask if there is a horizontal line such that the graph of $\mathbf{f}$ is as close as we please to the line for arguments that are chosen large enough, but does not coincide with the graph of $\mathbf{f}$ for these arguments. If there is such a line we call it a *horizontal asymptote* of the graph of $\mathbf{f}$. Since every horizontal line is the graph of a constant function $\mathbf{k}$ the question we ask is whether, for any number $c > 0$, we can show that for large enough arguments t

$$|\mathbf{f}(t) - k| < c.$$

Note that this is exactly the same question we ask when we want to know whether a sequence has a limit. The only difference is that the terms of a sequence are values of a function for positive integer arguments only, while here any real number can be an argument.

What we are asking is whether given $c > 0$ there is a number N such that $t > N \rightarrow |\mathbf{f}(t) - k| < c$ is true. If this can be shown we say that k is the *limit of* $\mathbf{f}$ *at infinity* and write $\lim_{\infty} \mathbf{f} = k$. The reason for the subscript ∞ is to distinguish this notion of limit from others we consider in the following sections.

Because of the similarity of this notion of limit and the notion of limit of a sequence, the properties $Q1$–25 of Sections 8–9, Chapter 2, hold without change. If $\lim_{\infty} \mathbf{f} = k$, then the graph of $\mathbf{f}$ gets closer and closer to the horizontal line at height k the larger the argument chosen.

Since the properties $Q1$–25 hold, it is easy to see that

$$\lim_{\infty} \frac{x^2 + 1}{x^2 - 1} = 1$$

so that the graph of $\mathbf{1}$ is a horizontal asymptote to the graph of $\dfrac{x^2 + 1}{x^2 - 1}$. See Figure 26.

Analogous to $\lim_{\infty} \mathbf{f} = k$ we define $\lim_{-\infty} \mathbf{f} = k$ so that the difference

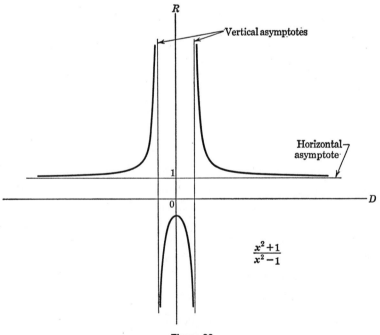

Figure 26

$|\mathbf{f}(t) - k|$ can be made as small as we please by choosing the argument t *small* enough. Thus, given $c > 0$, if there is a number M such that $t < M \rightarrow |\mathbf{f}(t) - k| < c$, we say that the *limit at minus infinity of* $\mathbf{f}$ *is* k and write $\lim_{-\infty} \mathbf{f} = k$. This means that the vertical distance between the graph of $\mathbf{f}$ and the horizontal line through k is small when the argument is far to the left of the coordinate system.

EXERCISES

1. Sketch the graph of each of the following functions:
   - (a) $\mathbf{x}^{1/2}$
   - (b) $\mathbf{x}^{1/3}$
   - (c) $\mathbf{x}^3$
   - (d) $\mathbf{x}^2$
   - (e) $(4 - \mathbf{x}^2)^{1/2}$.

2. Using the addition principle and the graphs sketched in Exercise 1, sketch graphs of the following functions:
   - (a) $\mathbf{x}^2 + \mathbf{x}^{1/2}$
   - (b) $\mathbf{x}^3 + \mathbf{x}^2$
   - (c) $\mathbf{x}^{1/3} + \mathbf{x}^{1/2}$
   - (d) $\mathbf{x}^2 + (4 - \mathbf{x}^2)^{1/2}$
   - (e) $\mathbf{x}^2 - \mathbf{x}^3$.

3. Using the addition principle, sketch the following graphs:
   - (a) $\mathbf{x} + \mathbf{int}$
   - (b) $\mathbf{int} - \mathbf{x}$
   - (c) $\mathbf{x}^2 + \mathbf{int}$
   - (d) $\mathbf{x}^2 - \mathbf{int}$
   - (e) $\mathbf{x} + \mathbf{abs}$
   - (f) $2\mathbf{x} - \mathbf{abs}$.

4. Using the translation principle and the results of Exercise 1, sketch the following graphs:
   - (a) $(\mathbf{x} + 3)^{1/2} - 1$
   - (b) $2 + (\mathbf{x} - 4)^{1/3}$
   - (c) $(\mathbf{x} - 7)^3 + 3$
   - (d) $\mathbf{x}^2 + 2\mathbf{x} - 4$
   - (e) $7 + (4 - (\mathbf{x} + 1)^2)^{1/2}$.

5. For each function $\mathbf{f}$ listed below find functions whose graphs are symmetric to the graph of $\mathbf{f}$ in the D-axis, the R-axis, and the origin. Sketch all graphs.

(a) $2x + 3$

(b) $x^2 - 3x$

(c) $abs + 2$

6. Let f and g be even functions and h and j be odd functions. Prove that:

(a) $f + g$, fg, hj, $f[g]$, $f[h]$, f/g, h/j are even functions

(b) $h + j$, fh, g/j, $h[j]$ are odd functions.

7. Prove that $mx + b$ is even if and only if $m = 0$ and odd if and only if $b = 0$.

8. Find a function that is both even and odd.

9. Prove that a one-one correspondence f and its inverse g have graphs that are symmetric in the graph of x.

10. Prove that if s and t are any real numbers with $s + t = 1$, then the graph of $s(ax + b) + t(cx + d)$ passes through the point of intersection of the graphs of $ax + b$ and $cx + d$. Comment on the situation in case these two graphs coincide or fail to intersect.

11. Evaluate the following limits, and sketch the graph of the given function indicating horizontal asymptotes.

(a) $\lim_{\infty} x^2/(1 - x^2)$

(b) $\lim_{\infty} x^3/(3 + x^3)$

(c) $\lim_{\infty} (2 + x)/(x - 1)$

(d) $\lim_{\infty} 3x^2/(5 - 2x + x^2)$

12. We say that f *is greater than* g ($f > g$) if $f - g$ is a positive function. Find the domain, if there is one, in which the first function listed is greater than the second.

(a) x^2, x^3

(b) x^2, $x^{1/2}$

(c) $2x + 3$, $x - 1$

(d) x^2, x

Prove your results.

13. A function f is *bounded above* if there is a constant function k such that $k \geq f$, and is *bounded below* if there is a constant function k such that $f \geq k$. If f is bounded both above and below then it is *bounded*. Show that if f is bounded in an interval, then its graph is contained between two horizontal lines there. For each function in Exercises 1–5 tell whether it is bounded, bounded above, or bounded below over its entire domain.

14. Prove that the only bounded linear function is 0.

15. A function is *monotonic increasing* if $\mathbf{f}(a) \geq \mathbf{f}(b)$ whenever $a > b$, and *monotonic decreasing* if $\mathbf{f}(a) \leq \mathbf{f}(b)$ whenever $a > b$. Show that if $\mathbf{f}$ is monotonic increasing in an interval, then the height of its graph cannot decrease for increasing arguments there. Describe the situation for monotonic decreasing functions. For the functions in Exercises 1–5, find intervals over which each is monotonic increasing and those over which it is monotonic decreasing.

16. $\mathbf{fg} = \mathbf{0}$ and $\mathbf{g} \neq \mathbf{0}$, can we conclude that $\mathbf{f} = \mathbf{0}$? Explain.

3 · LIMITS OF FUNCTION VALUES

In the preceding section the notion of limit of function values at infinity was introduced. We noted that this notion was entirely analogous to the notion of the limit of a sequence, since the terms of a sequence are values of a function. The only distinction between these two ideas is that the domains of functions that define sequences consist only of positive integers, while the functions that concern us here take real numbers as arguments. However, if a function $\mathbf{f}$ has in its domain all real numbers greater than a given number a, then the definition of $\lim_{\infty} \mathbf{f}$ is exactly the same as the definition of $\lim_{\infty} f_n$ for a sequence (f_n), and, as a result, the properties of $Q1$–25 of limits hold for the new notion of limit. Similar remarks hold for $\lim_{-\infty} \mathbf{f}$, for we can show that if this limit exists, then it is equal to $\lim_{\infty} \mathbf{f}[-\mathbf{x}]$.

Since the real numbers are dense, it is possible and useful to introduce the notion of the limit of a function $\mathbf{f}$ near an argument a so that it also has the properties $Q1$–25. The present section is devoted to this task.

If k is a real number, $\mathbf{f}$ a real function, and a an argument of $\mathbf{f}$ such that each point in the interval (a, b) for some number $b > a$ is also an argument of $\mathbf{f}$, we ask if the value $\mathbf{f}(t)$ is close to k when t is close to a. Again we are interested in showing that we can make $|\mathbf{f}(t) - k|$ as small as we wish, but the condition on t is not that it be large, as with $\lim_{\infty} \mathbf{f}$, but rather that it be close to a. Thus we wish to know if for any neighborhood of k we can find a neighborhood of a so that every argument to the right of a in the latter, except possibly a, is assigned a value by $\mathbf{f}$ that lies in the former interval. Figure 27 illustrates this idea. Note that we are interested only in values of $\mathbf{f}$ for arguments greater than and close to a. The value of $\mathbf{f}$ at a or at arguments to the left of a do not interest us at all.

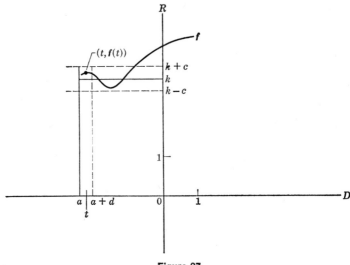

Figure 27

If k has the property described above for some function $\mathbf{f}$ and argument a we call k the *limit of $\mathbf{f}$ at a from the right* and write $k = \lim_{a+} \mathbf{f}$.
Thus, using algebraic notation, we define the statement $\lim_{a+} \mathbf{f} = k$ to mean

$$(c)[c > 0 \rightarrow (\text{E } d)(t)(0 < t - a < d \rightarrow |\mathbf{f}(t) - k| < c)].$$

Note that $0 < t - a < d$ means that t is in the interval $(a, a + d)$ lying to the right of a.

This notion of limit is important in cases in which we wish to approximate k by values of $\mathbf{f}$ near a to within c. If $\lim_{a+} \mathbf{f} = k$, then we know that if t is less than d units from a and to the right of a, then the desired accuracy is guaranteed. Thus, for example, $\lim_{0+} \mathbf{x}^{1/2} = 0$, since we can make

$$|t^{1/2} - 0| = t^{1/2}$$

as small as we please by making $t - 0 = t$ small enough and positive. In fact, if we wish to make $t^{1/2} < c$, where $c > 0$, we need take any argument t such that $0 < t < c^2$. The fact that $x^{1/2}(0) = 0$ is convenient, as we shall see, but completely beside the point. The fact is that $\lim_{0+} x^{1/2}$ is independent of what $x^{1/2}(0)$ is. Let

$$\mathbf{f} = \begin{cases} \mathbf{122} & \text{at} \quad 0 \\ \mathbf{x}^{1/2} & \text{on} \quad (0, \infty) \end{cases}$$

then $\lim_{0+} \mathbf{f} = 0$, by the above argument, since $\mathbf{f}$ differs from $\mathbf{x}^{1/2}$ only at the argument 0. See Figure 28.

We define an analogous notion for cases in which we are primarily

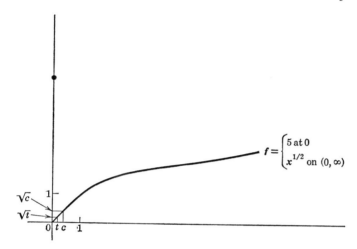

Figure 28

interested in approximating k by values of $\mathbf{f}$ at arguments close to and to the left of a. Then we must confine the argument t to some interval $(a - d, a)$ for some $d > 0$ in order to obtain the desired accuracy. Accordingly we say that k *is the limit of* $\mathbf{f}$ *at a from the left* if

$$(c)[c > 0 \rightarrow (\mathrm{E}\, d)(t)(0 < a - t < d \rightarrow |\mathbf{f}(t) - k| < c)]$$

is true. Note that $0 < a - t < d$ means that t is in the interval $(a - d, a)$.

For example, $\lim_{2-} \mathbf{int} = 1$, because $\mathbf{int}(t) = 1$ when t is in a small enough interval $(2 - d, 2)$ to the left of 2. Note that $\lim_{0-} \mathbf{x}^{1/2}$ does not exist, since $\mathbf{x}^{1/2}$ has no argument to the left of 0.

One can determine left-hand and right-hand limits of a function $\mathbf{f}$ at an argument a by glancing at a graph. Figure 29 shows functions $\mathbf{f}$ such that

$$\lim_{a-} \mathbf{f} = b \quad \text{and} \quad \lim_{a+} \mathbf{f} = c$$

in (a), $b > c$, in (b) $b = c$, and in (c) $b < c$.

If in approximating k by values of $\mathbf{f}$ at a there is no reason to specify that the argument is to be chosen from one side of a or the other, then to obtain the desired degree of accuracy we need specify only that t is in some interval with a at its center. For a positive number d, such an

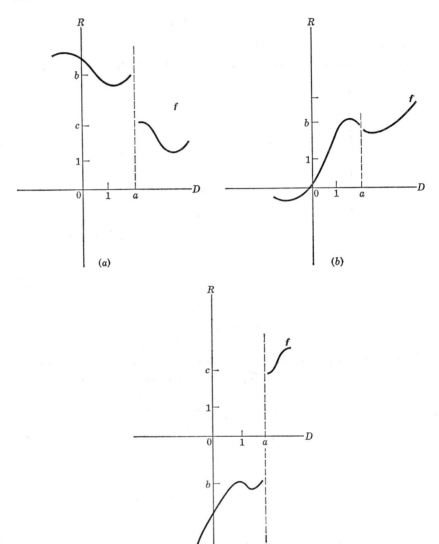

(a)

(b)

(c)

Figure 29

interval is $(a - d, a + d)$. Since we wish t to be a member of this interval, and since we are not concerned with $\mathbf{f}(a)$ itself we must have $0 < |t - a| < d$ true. Thus we say that k is *the limit of* $\mathbf{f}$ *at* a and write $k = \lim_{a} \mathbf{f}$ if and only if

$$(c)[c > 0 \rightarrow (\mathrm{E}\ d)(t)(0 < |t - a| < d \rightarrow |\mathbf{f}(t) - k| < c)]$$

is true.

Note that $\lim_{2} \mathbf{int}$ does not exist, since there is no interval centered at 2 such that all arguments t in the interval give values $\mathbf{int}(t)$ near some number. This is because the left-hand and right-hand limits of $\mathbf{int}$ at 2 are distinct. Note also that $\lim_{0} \mathbf{x}^{1/2}$ does not exist because the function is not defined for every argument in some neighborhood of 0. However,

$$\lim_{2} 3\mathbf{x} = 6$$

since if $c > 0$, $|3t - 6| < c$ whenever

$$0 < |t - 2| < c/3.$$

Thus, arguments in the interval $(2 - c/3, 2 + c/3)$ give values of the function $3\mathbf{x}$ in the interval $(6 - c, 6 + c)$. See Figure 30.

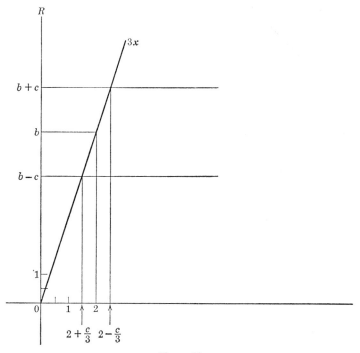

Figure 30

Again note that the value of $\mathbf{f}$ at a does not concern the determination of $\lim_{a} \mathbf{f}$. Consider the function $(\mathbf{x}^2 - 4)/(\mathbf{x} - 2)$, which is defined for all real numbers except 2. However,

$$\lim_{2} \frac{x^2 - 4}{x - 2} = 4$$

as we shall show. Note that, except at 2,

$$\frac{x^2 - 4}{x - 2} = x + 2.$$

Thus, the value of the function at an argument $t \neq 2$ is $t + 2$. Now for any positive number c, $t + 2$ is in the interval $(4 - c, 4 + c)$ whenever t is in the interval $(2 - c, 2 + c)$ and $t \neq 2$. See Figure 31.

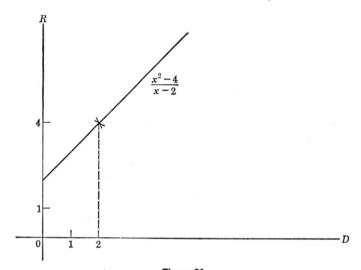

Figure 31

The proofs of properties $Q1$–25 require that statements of the form $n > N$ be replaced by statements of the form

$$0 < |t - a| < d$$

and where for sequences we seek the largest of a finite collection of numbers N_j, here we would seek the smallest of a collection of numbers d_j. Proofs of the following additional properties are left to the reader:

(a) $\lim_{a} \mathbf{x} = a$ (19)

(b) $\lim_{a} \mathbf{abs} = |a|$. (20)

If k is a real number, then

(a) $\lim_{a} \mathbf{k} = k$. (21)

From these properties and Q1–25, one can show that if $\mathbf{f}$ is a polynomial function, then for every real number a, $\lim_a \mathbf{f}$ exists and equals $\mathbf{f}(a)$. The same is true of rational functions except at the zeros of their denominators.

To say that $\lim_a \mathbf{f} = k$ means that each argument $t \neq a$ in some neighborhood of a gives a value $\mathbf{f}(t)$ in some neighborhood of k chosen at will. To prove that $\lim_a \mathbf{f} \neq k$, it is sufficient to show that there is a neighborhood of k that excludes a value $f(t)$ for some argument t in *every* neighborhood of a. In Figure 32 the situation of

$$\lim_a \mathbf{f} = k \quad \text{and} \quad \lim_a \mathbf{f} \neq h$$

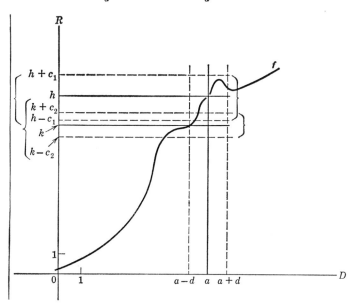

Figure 32

is sketched. Note in the first case that a rectangle is determined in which every point of the graph in $(a - d, a + d)$ lies, except possibly $(a, \mathbf{f}(a))$. In the second case, every such rectangle excludes at least one point of the graph other than $(a, \mathbf{f}(a))$.

If $\lim_a \mathbf{f} = k$ then values of $\mathbf{f}$ at arguments near a are near k, so we are sometimes led to expect that the value of $\mathbf{f}$ at a should equal k. If this is not the case, then the graph of $\mathbf{f}$ has a break, or *discontinuity* at a. If $\lim_a \mathbf{f}$ exists, but does not equal $\mathbf{f}(a)$, then a single point is missing from the graph of **f**. Such a discontinuity is called a *gap*, whether or not $\mathbf{f}(a)$ exists and the curve can be made continuous by redefining $\mathbf{f}(a)$ to equal $\lim_a \mathbf{f}$. If $\lim_a \mathbf{f}$ does not exist, it may be that $\lim_{a+} \mathbf{f}$ and $\lim_{a-} \mathbf{f}$ both exist but are unequal. In this case the break is called a *finite jump*, and the function cannot be redefined at a single argument to repair the break. If $\lim_{a+} \mathbf{f}$ or $\lim_{a-} \mathbf{f}$ or both are infinite (see Exercises 1–2), then the break is called an *infinite jump* and is also irreparable.

The case that $\lim_a \mathbf{f}$ and $\mathbf{f}(a)$ both exist and are equal is of special importance to us, for in this case, there is a neighborhood of a over which the graph of **f** is unbroken. If

$$\lim_a \mathbf{f} = \mathbf{f}(a)$$

we say that **f** *is continuous at a*, and is *discontinuous at a* otherwise. To be discontinuous either $\lim_a \mathbf{f}$ or $\mathbf{f}(a)$ or both fail to exist, or they both exist and are unequal. If **f** is continuous at a then

$$(c)[c > 0 \to (\mathrm{E}\, d)(t)(0 < |t - a| < d \to |\mathbf{f}(t) - \mathbf{f}(a)| < c)] \quad (22)$$

must be true.

If **f** is continuous at every argument a of an interval, then we say that **f** is *continuous on the interval*. This means that (22) must be true for every argument a in the interval. Thus, if $p(\mathbf{f}, a)$ represents the predicate that is defined by formula (22), then

$$(a)[q < a < r \to p(\mathbf{f}, a)] \quad (23)$$

is the statement that **f** is continuous in the interval (q, r). Note that the number d that is part of $p(\mathbf{f}, a)$ is determined only after both c and a are chosen. For each $a \in (q, r)$, d depends on c, and we usually expect that d must be small when c is small. Similarly, for each choice of $c > 0$ it may be necessary to choose d smaller for some arguments a than for others.

In Figure 33 we have sketched the graph of $1/\mathbf{x}$ in $(0, 1)$. Note that for the argument .2 the value is 5 and the interval $(5 - c, 5 + c)$ about 5 determines a small neighborhood of .2 from which approximating arguments can be chosen. For the argument .7 the value is $\frac{10}{7}$ and the same accuracy interval about $\frac{10}{7}$ determines a longer interval about .7 from which approximating arguments can be chosen, allowing more latitude.

It is interesting that if a function **f** is continuous in some intervals, then we can show that the choice of d does not depend upon a, the argument at which approximation takes place, but only on the measure of

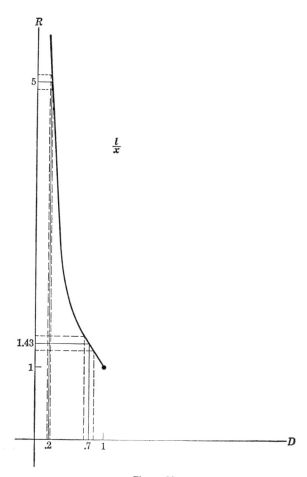

Figure 33

accuracy c. This means that when $c > 0$ is chosen, a positive number d is determined so that if a is *any* argument in the interval, all arguments in the d-neighborhood of a give values in the c-neighborhood of $\mathbf{f}(a)$. We describe this situation by saying that $\mathbf{f}$ is *uniformly continuous* in the given interval. We can now prove the following useful theorem.

*F*1. If $\mathbf{f}$ is continuous on a closed interval $[q, r]$ then $\mathbf{f}$ is uniformly continuous there.

Proof:

Choose any number $c > 0$. Then for every argument a in $[p, q]$ there is a positive number d_a so that if t is in the d_a-neighborhood of a, then $\mathbf{f}(t)$ is in the $c/2$-neighborhood of $f(a)$. Thus the interval $[p, q]$ is covered by a collection of open intervals, the $d_a/2$-neighborhoods. By the Heine-Borel property, a finite subcollection must cover $[p, q]$. Let d be the length of the shortest neighborhood of this subcollection and let t and a be arguments in $[q, r]$ with $|t - a| < d/2$. Now there is a number b in $[q, r]$ such that t is in the d_b-neighborhood of b, and such that this interval is in the finite subcollection that covers $[q, r]$. Then

$$|b - a| \leq |b - t| + |t - a|$$

$$< \frac{d_b}{2} + \frac{d}{2}$$

$$< d_b$$

since $d \leq d_b$. Thus,

$$|\mathbf{f}(t) - \mathbf{f}(a)| \leq |\mathbf{f}(t) - \mathbf{f}(b)| + |\mathbf{f}(b) - \mathbf{f}(a)|$$

$$< \frac{c}{2} + \frac{c}{2} = c.$$

This shows that for any $c > 0$ there is a $d > 0$ so that any arguments that differ by less than $d/2$ have values that differ by less than c, and thus proves the theorem.

Let $\mathbf{f}$ be continuous on $[q, r]$ and let $c = 1$. Choose d so that if

$$|t - a| < d$$

then

$$|\mathbf{f}(t) - \mathbf{f}(a)| < 1.$$

Since the interval can be covered by a finite number (say n) of open intervals of length d, no two values of $\mathbf{f}$ can differ by more than n. This means that if $\mathbf{f}(a)$ is any value, then

$$|\mathbf{f}(t)| \leq |\mathbf{f}(a)| + n$$

for each argument t in $[q, r]$, so that the following theorem holds.

F2. If $\mathbf{f}$ is continuous on a closed interval $[q, r]$, then it is bounded there, that is, there is a number $M > 0$ such that $\mathbf{f} \leq \mathbf{M}$.

Suppose that $\mathbf{f}$ is continuous in $[q, r]$. Since it is bounded, its values must have a least upper bound M. We call M the *maximum* of $\mathbf{f}$ on $[q, r]$. Choose a sequence (t_n) of arguments from $[q, r]$ such that

$$M - \mathbf{f}(t_n) < \frac{1}{n}$$

for each n. If this were not possible, then we would have

$$\mathbf{f}(t) < M - \frac{1}{n}$$

for some n and all t, and M would not be the least upper bound. Now $[q, r]$ is a closed interval, so that (t_n) is bounded, and must have a limit t in the interval. We leave it to the reader to show that $\mathbf{f}(t) = M$. Thus, we prove the following property.

F3. If $\mathbf{f}$ is continuous on a closed interval $[q, r]$, it attains its maximum, that is, if M is its maximum, then there is an argument t in $[q, r]$ such that $\mathbf{f}(t) = M$.

F4. If $\mathbf{f}$ is continuous on a closed interval $[q, r]$, then it attains its minimum, that is, if m is the greatest lower bound of the values of $\mathbf{f}$ in $[q, r]$ then there is an argument t in $[q, r]$ such that $\mathbf{f}(t) = m$.

Proof:

If m is the minimum of $\mathbf{f}$, then $-m$ is the maximum of $-\mathbf{f}$ (see Exercise 11). Thus, there is an argument t by *F3* such that $-\mathbf{f}(t) = -m$, so $\mathbf{f}(t) = m$.

We leave it to the reader to show that the following property holds,

F5. If $\mathbf{f}$ is continuous in $[q, r]$, m and M are its minimum and maximum. respectively, and c any number in the interval (m, M), then there is an argument t in $[q, r]$ such that $\mathbf{f}(t) = c$.

These properties show that if $\mathbf{f}$ is continuous in a closed interval, then its graph in that interval crosses every horizontal line from height m to height M.

EXERCISES

1. We say that $\lim\limits_{a+} \mathbf{f} = \infty$ if given $M > 0$ there is a number $d > 0$ such that

$$(t)[0 < t - a < d \rightarrow \mathbf{f}(t) > M]$$

Show that this means that $\mathbf{f}$ assumes arbitrarily large values in an interval $(a, a + d)$, so that the vertical line through a is an asymptote of the graph of $\mathbf{f}$.

2. Give definitions of $\lim\limits_{a-} \mathbf{f} = \infty$, $\lim\limits_{a+} \mathbf{f} = -\infty$, and $\lim\limits_{a-} \mathbf{f} = -\infty$ that are analogous to the definition given in Exercise 1. Interpret these notions as in Exercise 1.

3. Find $\lim\limits_{3+} \mathbf{f}$, $\lim\limits_{3-} \mathbf{f}$, and $\lim\limits_{3} \mathbf{f}$ if they exist for the following functions $\mathbf{f}$, and sketch their graphs in a neighborhood of 3:

   (a) $\mathbf{f} = 2\mathbf{x} + 7$
   (b) $\mathbf{f} = 1/(\mathbf{x} - 3)$

(c) $\mathbf{f} = (\mathbf{x} - 3)/\mathbf{x}$

(d) $\mathbf{f} = \mathbf{int} - \mathbf{x}$

(e) $\mathbf{f} = \begin{cases} \mathbf{x} \text{ on } (0, 3) \\ \mathbf{x}^2 - 6 \text{ on } (3, 7) \end{cases}$

(f) $\mathbf{f} = \begin{cases} \mathbf{x}^2 \text{ on } (0, 3) \\ 2\mathbf{x} + 3 \text{ on } (3, 7) \end{cases}$

(g) $f = \begin{cases} \mathbf{x}/(\mathbf{x} - 3) \text{ on } (1, 3) \\ \mathbf{x} - 2 \text{ on } (3, 4) \end{cases}$

(h) $f = \begin{cases} 2 \text{ on } (0, 3) \\ 1/(\mathbf{x} - 3)^2 \text{ on } (3, 7). \end{cases}$

4. Prove that $\lim\limits_{a} \mathbf{f}$ exists if and only if $\lim\limits_{a+} \mathbf{f}$ and $\lim\limits_{a-} \mathbf{f}$ both exist and are equal to a number k. Show that $\lim\limits_{a} \mathbf{f} = k$ in this case.

5. Verify that the proofs of $Q1$–25 for the notions $\lim\limits_{a} \mathbf{f}$, $\lim\limits_{a-} \mathbf{f}$, and $\lim\limits_{a+} \mathbf{f}$ remain valid under the changes suggested in the text.

6. Prove (19)–(21).

7. For the functions of Exercise 3 that are discontinuous at 3, characterize the discontinuity as a gap, a finite jump, or an infinite jump.

8. Show that $1/\mathbf{x}$ is not uniformly continuous in $(0, 1)$ even though it is continuous there. This shows that the condition that the interval of continuity be closed is necessary to the validity of the property. Do this by showing that there is a real number $c > 0$, such that for any $d > 0$ there are numbers s and t with
$$|s - t| < d \quad \text{and} \quad |(1/s) - (1/t)| \geq c.$$

9. Prove that $\lim\limits_{2} 4\mathbf{x} \neq 7$.

10. In the proof of $F3$, show that $\mathbf{f}(t) = M$.

11. Show that if M is the maximum value of a continuous function $\mathbf{f}$ in an interval $[q, r]$, then

(a) kM is the maximum of $k\mathbf{f}$ if $k > 0$

(b) kM is the minimum of $k\mathbf{f}$ if $k < 0$

(c) $k + M$ is the maximum of $\mathbf{k} + \mathbf{f}$

(d) $k - M$ is the minimum of $\mathbf{k} - \mathbf{f}$

where k is a real number.

12. Fill in the details of the proof of $F4$.

13. Prove $F5$. [Hint: Let $\mathfrak{A}$ be the set of arguments t such that $\mathbf{f}(t) > c$, and $\mathfrak{B}$ be the set of arguments t such that $\mathbf{f}(t) < c$. Show that neither $\mathfrak{A}$ nor $\mathfrak{B}$ is empty and each has an accumulation point. Show that there is at least

one number t^* that is an accumulation point of both α and β. Prove that $\mathbf{f}(t^*) = c$.]

14. Prove that if $\mathbf{f}$ is defined and monotonic (increasing or decreasing) in an interval $[q, r]$, then it assumes a maximum and a minimum value there. Express these in terms of q and r in each case.

4 · DERIVATIVES OF FUNCTIONS

Consider a function $\mathbf{f}$ that describes the motion of a particle along some path so that for each argument t in an interval $[q, r]$, $\mathbf{f}(t)$ is the distance from some fixed point on the path to the position of the particle at time t. Thus the path could be a straight line, as in Figure 34 with the ori-

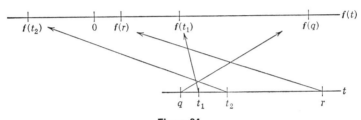

Figure 34

gin of its scale as the fixed point from which distance is measured. Then $\mathbf{f}(t)$ is the coordinate on that scale of the position of the particle at time t. For a line oriented as in Figure 34 the particle is to the right of 0 when $\mathbf{f}(t) > 0$ and to the left when $\mathbf{f}(t) < 0$. Of course the path of a particle could be more complicated, but we shall confine ourselves to this simple case for illustrative purposes.

Suppose now that the particle moves, starting at a position with co-ordinate $\mathbf{f}(a)$, through a time interval of length $h \neq 0$. For concreteness, we suppose that $h > 0$, for the time being. Then the time interval is $(a, a + h)$, and the distance traveled is $\mathbf{f}(a + h) - \mathbf{f}(a)$, the difference of the two position coordinates. (See Figure 35.) We define the average rate of velocity for this motion as the fraction

$$\frac{\mathbf{f}(a + h) - \mathbf{f}(a)}{h} \tag{24}$$

in the familiar way. Note that since $h > 0$ motion to the right makes the average rate positive, and motion to the left makes it negative.

In order to find average velocity for a given function, we need an interval of positive length over all of which the function is defined. For a particular choice of a, the average velocity depends only on h, the length

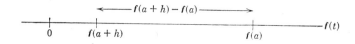

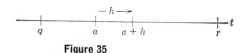

Figure 35

of the interval. Thus, we may consider (21) to be the value at h of some function $\mathbf{g}_a$. Apparently

$$\mathbf{g}_a = \frac{\mathbf{f}[a + x] - \mathbf{f}[a]}{x} \qquad (25)$$

and we call $\mathbf{g}_a$ the *difference quotient of* $\mathbf{f}$ *at* a.

Sometimes we ask the question: How fast is the particle moving at time $t = a$? We emphasize that this question has no relation to experimental phenomena, for in experiment we need a time interval of positive length to compute velocity. The question of velocity at a particular instant of time must then be a theoretical or abstract idea, one that is to be sure very useful. Thus a prior question that must concern us is: How shall we define instantaneous velocity?

We must take our clue from experiment. If instantaneous velocity is to have a useful meaning, then it must be close to average velocities taken over small intervals of time near the time $t = a$. Thus, a guide to instantaneous velocity is the set of values of $\mathbf{g}_a$ for small arguments h. Since $h > 0$, it is thus reasonable to define instantaneous velocity of $\mathbf{f}$ at a as

$$\lim_{0+} \mathbf{g}_a$$

We could just as well have used small intervals of arguments to the left of a, as we might if a is the last instant of time at which the motion of the particle is recorded. Then we would define instantaneous velocity as

$$\lim_{0-} \mathbf{g}_a$$

if a is such that we may use intervals that extend on either side of a. Then we might use

$$\lim_{0} \mathbf{g}_a$$

as a definition of instantaneous velocity of $\mathbf{f}$ at a. In all cases we would have to leave instantaneous velocity undefined if the limit failed to exist.

Another application from the field of geometry lends itself to a similar analysis. Let **f** be a function defined on an interval $[q, r]$ and let a be an argument of **f** in the interval, as in Figure 36. We ask: What is the slope of

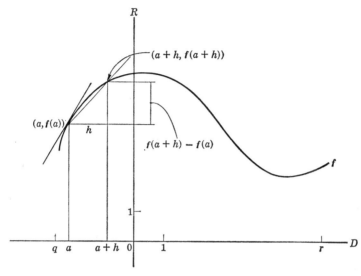

Figure 36

the line that is tangent to the graph of **f** at $(a, \mathbf{f}(a))$? To determine the slope of a line, however, it is necessary to know two distinct points on it, hence some abstraction is again indicated. We take our clue to the slope of the tangent line from the slopes of chords joining $(a, \mathbf{f}(a))$ to neighboring points $(a + h, \mathbf{f}(a + h))$ for h small and nonzero. But such slopes are given by the difference quotient (25). Thus we are led to define the slope of the tangent line in one of the three ways in which instantaneous velocity was defined above. Which of the definitions is chosen depends on whether the conditions of the problem require that $h > 0$, $h < 0$, or simply $h \neq 0$.

Given the function **f**, each of the limits $\lim_{0+} \mathbf{g}_a$, $\lim_{0-} \mathbf{g}_a$, and $\lim_0 \mathbf{g}_a$ associates with each member of a set of arguments a of **f** a unique number. In each case a function is defined whose domain is this set of arguments. If the function assigns $\lim_{0+} \mathbf{g}_a$ to each argument a we call it the *right-hand derivative of* **f** and denote it by **D⁺f**. If it associates $\lim_{0-} \mathbf{g}_a$ with each argument a, we call it the *left-hand derivative of* **f** and denote it by **D⁻f**. If it assigns $\lim_0 \mathbf{g}_a$ to each argument, we call it the *derivative of* **f** and denote it by $\mathbf{Df}$. If $\mathbf{Df}(a)$ exists, we say that $\mathbf{f}$ is *differentiable* at a. We can show that $\mathbf{Df}(a)$ exists if and only if $\mathbf{D^+f}(a)$ and $\mathbf{D^-f}(a)$ both exist and are equal. Left-hand and right-hand derivatives are most useful at the end-points of an interval of the domain of $\mathbf{f}$. If they exist at a and are distinct, then the graph of $\mathbf{f}$ has a *corner* at a, which is the argument at which there is an abrupt change in the slope of the tangent to the graph of $\mathbf{f}$.

To evaluate the derivative of $\mathbf{f}$ at a, we compute the difference quotient function $\mathbf{g}_a$ and take its limit at 0. If $\mathbf{f} = \mathbf{x}^2$, then

$$\mathbf{g}_a = \frac{(\mathbf{a} + \mathbf{x})^2 - \mathbf{a}^2}{\mathbf{x}}$$

$$= \frac{2\mathbf{a}\mathbf{x} + \mathbf{x}^2}{\mathbf{x}}$$

$$= 2\mathbf{a} + \mathbf{x}$$

except at 0. Hence

$$\mathbf{Df}(a) = \lim_0 (2\mathbf{a} + \mathbf{x}) = 2a$$

Thus, for the derivative function of $\mathbf{f}$ we have $\mathbf{Df} = 2\mathbf{x}$.

If $\mathbf{f} = \mathbf{x}^{1/2}$, then for an argument a,

$$\mathbf{g}_a = \frac{(\mathbf{a} + \mathbf{x})^{1/2} - \mathbf{a}^{1/2}}{\mathbf{x}}$$

$$= \frac{(\mathbf{a} + \mathbf{x})^{1/2} - \mathbf{a}^{1/2}}{\mathbf{x}} \frac{(\mathbf{a} + \mathbf{x})^{1/2} + \mathbf{a}^{1/2}}{(\mathbf{a} + \mathbf{x})^{1/2} + \mathbf{a}^{1/2}}$$

$$= \frac{\mathbf{x}}{\mathbf{x}[(\mathbf{a} + \mathbf{x})^{1/2} + \mathbf{a}^{1/2}]}$$

$$= \frac{1}{(\mathbf{a} + \mathbf{x})^{1/2} + \mathbf{a}^{1/2}}$$

except at 0. Thus,

$$\mathbf{Df}(a) = \lim_0 \mathbf{g}_a = \frac{1}{2a^{1/2}}$$

Note that $\mathbf{Df}(a)$ does not exist at 0 in this case. Since the formula is valid for other arguments a, we have

$$\mathbf{Dx}^{1/2} = \frac{1}{2\mathbf{x}^{1/2}}$$

Derivatives of other functions can be found in the same way. It is useful to know the derivatives of basic functions and formulas for computing the derivative of the result of an operation once the derivatives

of its parts are known. We list some of these properties here and leave
their proofs to the reader.

If k is a real number, $\mathbf{D}k = \mathbf{0}$ (26)

$\mathbf{D}\mathbf{x} = \mathbf{1}$ (27)

$\mathbf{D}(\mathbf{f} + \mathbf{g}) = \mathbf{D}\mathbf{f} + \mathbf{D}\mathbf{g}$ (28)

$\mathbf{D}(\mathbf{f} - \mathbf{g}) = \mathbf{D}\mathbf{f} - \mathbf{D}\mathbf{g}$ (29)

$\mathbf{D}(\mathbf{f}\mathbf{g}) = \mathbf{f}\mathbf{D}\mathbf{g} + \mathbf{g}\mathbf{D}\mathbf{f}$ (30)

$\mathbf{D}\dfrac{\mathbf{f}}{\mathbf{g}} = \dfrac{\mathbf{g}\mathbf{D}\mathbf{f} - \mathbf{f}\mathbf{D}\mathbf{g}}{\mathbf{g}^2}$ (31)

$\mathbf{D}\mathbf{x}^n = n\mathbf{x}^{n-1}$ (32)

We prove now a number of abstract properties of the derivative that
give examples of kinds of information the derivative of a function can
give.

F6. If $\mathbf{D}\mathbf{f}(a)$ exists, then $\mathbf{f}$ is continuous at a.

Proof:

If $\mathbf{D}\mathbf{f}(a)$ exists, then there is a neighborhood of a in which $\mathbf{f}$ is defined
and

$$\left|\frac{\mathbf{f}(a + h) - \mathbf{f}(a)}{h}\right| \le M$$

for some $M > 0$. Then

$$|\mathbf{f}(a + h) - \mathbf{f}(a)| \le M|h|$$

so that $\mathbf{f}(a + h)$ is as close to $\mathbf{f}(a)$ as we please when h is small.

F7. If $\mathbf{f}$ is continuous and monotone increasing in $[a, b]$, and $\mathbf{D}\mathbf{f}$ exists
there, then $\mathbf{D}\mathbf{f} \ge \mathbf{0}$ there.

Proof:

Since $\mathbf{f}$ is monotone increasing, the difference quotient $\mathbf{g}_t \ge 0$ for every
t in $[a, b]$. Hence $\mathbf{D}\mathbf{f}(t) \ge 0$.

F8. If $\mathbf{f}$ is monotone decreasing in $[a, b]$ and $\mathbf{D}\mathbf{f}$ exists there, then
$\mathbf{D}\mathbf{f} \le \mathbf{0}$ there.

The proofs of *F8* and the converses of both *F7* and *F8* are left to the
reader.

The mean value theorem implies a number of these properties and is
proved as *F10*. *F9* is called Rolle's theorem and is used in the proof of *F10*.

*F*9. Let **f** be continuous on $[a, b]$ (with $a < b$), and let **Df** exist on the open interval (a, b). If $\mathbf{f}(a) = \mathbf{f}(b)$, then there is an argument t in (a, b) such that $\mathbf{Df}(t) = 0$.

Proof:

Note as in Figure 37, that the conclusion means that under the specified conditions, the graph must have a horizontal tangent at some point in

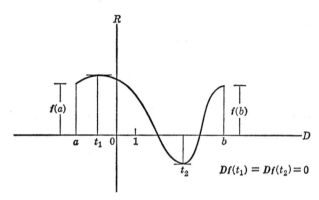

Figure 37

the interval. If **f** is a constant function, then $\mathbf{Df} = 0$ at every point of $[a, b]$, so that the theorem holds. Suppose that **f** is not a constant function—say there is an argument c in (a, b) such that $\mathbf{f}(c) > \mathbf{f}(a)$. The proof in the opposite case is similar. Let M be the maximum of **f** in $[a, b]$. Then

$$M \neq \mathbf{f}(a) \quad \text{and} \quad M \neq \mathbf{f}(b)$$

but by *F*3 there is a number t in $[a, b]$ such that $\mathbf{f}(t) = M$. Since $t \neq a$ and $t \neq b$, t is in (a, b). We shall show that $\mathbf{Df}(t) = 0$.

Consider the difference quotient

$$\mathbf{g}_t = \frac{\mathbf{f}[t + x] - \mathbf{f}[t]}{x}.$$

Since $\mathbf{f}(t)$ is maximum, the numerator of $\mathbf{g}_t$ is negative for arguments $h \neq 0$ and small enough for $t + h$ to belong to $[a, b]$. Hence if $h > 0$, $\mathbf{g}_t(h) < 0$, so by Q, $\mathbf{D^+f}(t) \leq 0$. If $h < 0$, $\mathbf{g}_t(h) > 0$, so that $\mathbf{D^-f}(t) \geq 0$. But if $\mathbf{Df}(t)$ exists, we must have

$$\mathbf{D^+f}(t) = \mathbf{D^-f}(t) = 0$$

which proves that $\mathbf{Df}(t)$ must be 0.

*F*10. Let **f** be continuous in $[a, b]$ and let **Df** exist on (a, b). Then there is an argument t in (a, b) such that

$$\frac{\mathbf{f}(b) - \mathbf{f}(a)}{b - a} = \mathbf{Df}(t).$$

Proof:

We are proving that if **f** satisfies the hypotheses of the theorem, then there is a point t of the interval such that the tangent to the graph of **f** at $(t, \mathbf{f}(t))$ is parallel to the chord joining the endpoints of the curve in the interval. See Figure 38. If **f** represents the position of a particle in

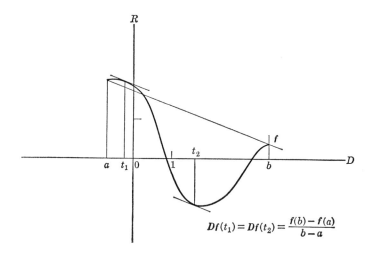

$$Df(t_1) = Df(t_2) = \frac{f(b) - f(a)}{b - a}$$

Figure 38

motion, then the interpretation is that the average velocity in an interval must equal the instantaneous velocity at some time within the interval. We proceed by constructing from **f** a function **g** that satisfies the hypotheses of *F*9, and use that property. Let

$$\mathbf{g} = \mathbf{f} - \frac{\mathbf{x} - \mathbf{a}}{b - a}(\mathbf{f}(b) - \mathbf{f}(a)).$$

Then, for each t, $\mathbf{g}(t)$ is the vertical distance of the point $(t, \mathbf{f}(t))$ of the graph of **f** from the chord joining $(a, \mathbf{f}(a))$ and $(b, \mathbf{f}(b))$. Note that

$$\mathbf{g}(a) = \mathbf{g}(b) = \mathbf{f}(a)$$

g is continuous in $[a, b]$ and

$$\mathbf{Dg} = \mathbf{Df} - \frac{\mathbf{f}[b] - \mathbf{f}[a]}{b - a}$$

exists in (a, b). Thus, by $F9$, there is a t in the interval with $\mathbf{Dg}(t) = 0$, and the conclusion follows easily.

The next property is called the *generalized mean value theorem*. It compares the ratio of two function value differences to the ratio of derivatives of these functions at an argument in their common domain.

$F11$. If $\mathbf{f}$ and $\mathbf{g}$ are continuous in $[a, b]$ and if $\mathbf{Df}$ and $\mathbf{Dg}$ exist in (a, b), then there is an argument t in (a, b) such that

$$\frac{\mathbf{f}(b) - \mathbf{f}(a)}{\mathbf{g}(b) - \mathbf{g}(a)} = \frac{\mathbf{Df}(t)}{\mathbf{Dg}(t)}$$

provided $\mathbf{Dg}$ does not take the value 0 in $[a, b]$.

Proof:
Consider the function

$$\mathbf{h} = \mathbf{f} - (\mathbf{x} - \mathbf{a})\frac{\mathbf{f}(b) - \mathbf{f}(a)}{b - a} - \mathbf{g} + (\mathbf{x} - \mathbf{a})\frac{\mathbf{g}(b) - \mathbf{g}(a)}{b - a}.$$

The function $\mathbf{h}$ satisfies the hypotheses of Rolle's theorem. For $\mathbf{h}$ is continuous,

$$\mathbf{h}(a) = \mathbf{h}(b) = \mathbf{f}(a) - \mathbf{g}(a)$$

and

$$\mathbf{Dh} = \mathbf{Df} - \frac{\mathbf{f}[\mathbf{b}] - \mathbf{f}[\mathbf{a}]}{b - a} - \mathbf{Dg} + \frac{\mathbf{g}[\mathbf{b}] - \mathbf{g}[\mathbf{a}]}{b - a}$$

exists in (a, b). Thus there is a t in (a, b) such that $\mathbf{Dh}(t) = 0$. So the conclusion holds, provided

$$\mathbf{g}(b) - \mathbf{g}(a) \neq 0.$$

Note that if

$$\mathbf{g}(b) - \mathbf{g}(a) = 0$$

we could not perform the required division. But if

$$\mathbf{g}(b) = \mathbf{g}(a)$$

$\mathbf{g}$ would satisfy the hypotheses of Rolle's theorem, and we would have $\mathbf{Dg}(s) = 0$ for some s in (a, b), contrary to hypothesis.

Some of the consequences of the generalized mean value theorem are explored in the exercises. We close the section by using it to prove an important formula, called the *chain rule* which allows us to evaluate the derivative of the composition $\mathbf{f}[\mathbf{g}]$ if $\mathbf{Df}$ and $\mathbf{Dg}$ are known.

$$\mathbf{D}(\mathbf{f}[\mathbf{g}]) = \mathbf{Df}[\mathbf{g}] \cdot \mathbf{Dg} \tag{33}$$

To prove (30) we investigate the value at h of the difference quotient of $\mathbf{f}[\mathbf{g}]$ at a:

$$\frac{\mathbf{f}(\mathbf{g}(a+h)) - \mathbf{f}(\mathbf{g}(a))}{h}$$

where $h \neq 0$. We are interested in this value for $|h|$ small, say for h in the interval $(-d, d)$ for some $d > 0$. If every such interval has an argument t for which $\mathbf{Dg}(a + t) = 0$, then, since $\mathbf{Dg}$ exists and $\mathbf{g}$ is continuous, there must be a subinterval $(-d_1, d_1)$ of $(-d, d)$ such that $\mathbf{Dg}(a + t) = 0$ for every t in the subinterval. Then $\mathbf{g}$ is a constant function there. (See Exercise 20.) It follows that $\mathbf{f}[\mathbf{g}]$ is also a constant function there, and

$$\mathbf{D}(\mathbf{f}[\mathbf{g}])(a) = 0.$$

Thus, (33) holds in this case.

Suppose now that there is an interval $(-d, d)$ such that

$$\mathbf{Dg}(a + t) \neq 0$$

for t in $(-d, d)$. Then

$$\mathbf{g}(a + t) \neq \mathbf{g}(a)$$

and we may write the difference quotient

$$\frac{\mathbf{f}(\mathbf{g}(a+h)) - \mathbf{f}(\mathbf{g}(a))}{\mathbf{x}(\mathbf{g}(a+h)) - \mathbf{x}(\mathbf{g}(a))} \cdot \frac{\mathbf{g}(a+h) - \mathbf{g}(a)}{\mathbf{x}} \qquad (34)$$

since $\mathbf{x}[\mathbf{g}] = \mathbf{g}$, and h is in $(-d, d)$. Since $\mathbf{Df}$ and $\mathbf{Dg}$ exist at a, they exist in a subinterval of $(-d, d)$ and the hypotheses of both mean value theorems are satisfied. Thus there are numbers s and s' in this subinterval such that (34) is equal to

$$\frac{\mathbf{Df}(g(s))}{\mathbf{Dx}(g(s))} \mathbf{Dg}(s').$$

But as h becomes small, s and s' are arbitrarily close to a, so that, evaluating limits, we have

$$\mathbf{D}(\mathbf{f}[\mathbf{g}])(a) = \frac{\mathbf{Df}(\mathbf{g}(a))\mathbf{Dg}(a)}{\mathbf{Dx}(\mathbf{g}(a))}$$

and since $\mathbf{Dx} = 1$, the chain rule is proved.

EXERCISES

1. Each of the following functions describes the motion of a particle along a real number scale. Find the average velocity of the motion in the interval given.

   (a) $\mathbf{x}^2 + 2\mathbf{x} - 1$: $[1, 6]$
   (b) $\mathbf{x} + 1/\mathbf{x}$: $[2, 8]$
   (c) $\mathbf{abs} - \mathbf{x}$: $[-5, -2]$
   (d) $\mathbf{x}^3 + \mathbf{int}$: $[1, 4]$

2. For the function of the corresponding part of Exercise 1, find the average rate of the function over the indicated interval, where $h \neq 0$.

(a) $[1, 1 + h]$
(b) $[2, 3 + h]$
(c) $[-5, -5 + h]$
(d) $[1, 1 + h]$

In part (d) find the average rates for $h > 0$ and for $h < 0$ separately.

3. In each part of Exercise 1 graph the function in the given interval and draw the chord whose slope is given to be the average rate.

4. For the function of the corresponding part of Exercise 1, find the instantaneous rate of change at the indicated argument.

(a) $a = 1$
(b) $a = 2$
(c) $a = -5$
(d) $a = 1$

5. For the given function, find the value of the derivative at the indicated argument:

(a) $3x - 1: a = 5$
(b) $(x - 1)^3 + x: a = 1$
(c) $x^2 + \mathbf{abs}: a = -2$
(d) $x - \mathbf{abs}: x = 0$.

In part (d) find the left-hand and right-hand derivatives.

6. Using the definition of derivative, find the derivative function and its domain for each of the following functions:

(a) $x^2 + \dfrac{1}{x}$

(b) $x - \mathbf{int}$

(c) $(x - a)^{1/2}$

(d) $\dfrac{x}{x + 1}$.

7. Find $\mathbf{D^{+}abs}(0)$ and $\mathbf{D^{-}abs}(0)$, and show that $\mathbf{Dabs}(0)$ does not exist. What is $\mathbf{Dabs}(a)$ for $a \neq 0$?

8. Show that $\mathbf{Df}$ does not exist at the zeros of $\mathbf{g}$ if $\mathbf{f} = \mathbf{abs}[\mathbf{g}]$.

9. Prove (26)–(32).

10. Prove that $\mathbf{Df}$ exists for every argument, where $\mathbf{f}$ is a polynomial function.

11. If $\mathbf{f}$ is an odd polynomial function, show that $\mathbf{Df}$ is even. If $\mathbf{f}$ is an even polynomial function, show that $\mathbf{Df}$ is odd.

12. If **f** and **g** are polynomial functions, show that $\mathbf{D(f/g)}$ exists except at the zeros of **g**.

13. To disprove the converse of $F6$, exhibit a function that is continuous at an argument a, such that $\mathbf{Df}(a)$ fails to exist.

14. To show that all hypotheses of Rolle's theorem are necessary, give an example of a function **f** and an interval $[a, b]$ for which the conclusion is false, such that

    (a) **f** is not continuous in $[a, b]$
    (b) $\mathbf{Df}(c)$ does not exist for some c in (a, b)
    (c) $\mathbf{f}(a) \neq \mathbf{f}(b)$.

15. Use the chain rule to find the derivative function of each of the following:

    (a) $(\mathbf{x}^2 + \mathbf{x} - 1)^2$

    (b) $\left(\dfrac{\mathbf{x}+1}{\mathbf{x}-1}\right)^2$

    (c) $\{(3\mathbf{x} - 1)^{1/2} - \mathbf{x}\}^2$.

16. If n is a positive integer, prove by induction that $\mathbf{Dx}^n = n\mathbf{x}^{n-1}$.

17. Show that $\mathbf{Dx}^{-1} = -\mathbf{x}^{-2}$. Prove by induction that $\mathbf{Dx}^n = n\mathbf{x}^{n-1}$ if n is a negative number.

18. Prove that if $\mathbf{f} = \mathbf{g}$, then $\mathbf{Df} = \mathbf{Dg}$.

19. Let $\mathbf{f} = \mathbf{x}^n$, where $n = p/q$, a rational number. Then $\mathbf{f}^q = \mathbf{x}^p$. Use Exercise 19 and the chain rule to prove that $\mathbf{Dx}^n = n\mathbf{x}^{n-1}$.

20. Show that if $\mathbf{Df} = \mathbf{0}$ is in $[a, b]$, then **f** is a constant function there.

5 · THE DEFINITE INTEGRAL

In applications of mathematics it is often the case that some quantity is expressed as the product of two other quantities. As examples, consider the following:

1. area = height $\times$ base (rectangles)
2. volume = cross-section area $\times$ height (solids with congruent cross sections)
3. work = force $\times$ distance (constant force)
4. mass = density $\times$ volume (constant density)
5. distance = rate $\times$ time (constant rate).

In each of these formulas the quantity in the second factor is any number, but to apply the formula to a particular problem we must know that no matter what that number is, the quantity in the first factor is always the same in the given problem.

If the number in the first factor is not the same for all numbers in the second, then these simple formulas are no longer valid. This would be the case in 1, for example, if, instead of a rectangle, we were to be asked for the area of a region like that of Figure 39. The formula in 2 may be

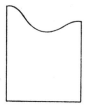

Figure 39

valid for solids like those of Figure 40, but not for those of Figure 41. We cannot use the formula in 3 if the force changes from point to point along the path of motion, nor the formula in 5 if the rate changes during

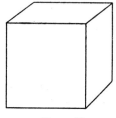 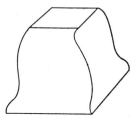

Figure 40   **Figure 41**

the period of motion. The formula in 4 is only valid when the solid is homogeneous and the density is the same at each point of it.

In this section we consider a way that formulas like those above can be used to define an abstract mathematical idea, the definite integral, that enables us to define in turn quantities like those computed in the formulas, even when the number in the first factor is not fixed. We shall use a new notion of limit, similar in many ways to the limit notions already introduced, that enables us to be sure that the number defined in each case is approximated by numbers obtained in situations that are similar enough, and such that the given formulas are valid. We shall confine ourselves to the question of the area of a plane region in what follows. The theory is entirely similar in the other cases.

What we wish to do is to define a function **m**, called an *area measure function* whose domain is the set of regions in a given plane and whose range is the set of real numbers, such that if ⊕ is any region in the plane, then $\mathbf{m}(\mathcal{R})$ is its *area*. Some reasonable properties to expect for the function $\mathbf{m}$ are:

m1. If $\mathcal{R}$ is a rectangle with height h and base b, then
$$\mathbf{m}(\mathcal{R}) = hb.$$

m2. If R_1 and R_2 are regions that intersect at most along a union of curves in the plane, then
$$\mathbf{m}(\mathcal{R}_1 \cup \mathcal{R}_2) = \mathbf{m}(\mathcal{R}_1) + \mathbf{m}(\mathcal{R}_2).$$

m3. If $\mathcal{R}_1$ and $\mathcal{R}_2$ are congruent, then
$$\mathbf{m}(\mathcal{R}_1) = \mathbf{m}(\mathcal{R}_2).$$

The properties *m2* and *m3* are illustrated in Figures 42 and 43.

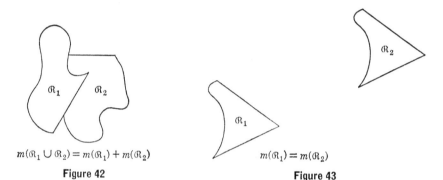

$$m(\mathcal{R}_1 \cup \mathcal{R}_2) = m(\mathcal{R}_1) + m(\mathcal{R}_2)$$

Figure 42

$$m(\mathcal{R}_1) = m(\mathcal{R}_2)$$

Figure 43

Property *m2* is similar to a property of the function $\mathbf{n}$ of sets defined earlier such that $\mathbf{n}(\mathcal{C})$ is the number of elements in the set $\mathcal{C}$. As with the function $\mathbf{n}$, $\mathbf{m}$ also has the following property:

m4. If $\mathcal{R}_1$ and $\mathcal{R}_2$ are any regions, then
$$\mathbf{m}(\mathcal{R}_1 \cup \mathcal{R}_2) = \mathbf{m}(\mathcal{R}_1) + \mathbf{m}(\mathcal{R}_2) - \mathbf{m}(\mathcal{R}_1 \cap \mathcal{R}_2).$$

The proof is left to the reader. Two other convenient properties to note are:

m5. If $m(\mathcal{R}_1) \geq 0$ and $m(\mathcal{R}_2) \geq 0$ and $\mathcal{R}_1 \subset \mathcal{R}_2$, then
$$m(\mathcal{R}_1) \leq m(\mathcal{R}_2).$$

m6. If $\mathcal{R}$ is a single point, or a curve, then $m(\mathcal{R}) = 0$.

Consider now a function $\mathbf{f}$ defined on an interval $[a, b]$. Assuming for the present that $a < b$ and $\mathbf{f} > 0$ on $[a, b]$, a region $\mathcal{R}$ is defined as in Figure 44. This region is bounded by the graph of $\mathbf{f}$, the domain axis, and

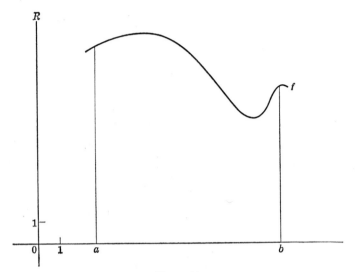

Figure 44

the vertical lines through a and b. We attempt now to define $\mathbf{m}(\mathfrak{R})$ in accordance with the properties in $m1$–6.

Choose $n + 1$ arguments $t_0, t_1, \ldots, t_n$ in $[a, b]$ with

$$a = t_0 \leq t_1 \leq t_2 \leq \cdots \leq t_n = b.$$

These numbers determine a partition P of $[a, b]$ into subintervals

$$[t_0, t_1], [t_1, t_2], \ldots, [t_{n-1}, t_n].$$

The lengths of these subintervals are

$$t_1 - t_0, t_2 - t_1, \ldots, t_n - t_{n-1}$$

none of which is negative. The largest of these numbers is unique for each partition P and is called the *mesh* of P. (See Figure 45.)

Suppose that $\mathbf{f}$ has a maximum value and a minimum value in each closed subinterval of $[a, b]$. Let m_i be the minimum value of $\mathbf{f}$ and M_i be the maximum value of $\mathbf{f}$ in the interval $[t_{i-1}, t_i]$, for $i = 1, 2, \ldots, n$.

Consider now the sums:

$$\underline{S}_P = m_1(t_1 - t_0) + m_2(t_2 - t_1) + \cdots + m_n(t_n - t_{n-1})$$
$$\overline{S}_P = M_1(t_1 - t_0) + M_2(t_2 - t_1) + \cdots + M_n(t_n - t_{n-1})$$

respectively called *lower* and *upper Riemann sums of* P. These sums are areas of unions $\mathfrak{R}_1$ and $\mathfrak{R}_2$ of rectangles that respectively are inscribed in and circumscribed about $\mathfrak{R}$. Thus $\mathfrak{R}_1 \subset \mathfrak{R} \subset \mathfrak{R}_2$, and since $\mathbf{f} > 0$, we have

$$\underline{S}_P \leq \mathbf{m}(\mathfrak{R}) \leq \overline{S}_P \qquad (35)$$

using $m5$.

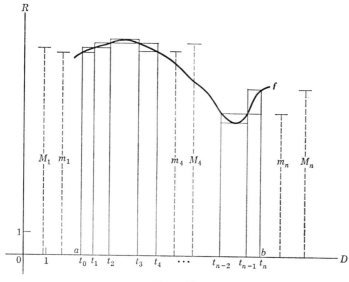

Figure 45

We leave it to the reader to show that $\underline{S}_P \leq \overline{S}_P$ even if $\mathbf{f} \not> 0$. Thus, if $\mathbf{m}(\mathfrak{R})$ is the area to be defined, then it must satisfy (35) for every partition P of $[a, b]$.

Next we investigate the consequences of using partitions P whose mesh is small. Intuitively, if the mesh of P is small, we expect that the portion of the region $\mathfrak{R}$ not in $\mathfrak{R}_1$ and the portion of $\mathfrak{R}_2$ not in $\mathfrak{R}$ will be small as well. If we can show that we can make these portions as small as we wish by choosing P to have small enough mesh, then $\mathbf{m}(\mathfrak{R})$ can be defined.

We show now that if Q is a partition that is finer than P, then $\underline{S}_P \leq \underline{S}_Q$ and $\overline{S}_Q \leq \overline{S}_P$. This result would mean that passing *to* partitions of small mesh cannot decrease a lower sum and cannot increase an upper sum. Of course if Q is finer than P its mesh is at most that of P.

We prove the result in case Q is obtained by adding to P a single partition point s. Then the result for any Q finer than P follows by induction. Suppose that

$$t_{i-1} \leq s \leq t_i$$

for some $i = 1, 2, \ldots, n$. Then the lower sums for P and Q are the same except for the i-th term of $\underline{S}_P$ which is $m_i(t_i - t_{i-1})$. The number in this position in $\underline{S}_Q$ is

$$m_i'(s - t_{i-1}) + m_i''(t_i - s)$$

where m_i' and m_i'' are minima of f in $[t_{i-1}, s]$ and $[s, t_i]$. But since m_i is the minimum over the whole interval, we have

$$m_i \leq m_i' \quad \text{and} \quad m_i \leq m_i'',$$

so $\underline{S}_P \leq \underline{S}_Q$ as required. The reasoning for upper sums is similar and is left to the reader.

The set of lower sums is thus bounded below by $m(b - a)$, where m is the minimum of $\mathbf{f}$ on $[a, b]$, and it is bounded above by every upper sum. By the completeness property for real numbers it follows that this set has a least upper bound, which we call the *lower integral of $\mathbf{f}$ from a to b*, and denote by

$$\underline{\int_a^b} \mathbf{f}$$

Similarly, the set of upper sums is bounded. Its greatest lower bound is called the *upper integral of $\mathbf{f}$ from a to b*, and is denoted by

$$\overline{\int_a^b} \mathbf{f}.$$

Of course we have

$$\underline{\int_a^b} \mathbf{f} \leq \overline{\int_a^b} \mathbf{f}$$

and we must define $\mathbf{m}(\Re)$ so that

$$\underline{\int_a^b} \mathbf{f} \leq \mathbf{m}(\Re) \leq \overline{\int_a^b} \mathbf{f}.$$

If the upper and lower integrals coincide, then their common value is called the *definite integral* of $\mathbf{f}$ from a to b and is denoted by $\int_a^b \mathbf{f}$. If $\int_a^b \mathbf{f}$ exists, then considering the discussion above, it is reasonable to define $\mathbf{m}(\Re)$ so that

$$\mathbf{m}(\Re) = \int_a^b \mathbf{f}.$$

If not, then $\mathbf{m}(\Re)$ is not defined. If the definite integral exists, then we can show that

$$\overline{S}_P - \int_a^b \mathbf{f}$$

and

$$\int_a^b \mathbf{f} - \underline{S}_P$$

are nonnegative and can be made as small as we please by choosing P with small enough mesh. We describe this situation by saying that the definite integral is the *P-limit* of the set of upper sums and of the set of lower sums. Thus,

$$\int_a^b \mathbf{f} = \lim_P \overline{S}_P = \lim_P \underline{S}_P.$$

If **f** has a minimum and a maximum value in every subinterval of $[a, b]$, then all we need prove is that

$$\lim_P (\overline{S}_P - \underline{S}_P) = 0$$

for this will assure us that the upper and lower integrals of **f** coincide. This means that $\overline{S}_P - \underline{S}_P$ can be made as small as we wish by choosing P with small enough mesh. We shall prove this for two important classes of functions: monotonic functions and continuous functions. Note that

$$\overline{S}_P - \underline{S}_P = (M_1 - m_1)(t_1 - t_0) + (M_2 - m_2)(t_2 - t_1) +$$
$$\cdots + (M_n - m_n)(t_n - t_{n-1}). \qquad (36)$$

*F*9. If **f** is defined and monotonic increasing in $[a, b]$, then $\int_a^b \mathbf{f}$ exists.

Proof:

If **f** is monotonic increasing then it has a maximum and a minimum value in every subinterval for

$$M_i = \mathbf{f}(t_i) \quad \text{and} \quad m_i = \mathbf{f}(t_{i-1})$$

for $i - 1, 2, \ldots, n$ in a partition P into n subintervals. We must show that for any $c > 0$ there is a d such that the difference in (36) is less than c whenever mesh $P < d$. Choose $c > 0$ and let

$$d < \frac{c}{f(b) - f(a)}.$$

If P is a partition of mesh less than d, then $t_i - t_{i-1} < d$ for $i = 1,$ $2, \ldots, n$, so that the difference in (36) is less than

$$d\{(M_1 - m_1) + (M_2 - m_2) + \cdots + (M_n - m_n)\}.$$

Since **f** is monotonic increasing,

$$\mathbf{f}(a) = m_1, \quad \mathbf{f}(b) = M_n, \quad \text{and} \quad m_{i+1} = M_i$$

so that the sum is less than $d[\mathbf{f}(b) - \mathbf{f}(a)]$. Since this is c, the theorem is proved.

*F*10. If **f** is defined and monotonic decreasing in $[a, b]$, then $\int_a^b \mathbf{f}$ exists.

The proof of *F*10 is left for the reader.

*F*11. If **f** is continuous in $[a, b]$ then $\int_a^b \mathbf{f}$ exists.

Proof:

We have shown that if **f** is continuous in $[a, b]$, then it has maximum and minimum values in subintervals of $[a, b]$, so all that remains to be proved is (36). Choose $c > 0$. Since $[a, b]$ is closed, $\mathbf{f}$ is uniformly continuous on $[a, b]$. Thus, there is a number d such that

$$|\mathbf{f}(t) - \mathbf{f}(s)| < \frac{c}{b - a}$$

if $|t - s| < d$. For a partition P with mesh less than d, we have

$$M_i - m_i < \frac{c}{b - a}$$

for $i = 1, 2, \ldots, n$. Thus, the sum in (33) is less than

$$\frac{c}{b - a} \cdot (b - a) = c$$

and the theorem is proved.

EXERCISES

1. Prove $m4$–6, using $m3$.

2. Let P be a partition of the interval $[0, 1]$ into n subintervals of equal length. List the partition points of P, and express in terms of n the upper and lower sums for the following functions:
   (a) $\mathbf{2}$
   (b) $\mathbf{x}$
   (c) $\mathbf{x}^2$
   (d) $\mathbf{int}$.

3. If $\mathbf{k}$ is a constant function and $a \leq b$, show that $\int_a^b \mathbf{k}$ exists and equals $k(b - a)$.

4. Show that (35) holds even if $\mathbf{f}$ is not positive on $[a, b]$.

5. Prove that if Q has all the partition points of P and one more, then $\overline{S}_Q \leq \overline{S}_P$.

6. Prove by induction that if Q is finer than P, then
$$\underline{S}_P \leq \underline{S}_Q \leq \overline{S}_Q \leq \overline{S}_P.$$

7. The cross-partition R of P and Q is finer than both of them. Show that $\overline{S}_R - \underline{S}_R$ is not greater than $\overline{S}_P - \underline{S}_P$.

8. Use the result of Exercise 7 to show that if
$$\int_a^b \mathbf{f} \quad \text{and} \quad \int_a^b \mathbf{g}$$
exist, then
$$\int_a^b (\mathbf{f} + \mathbf{g}) \quad \text{and} \quad \int_a^b (\mathbf{f} - \mathbf{g})$$

exist and

$$\int_a^b (\mathbf{f} + \mathbf{g}) = \int_a^b \mathbf{f} + \int_a^b \mathbf{g}$$

and

$$\int_a^b (\mathbf{f} - \mathbf{g}) = \int_a^b \mathbf{f} - \int_a^b \mathbf{g}.$$

9. If $\int_a^b \mathbf{f}$ exists and k is a real number, show that $\int_a^b (k\mathbf{f})$ exists and equals $k \int_a^b \mathbf{f}.$

10. Show that if $\int_a^b \mathbf{f}$ exists and c is any point in $[a, b]$, then

$$\int_a^b \mathbf{f} = \int_a^c \mathbf{f} + \int_c^b \mathbf{f}.$$

11. Use Exercise 3 and 10 to evaluate $\int_{-1}^7 \mathbf{int}.$

12. Define

$$\int_a^b \mathbf{f} = -\int_b^a \mathbf{f}$$

if $a > b$, and $\int_a^a \mathbf{f} = 0$ for all a. If the integrals of Exercise 10 exist, prove that the conclusion of Exercise 10 holds for any three numbers a, b, and c.

13. Prove $F10$.

14. For each $i = 1, 2, \ldots, n$, let s_i be in the subinterval $[t_{i-1}, t_i]$ of a partition P, of $[a, b]$. Consider the sum

$$S_P = f(s_1)(t_1 - t_0) + f(s_2)(t_2 - t_1) + \cdots + f(s_n)(t_n - t_{n-1}).$$

Prove that:

(a) $\underline{S}_P \le S_P \le \overline{S}_P$

(b) If $\int_a^b \mathbf{f}$ exists, then $\int_a^b \mathbf{f} = \lim_P S_P.$

15. Show that if $\int_a^b \mathbf{f}$ exists and (P_n) is any sequence of partitions of $[a, b]$ whose meshes have limit 0, then

$$\int_a^b \mathbf{f} = \lim \underline{S}_{P_n} = \lim S_{P_n} = \lim \overline{S}_{P_n}$$

where "lim" indicates limit of a sequence.

16. Use Exercises 2 and 15 to find

(a) $\int_0^1 \mathbf{x}$

(b) $\int_0^1 \mathbf{x}^2.$

17. Prove that if $\mathbf{f}$ is even and if $\int_0^a \mathbf{f}$ exists, then $\int_{-a}^a \mathbf{f} = 2 \int_0^a \mathbf{f}$.

18. Prove that if $\mathbf{f}$ is odd and if $\int_0^a \mathbf{f}$ exists, then $\int_{-a}^a \mathbf{f} = 0$.

6 · THE FUNDAMENTAL THEOREM OF CALCULUS

In the preceding section, the definite integral of a function $\mathbf{f}$ in an interval $[a, b]$ was defined and interpreted. We were able to prove from the definition that continuous functions and monotone functions have integrals, and that certain algebraic properties hold for definite integrals. These properties enable us to evaluate certain integrals once the values of others are known. But the procedure that the definition provides for finding the definite integral of even a simple function like $\mathbf{x}^2$ is somewhat complicated. We review the procedure for evaluating $\int_0^1 \mathbf{x}^2$ here, which was assigned to the reader in the preceding exercises, and also evaluate $\int_0^1 \mathbf{x}^{1/2}$. Then we consider the fundamental theorem which provides a simpler procedure for evaluating $\int_a^b \mathbf{f}$ for a large class of functions $\mathbf{f}$. Finally, we prove two mean value theorems for definite integrals similar to those proved for derivatives in Section 4.

Note that $\mathbf{x}^2$ is continuous and monotone in $[0, 1]$. It follows that

$$\int_0^1 \mathbf{x}^2$$

exists, and that its value may be found by considering a sequence of Riemann sums obtained from any sequence (P_n) of partitions whose meshes have limit 0. For each n, we shall let P_n be a partition of $[0, 1]$ into n intervals of equal length. Then the partition points are the numbers i/n for $i = 0, 1, \ldots, n$, and the length of each subinterval is $1/n$, which is the mesh of P_n. (See Figure 46.) Since $\lim (1/n) = 0$, this sequence (P_n) is appropriate for computing the integral. Since $\mathbf{x}^2$ is increasing in $[0, 1]$, its maximum in each subinterval $[t_{i-1}, t_i]$ is at the right-hand endpoint $t_i = i/n$. Thus, for each

$$i = 1, 2, \ldots, n$$

$$M_i = \mathbf{x}^2\left(\frac{i}{n}\right) = \frac{i^2}{n^2}.$$

Similarly, the minimum in each interval is

$$m_i = \frac{(i-1)^2}{n^2}$$

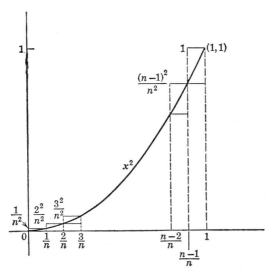

Figure 46

Thus,

$$\overline{S}_{P_n} = \frac{1}{n^2} \cdot \frac{1}{n} + \frac{4}{n^2} \cdot \frac{1}{n} + \frac{9}{n^2} \cdot \frac{1}{n} + \cdots + \frac{n^2}{n^2} \cdot \frac{1}{n}$$

$$= \frac{1}{n^3} (1 + 4 + 9 + \cdots + n^2)$$

Since for each n, the sum in parentheses in the last expression is $n(n + 1)(2n + 1)/6$, we have

$$\overline{S}_{P_n} = \frac{1}{n^3} \frac{n(n + 1)(2n + 1)}{6}$$

$$= \frac{2n^2 + 3n + 1}{6n^2}$$

from which it follows that

$$\int_0^1 \mathbf{x}^2 = \lim \overline{S}_{P_n} = \frac{1}{3}.$$

Using lower sums, we get the same result, of course, since

$$\underline{S}_{P_n} = \frac{1}{n^3} (0 + 1 + 4 + \cdots + (n - 1)^2)$$

$$= \frac{1}{n^3} \frac{n(n - 1)(2n - 1)}{6}$$

$$= \frac{2n^2 - 3n + 1}{6n^2}.$$

Note that for each n,

$$\overline{S}_{P_n} - \underline{S}_{P_n} = \frac{6n}{6n^2} = \frac{1}{n}$$

so that this difference has limit 0.

To evaluate $\int_0^1 \mathbf{x}^{1/2}$ we note that $\mathbf{x}^{1/2}$ is monotonic increasing in $[0, 1]$, and continuous, except at 0, where it is continuous from the right, since

$$\lim_{0+} \mathbf{x}^{1/2} = \mathbf{x}^{1/2}(0) = 0$$

but $\lim_{0} \mathbf{x}^{1/2}$ does not exist. This time for each n we choose a partition P_n that has partition points

$$\frac{0}{n^2}, \frac{1}{n^2}, \frac{4}{n^2}, \cdots, \frac{n^2}{n^2}.$$

The subintervals of this partition do not have equal length but we note that the longest of the subintervals (see Figure 47) is

$$\left[\frac{(n-1)^2}{n^2}, \frac{n^2}{n^2}\right]$$

which has length

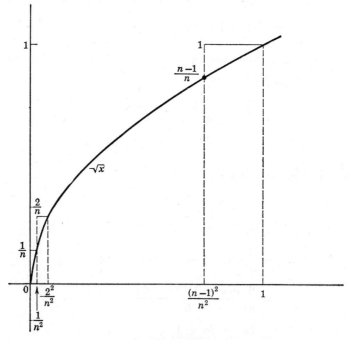

Figure 47

$$\frac{n^2 - (n-1)^2}{n^2} = \frac{2n-1}{n^2}$$

whose limit is zero. Thus, (P_n) is an appropriate sequence of partitions to use for evaluating the integral. For $i = 1, 2, \ldots, n$, the maximum value of $\mathbf{x}^{1/2}$ is

$$M_i = \mathbf{x}^{1/2}\left(\frac{i^2}{n^2}\right) = \frac{i}{n}.$$

Thus,

$$\bar{S}_{P_n} = \frac{1}{n}\left(\frac{1-0}{n^2}\right) + \frac{2}{n}\left(\frac{4-1}{n^2}\right) + \frac{3}{n}\left(\frac{9-4}{n^2}\right)$$

$$+ \cdots + \frac{n}{n}\left(\frac{n^2 - (n-1)^2}{n^2}\right)$$

$$= \frac{1}{n^3}\{1(1-2) + 4(2-3) + 9(3-4)$$

$$+ \cdots + (n-1)^2\left[(n-1) - n\right] + n \cdot n^2\}$$

$$= 1 - \frac{1}{n^3}\{1 + 4 + 9 + \cdots + (n-1)^2\}$$

$$= 1 - \frac{1}{n^3}\frac{n(n-1)(2n-1)}{6}$$

$$= 1 - \frac{2n^2 - 3n + 1}{6n^2}.$$

Thus,

$$\int_0^1 \mathbf{x}^{1/2} = \lim \bar{S}_{P_n} = 1 - \frac{1}{3} = \frac{2}{3}.$$

We leave it to the reader to show that since $\mathbf{x}^2$ and $\mathbf{x}^{1/2}$ are inverses of each other in $[0, 1]$, we might have expected that the sums of their integrals there would be 1.

We can use definite integrals to define functions. Let $\mathbf{f}$ be a function whose graph is sketched in Figure 48 and let a be an argument of $\mathbf{f}$. If t is any argument for which $\int_a^t \mathbf{f}$ exists, then we can consider this integral as the number assigned to t by a certain function $\mathbf{j}$. Thus $\mathbf{j}$ is defined so that for each t

$$\mathbf{j}(t) = \int_a^t \mathbf{f}.$$

The assignment that $\mathbf{j}$ makes to each of its arguments t depends, of course, on the choice of $\mathbf{f}$ and a. Once these are chosen, however, the function $\mathbf{j}$ is determined. Obviously

$$\mathbf{j}(a) = \int_a^a \mathbf{f} = 0$$

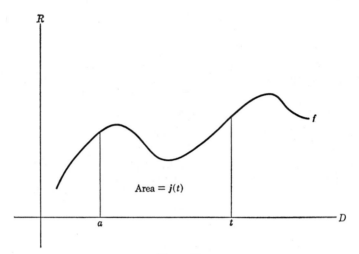

Figure 48

and since $\mathbf{j}(t)$ is the area under the graph of $\mathbf{f}$ from a to t if $t \neq a$, we call $\mathbf{j}$ the *area function of* $\mathbf{f}$ *with origin* a.

If we wish to evaluate $\int_a^b \mathbf{f}$, and if we can somehow find the area function $\mathbf{j}$ of f with origin a, then apparently,

$$\mathbf{j}(b) = \int_a^b \mathbf{f}.$$

We shall show below that $\mathbf{Dj} = \mathbf{f}$. Any function $\mathbf{j}$ for which $\mathbf{Dj} = \mathbf{f}$ is called an *antiderivative* of $\mathbf{f}$. Of course, there are many functions whose derivatives are equal to a given function $\mathbf{f}$, but we can show that there is at most one function $\mathbf{j}$ such that

$$\mathbf{Dj} = \mathbf{f} \quad \text{and} \quad \mathbf{j}(a) = 0.$$

*F*12. Given a function $\mathbf{f}$ and an argument a, there is at most one antiderivative $\mathbf{j}$ of $\mathbf{f}$ with $\mathbf{j}(a) = 0$.

Proof:

Let $\mathbf{h}$ and $\mathbf{j}$ both be antiderivatives of $\mathbf{f}$ with

$$\mathbf{h}(a) = \mathbf{j}(a) = 0.$$

Then $\mathbf{Dh} = \mathbf{Dj} = \mathbf{f}$. Thus,

$$\mathbf{D(h - j)} = \mathbf{Dh} - \mathbf{Dj} = 0.$$

It follows from the mean value theorem for derivatives that there is a constant function $\mathbf{k}$ such that $\mathbf{h} - \mathbf{j} = \mathbf{k}$. However,

$$\mathbf{k}(a) = \mathbf{h}(a) - \mathbf{j}(a) = 0$$

so that $\mathbf{k} = \mathbf{0}$. Thus,

$$\mathbf{h} - \mathbf{j} = \mathbf{0} \quad \text{and} \quad \mathbf{h} = \mathbf{j}.$$

We can now prove the fundamental theorem of the calculus which states that any area function of $\mathbf{f}$ is an antiderivative of $\mathbf{f}$.

$F13$. If $\mathbf{j}$ is the area function of $\mathbf{f}$ with origin a, then $\mathbf{Dj} = \mathbf{f}$.

Proof:
For each argument t of $\mathbf{j}$,

$$\mathbf{j}(t) = \int_a^t \mathbf{f}.$$

Thus,

$$\mathbf{j}(t + h) - \mathbf{j}(t) = \int_a^{t+h} \mathbf{f} - \int_a^t \mathbf{f} = \int_t^{t+h} \mathbf{f}$$

and the difference quotient $\mathbf{g}_t$ of $\mathbf{j}$ at $\mathbf{t}$ has the value

$$\mathbf{g}_t(h) = \frac{\mathbf{j}(t + h) - \mathbf{j}(t)}{h} = \frac{1}{h} \int_t^{t+h} \mathbf{f}$$

for an argument $h \neq 0$. If h is small enough then the integral in the last expression is the area under the graph $\mathbf{f}$ in $[t, t + h]$ if $h > 0$ and in $[t + h, t]$ if $h < 0$. The situation for $h > 0$ is sketched in Figure 49. Since the integral exists, for each h the function $\mathbf{f}$ has a minimum value m and a maximum value M in this interval, and the integral is bounded below by mh and above by Mh if $h > 0$. If $h < 0$ the upper and lower bounds are $-mh$ and $-Mh$ respectively. These statements hold for $\mathbf{f}$

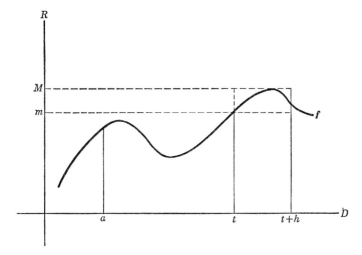

Figure 49

positive in the interval and similar statements hold under other conditions. (See Exercise 12.) In any case, we have

$$m \le \frac{1}{h} \int_t^{t+h} \mathbf{f} \le M.$$

The differences

$$M - \mathbf{f}(t) \quad \text{and} \quad \mathbf{f}(t) - m$$

can be made as small as we choose if $\int_a^b \mathbf{f}$ exists for some $b \ne a$ and if h is small enough. Then so can the difference

$$\left| \mathbf{f}(t) - \frac{1}{h} \int_t^{t+h} \mathbf{f} \right|.$$

This means that

$$\mathbf{D}j(t) = \lim_0 \mathbf{g}_t = \mathbf{f}(t)$$

which was to be proved.

As an example, we calculate again $\int_0^1 \mathbf{x}^2$. Note that

$$\mathbf{D}\frac{\mathbf{x}^3}{3} = \mathbf{x}^2 \quad \text{and} \quad \frac{\mathbf{x}^3}{3}(0) = 0$$

so that $\mathbf{x}^3/3$ is the area function of $\mathbf{x}^2$ with origin 0. Hence

$$\int_0^1 \mathbf{x}^2 = \frac{\mathbf{x}^3}{3}(1) = \frac{1}{3}$$

as before. Since

$$\mathbf{D}(\tfrac{2}{3}\mathbf{x}^{3/2}) = \mathbf{x}^{1/2} \quad \text{and} \quad \tfrac{2}{3}\mathbf{x}^{3/2}(0) = 0$$

we have

$$\int_0^1 \mathbf{x}^{1/2} = \tfrac{2}{3}\mathbf{x}^{3/2}(1) = \tfrac{2}{3}$$

again agreeing with previous results.

Given a function $\mathbf{f}$, not every antiderivative of $\mathbf{f}$ is an area function of $\mathbf{f}$ with some origin a. To see this, note that $\mathbf{x}^2 + 1$ is an antiderivative of $2\mathbf{x}$, but since there is no argument a for which $(\mathbf{x}^2 + 1)(a) = 0$, it is not an area function. However, we can show that *any* antiderivative of $\mathbf{f}$ can be used to evaluate $\int_a^b \mathbf{f}$.

*F*14. If $\mathbf{g}$ is any antiderivative of $\mathbf{f}$, then

$$\int_a^b \mathbf{f} = \mathbf{g}(b) - \mathbf{g}(a)$$

provided the integral exists.

Proof:

We have $\mathbf{Dg} = \mathbf{f}$. Let $\mathbf{j}$ be the area function of $\mathbf{f}$ with origin a. Then

$$\mathbf{Dj} = \mathbf{f}, \mathbf{j}(a) = 0 \quad \text{and} \quad \mathbf{j}(b) = \int_a^b \mathbf{f}.$$

Since $\mathbf{Dg} = \mathbf{Dj} = \mathbf{f}$, there is a constant function $\mathbf{k}$ such that $\mathbf{g} - \mathbf{j} = \mathbf{k}$. However,

$$\mathbf{k}(a) = \mathbf{g}(a) - \mathbf{j}(a) = \mathbf{g}(a)$$

so that $\mathbf{k} = \mathbf{g}[\mathbf{a}]$. Thus,

$$\mathbf{j} = \mathbf{g} - \mathbf{g}[\mathbf{a}]$$

and

$$\int_a^b \mathbf{f} = \mathbf{j}(b) = \mathbf{g}(b) - \mathbf{g}(a).$$

We have shown that if $\mathbf{g}$ and $\mathbf{g}_1$ are any antiderivatives of $\mathbf{f}$, then there is a constant function $\mathbf{k}$ such that $\mathbf{g} = \mathbf{g}_1 + \mathbf{k}$. It is immediate that if $\mathbf{g}_1$ is any antiderivative of $\mathbf{f}$, then $\mathbf{g}_1 + \mathbf{k}$ is also an antiderivative of $\mathbf{f}$ for every constant function $\mathbf{k}$. Since the set of all antiderivatives of a function $\mathbf{f}$ plays such an important part in the calculation of definite integrals of $\mathbf{f}$, we call this set the *indefinite integral* of $\mathbf{f}$ and denote it by $\int \mathbf{f}$. We leave it largely to the reader to show that the following properties of indefinite integrals hold:

1. $\int \mathbf{0} = \mathbf{k}$
2. If $n \neq -1$, then

$$\int \mathbf{x}^n = \frac{\mathbf{x}^{n+1}}{n+1} + \mathbf{k}$$

3. If $\mathbf{F}$ is an antiderivative of $\mathbf{f}$, then

$$\int \mathbf{f}[\mathbf{g}]\mathbf{Dg} = \mathbf{F}[\mathbf{g}] + \mathbf{k}$$

4. If m is any real number, then $\int m\mathbf{f} = m \int \mathbf{f}$
5. $\int (\mathbf{f} + \mathbf{g}) = \int \mathbf{f} + \int \mathbf{g}$
6. $\int \mathbf{f} \, \mathbf{Dg} = \mathbf{fg} - \int \mathbf{g} \, \mathbf{Df}$
7. $\int \mathbf{Df} = \mathbf{f} + \mathbf{k}$.

In order to prove a formula of the type $\int \mathbf{f} = \mathbf{g}$ it is sufficient to show that $\mathbf{Dg} = \mathbf{f}$. To prove 3, for example, we have

$$\mathbf{D}(\mathbf{F}[\mathbf{g}] + \mathbf{k}) = \mathbf{D}(\mathbf{F}[\mathbf{g}]) + \mathbf{Dk}$$

$$= \mathbf{DF}[\mathbf{g}]\mathbf{Dg} + 0$$

$$= \mathbf{f}[\mathbf{g}]\mathbf{Dg}.$$

To prove 6, we have

$$\mathbf{D}\{fg - \int g\,Df\} = \mathbf{D}(fg) - \mathbf{D}(\int g\,Df)$$
$$= f\,Dg + g\,Df - g\,Df$$
$$= f\,Dg$$

since $\mathbf{D}(\int \mathbf{g}\,\mathbf{Df}) = \mathbf{g}\,\mathbf{Df}$ is true by definition of antiderivative. In each formula in which it appears, "**k**" stands for any constant function. It is called an *arbitrary constant*, because any specification of **k** as a particular constant function results in an antiderivative of the same function.

We close this section with proofs of two important mean value theorems for definite integrals. In the first of these we show that in the interval (a, b) there is an argument t such that

$$\int_a^b \mathbf{f} = \mathbf{f}(t)(b - a).$$

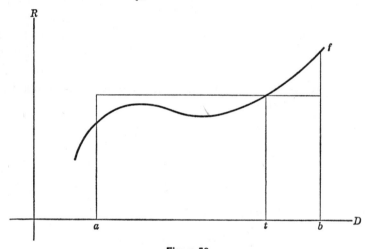

Figure 50

This means that there is a rectangle whose base is $b - a$, whose height is $\mathbf{f}(t)$ for some t in (a, b) and whose area is $\int_a^b \mathbf{f}$. See Figure 50.

*F*15. If **f** is continuous in $[a, b]$, then there is an argument t in (a, b) such that

$$\int_a^b \mathbf{f} = \mathbf{f}(t)(b - a).$$

Proof:
Let **j** be the area function of **f** with origin a. Then

$$\mathbf{j}(a) = 0, \quad \mathbf{j}(b) = \int_a^b \mathbf{f} \quad \text{and} \quad \mathbf{Dj} = \mathbf{f}$$

in $[a, b]$. Thus, $\mathbf{j}$ satisfies the mean value theorem for derivatives so that there is an argument t in (a, b) such that

$$\mathbf{j}(b) - \mathbf{j}(a) = \mathbf{Dj}(t)(b - a).$$

But this means that

$$\int_a^b \mathbf{f} = \mathbf{f}(t)(b - a)$$

since

$$\int_a^b \mathbf{f} = \mathbf{j}(b) = \mathbf{j}(b) - \mathbf{j}(a)$$

and $\mathbf{Dj}(t) = \mathbf{f}(t)$.

The last of these theorems is useful in finding bounds for integrals of products of functions.

$F16.$ Let $\mathbf{f}$ be continuous and $\mathbf{g}$ be nonnegative and integrable on $[a, b]$. Then there is an argument t such that

$$\int_a^b \mathbf{fg} = \mathbf{f}(t) \int_a^b \mathbf{g}.$$

Proof:

If $\mathbf{f}$ is continuous on $[a, b]$ it is bounded there and has a minimum value m and a maximum value M such that

$$\mathbf{m \leq f \leq M}$$

on $[a, b]$. Since $\mathbf{g}$ is nonnegative, we have

$$\mathbf{mg \leq fg \leq Mg}$$

and since the integrals of these three functions on $[a, b]$ are in the same order, we have

$$m \int_a^b \mathbf{g} \leq \int_a^b \mathbf{fg} \leq M \int_a^b \mathbf{g}.$$

Thus, there is a real number c in the interval $[m, M]$ such that

$$\int_a^b \mathbf{fg} = c \int_a^b \mathbf{g}.$$

But for every c in $[m, M]$ there is a t in (a, b) such that $\mathbf{f}(t) = c$, which was to be shown.

EXERCISES

1. Calculate the following integrals using $\lim \overline{S}_{P_n}$ for an appropriately chosen sequence (P_n) of partitions. Then check the result using the fundamental theorem.

   (a) $\displaystyle\int_0^1 \mathbf{x}^3$

(b) $\int_a^b \mathbf{x}$

(c) $\int_a^b \mathbf{x}^2$

(d) $\int_{-1}^1 \mathbf{abs}$

2. Let $\mathbf{f} = 1$ on $[0, 1]$ and $\mathbf{f} = 2$ on $(1, 2]$. Prove that $\int_0^2 \mathbf{f}$ exists and evaluate it. Let (P_n) be a sequence of partitions of $[0, 2]$ into n subintervals of equal length. Show that:

(a) If n is even, then $\underline{S}_{P_n} = \overline{S}_{P_n} = \int_0^2 \mathbf{f}$

(b) If n is odd, then $\underline{S}_{P_n} < \int_0^2 \mathbf{f} < \overline{S}_{P_n}$.

3. A function $\mathbf{f}$ is *piecewise monotone* on an interval $[a, b]$ if $[a, b]$ can be partitioned into a finite number of subintervals over each of which $\mathbf{f}$ is either monotonic increasing or monotonic decreasing. For the functions $\mathbf{f}$ defined by the graphs of Figure 51 in an interval $[a, b]$, tell whether $\mathbf{f}$ is continuous, monotonic increasing or decreasing, or piecewise monotone in $[a, b]$.

6. Prove that if $\mathbf{f}$ is piecewise monotone in $[a, b]$, then $\int_a^b \mathbf{f}$ exists.

7. Define a relation R so that if $\mathbf{f}$ and $\mathbf{g}$ are functions then $R(\mathbf{f}, \mathbf{g})$ is true if and only if $\mathbf{Df} = \mathbf{Dg}$. Show that R is an equivalence relation.

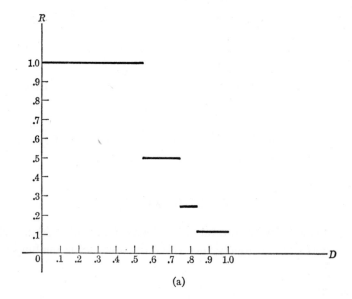

(a)

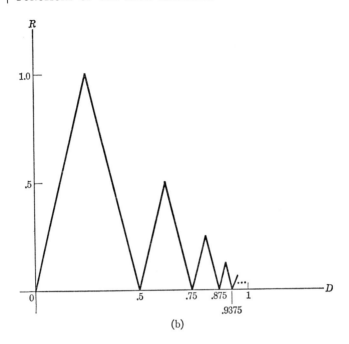

(b)

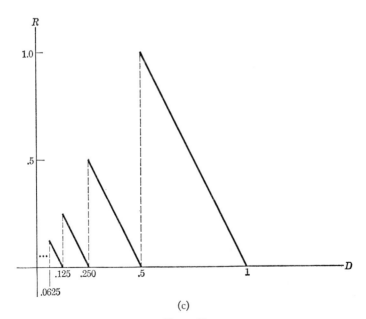

(c)

Figure 51

8. Define a relation R so that if $\mathbf{f}$ and $\mathbf{g}$ are functions integrable on $[0, 1]$ then $R(\mathbf{f}, \mathbf{g})$ is true if and only if

$$\int_0^1 \mathbf{f} = \int_0^1 \mathbf{g}.$$

Show that R is an equivalence relation.

9. Prove that if the region under the graph of a positive function $\mathbf{f}$ in an interval $[a, b]$ is rotated about the domain axis, then the volume of the solid obtained is $\pi \int_a^b \mathbf{f}^2$.

10. Prove that if the region of Exercise 9 is rotated about the range axis and if $0 < a < b$, then the volume of the solid obtained is $2\pi \int_a^b \mathbf{xf}$.

11. Find the area function with origin 3 for each of the following functions:
    (a) $\mathbf{x} + 2$
    (b) $\mathbf{x}^2 - 2\mathbf{x} - 2$
    (c) $\mathbf{x} - \mathbf{int}$
    (d) $\mathbf{abs}$.

12. In the proof of $F13$ it is shown that if $\mathbf{f}$ is positive then $mh \leq \int_t^{t+h} \mathbf{f} \leq Mh$ if $h > 0$, and $mh \geq \int_t^{t+h} \mathbf{f} \geq Mh$ if h is negative. Describe the situation when $\mathbf{f}$ is negative, in $(t, t + h)$. What if $\mathbf{f}$ is neither negative nor positive in $(t, t + h)$?

13. Prove properties 1–7 of indefinite integrals.

14. Define the natural logarithm function $\mathbf{ln}$ so that $\mathbf{ln}(t) = \int_1^t \mathbf{x}^{-1}$ for every real number $t > 0$.

    (a) Show that $\mathbf{ln}(t)$ exists if $t > 0$.
    (b) Show that $\mathbf{ln}(ts) = \mathbf{ln}(t) + \mathbf{ln}(s)$.
    (c) Show that for each real number k, $\mathbf{ln}(t^k) = k \, \mathbf{ln}(t)$.
    (d) Use the mean value theorem to show that for each real number k there is an argument t such that $\mathbf{ln}(t) = k$.
    (e) Show that $\int \mathbf{x}^{-1} = \mathbf{ln}[\mathbf{abs}] + \mathbf{k}$, where $\mathbf{k}$ is an arbitrary constant.
    (f) Prove that $\mathbf{ln}$ is a one-one correspondence.

15. Define the natural exponential function $\mathbf{exp}$ to be the inverse of $\mathbf{ln}$, and let e be the number such that $\mathbf{ln}(e) = 1$.

    (a) Show that $\mathbf{exp}(s + t) = \mathbf{exp}(s)\mathbf{exp}(t)$.
    (b) Show that $\mathbf{exp}$ is a positive function.
    (c) Show that $\mathbf{exp}(st) = \mathbf{exp}(s)^t$.
    (d) Show that for each argument t, $\mathbf{exp}(t) = e^t$.
    (e) Show that $\mathbf{Dexp} = \mathbf{exp}$.

(f) Show that $\int_0^1 \exp = e - 1$.

(g) Using mean value theorems, show that $2.5 < e < 3$.

16. Using the mean value theorem for derivatives, show that for each positive integer n,

$$\left(1 + \frac{1}{n}\right)^n < e < \left(1 + \frac{1}{n-1}\right)^n.$$

17. Prove that

$$e = \lim \left(1 + \frac{1}{n}\right)^n = \lim \left(1 + \frac{1}{n-1}\right)^n.$$

18. Show that if n is any real number, then

$$x^n = \exp\left[n \ln\right].$$

19. Use Exercise 18 to show that if n is any real number, then

$$Dx^n = nx^{n-1}.$$

BIBLIOGRAPHY

Apostol, *Calculus*, Blaisdell 1961.

Cogan, Norman, Thompson, *Calculus of Functions of One Argument*, Prentice-Hall 1960.

Courant, *Differential and Integral Calculus*, Interscience 1937.

Courant, Robbins, *What is Mathematics?*, Oxford 1941.

Johnson, Kiokemeister, *Calculus with Analytic Geometry*, Allyn and Bacon 1957.

Richmond, *Fundamentals of Calculus*, McGraw-Hill 1950.

Thomas, *Calculus with Analytic Geometry*, Addison-Wesley 1953.

Index